INTRODUCTORY MATHEMATICS FOR ECONOMIC ANALYSIS

THOMAS K. KIM

President, McMurry College

with a contribution by

JAMES P. GODFREY

Texas Tech University

SCOTT, FORESMAN AND COMPANY

Glenview, Illinois   *London*

To Martha Alice

Library of Congress Catalog Card No. 79-124659
Copyright © 1971 by Scott, Foresman and Company
Glenview, Illinois 60025
Philippines Copyright 1971 by Scott, Foresman and Company
All Rights Reserved
Printed in the United States of America
Regional offices of Scott, Foresman and Company are located in Dallas, Texas; Glenview,
Illinois; Palo Alto, California; Tucker, Georgia; and London, England.

PREFACE

This book is designed to serve as (1) the principal text in an undergraduate course in mathematical economics, and (2) a supplement in intermediate courses in micro and macroeconomics taught with some emphasis on mathematical analysis and model building. The book covers elementary algebra through differential equations, with building blocks provided along the way. The central purpose of providing mathematical background and showing economic applications of each topic is preserved throughout.

Treatments of set theory, mathematical programming, game theory, probability, input/output analysis, and other topics are omitted on the grounds that these topics are best covered in a separate volume.

The instructor using this book as the principal text may elect to discuss in class all the material in Chapter 2, or he may choose only certain topics in this chapter for class treatment, such as the solution of quadratics, the use of determinants, and the material on partial fractions. Chapter 3 was written with emphasis on the proofs of the various types of functions derived from conic sections, and the economic applications of each category of these functions. Proofs are carefully developed, step by step as aids to comprehension. Chapter 4 is devoted to the development and economic applications of such transcendental functions as exponential, logarithmic, and trigonometric functions and their geometric representations. The section on polar coordinates may be omitted without loss of continuity.

Differential calculus and its economic applications are covered in Chapters 5 through 8. Detailed proofs of each rule are carefully developed, and economic examples are liberally provided throughout. In Chapter 7, the rules of differentiation of trigonometric functions are included in the interest of completeness, but the section headed "Trigonometric Functions" may be skipped without loss of continuity in the remainder of the book. Chapter 9 is devoted to a discussion of maxima, minima, and points of inflection.

Integral calculus is a very broad topic; nevertheless, an effort has been made in Chapter 10 to give this topic a more complete and thorough treatment than is found in most books of this type. Chapter 11 is devoted to difference equations and their applications to economic models. Chapter 12 is a fairly complete treatment of differential equations, with each type of differential equation illustrated by economic examples.

Mr. James P. Godfrey, who was both an undergraduate and graduate student of mine, has made many invaluable contributions to this book. He read many versions in detail. He also contributed certain sections. He has been most generous with his help, both in time and in effort. Without his diligent assistance, I can truly say that the book would not have been possible. To him I want to express a very special word of gratitude.

I am also indebted to the following professors, who read and commented on the manuscript: W. David Maxwell, James E. Willis, Harold T. Shapiro, Chulson Khang, Richard B. Hoffman, Clark L. Allen, Donald Dewey, Harvey E. Brazer, and Edwin S. Mills. I am also indebted to my students at Texas Tech University, who read and studied various versions of this book in its several stages of development. However, I am solely responsible for any errors which may remain.

THOMAS K. KIM

CONTENTS

1 INTRODUCTION   1
  SELECTED DEFINITIONS   2
  Constants   2
  Variables: Continuous and Discrete   3
  Auxiliary Symbols   4
  THE NATURE OF ECONOMIC THEORIZING   4
  The Definition of the Problem and the Statement of Assumptions 4
  The Hypothesis   6
  Theory   6
  THE FUNCTION OF MATHEMATICS   7

2 REVIEW OF ELEMENTARY MATHEMATICS   9
  BASIC OPERATIONS AND ASSUMPTIONS OF ALGEBRA   9
  LAWS OF SIGNS   10
  LAWS OF EXPONENTS   11
  LOGARITHMS   13
  Laws of Logarithmic Operations   14
  Bases of Logarithms   18
  The Relation between Common and Natural Logarithms   19
  ALGEBRAIC EXPRESSIONS   20
  EQUATIONS AND IDENTITIES   21
  SOLUTION OF EQUATIONS   22
  Linear Equations   22
  Quadratic Equations   23
  Solution of Pure Quadratic Equations   25
  Solution of Complete Quadratic Equations   26
  The Character of the Roots of Quadratic Equations   32
  COMPLEX NUMBERS   33
  Algebraic Operations with Complex Numbers   34
  Graphic Solution of Quadratic Equations   36
  SYSTEMS OF EQUATIONS   38
  Systems of Linear Equations   38
  Determinants of Nth Order   46
  Systems of Equations Involving Quadratics   51
  THEORY OF EQUATIONS   53
  Fundamental Theorem of Algebra   53
  Remainder Theorem   56
  PARTIAL FRACTIONS   57
  PROBLEMS   63

CONTENTS

3 TYPES OF FUNCTIONS   69
LINEAR FUNCTION, STRAIGHT LINE   69
Slope   70
Equations of Straight Lines   74
Distance Between Two Points   78
QUADRATIC EQUATIONS, CONIC SECTIONS   79
The Circle   80
Economic Applications of The Circle   86
The Ellipse   89
Economic Applications of The Ellipse   94
The Parabola   96
Economic Applications of the Parabola   100
The Hyperbola   105
Economic Applications of The Hyperbola   113
OTHER ALGEBRAIC FUNCTIONS   118
PROBLEMS   120

4 TRANSCENDENTAL FUNCTIONS AND THEIR GRAPHS   128
EXPONENTIAL FUNCTIONS   128
Logarithmic Functions   135
TRIGONOMETRIC FUNCTIONS   141
Definitions   141
The Meanings and Uses of Trigonometric Functions   143
Trigonometric Identities   149
ECONOMIC APPLICATIONS
    OF TRIGONOMETRIC FUNCTIONS   150
Periodic Functions   150
Averages   152
POLAR EQUATIONS   155
COMPLEX NUMBERS   156
Polar Coordinates of a Complex Number   157
Addition of Complex Numbers   159
Multiplication of Complex Numbers   161
Division of Complex Numbers   162
PROBLEMS   163

5 LIMITS, CONTINUITY, AND DERIVATIVES   169
THE CONCEPT OF LIMITS   169
CONTINUITY   176
The Derivative   179
RULES OF DIFFERENTIATION   181
The Derivative of a Constant   181
The Derivative of a First-Degree Term   182
The Differentiation of a Power Function   184
The Differentiation of Sums and Differences   185
Differentiation of the Product of Two Functions   187

Differentiation of a Quotient 189
Differentiation of a Composite Function 191
Differentiation of an Inverse Function 194
Differentiation of Implicit Functions 195
Successive Differentiation 196
DIFFERENTIALS 199
Definition of a Differential 199
Geometric Interpretation of a Differential 200
Some Numerical Examples of Differentials 202
PROBLEMS 203

6 ECONOMIC APPLICATIONS OF DERIVATIVES 211
THE THEORY OF DEMAND 211
ELASTICITY 214
Price Elasticity 214
Gross Elasticity of Demand 218
Income Elasticity 219
ELASTICITY OF THE TOTAL REVENUE FUNCTION 219
MARGINAL REVENUE 222
MARGINAL COST 224
ELASTICITY OF TOTAL COST 226
LONG-RUN AND SHORT-RUN COSTS 228
THE NEOCLASSICAL MACROECONOMIC MODEL 234
MARGINAL PROPENSITY TO CONSUME AND TO SAVE 237
AN ANALYSIS OF INCOME TAXATION AND
    GOVERNMENT EXPENDITURES 239
PROBLEMS 243

7 DIFFERENTIATION OF TRANSCENDENTAL FUNCTIONS 249
DIFFERENTIATION OF LOGARITHMIC FUNCTIONS 249
DIFFERENTIATION OF EXPONENTIAL FUNCTIONS 255
DIFFERENTIATION OF LOGARITHMIC EXPRESSIONS
    TO ANY BASE 257
TRIGONOMETRIC FUNCTIONS 261
ECONOMIC APPLICATIONS OF DIFFERENTIATION
    OF TRANSCENDENTAL EXPRESSIONS 269
PROBLEMS 272

8 PARTIAL DIFFERENTIATION 278
PARTIAL DERIVATIVES 278
TOTAL DIFFERENTIAL 282
DIFFERENTIATION OF IMPLICIT FUNCTIONS 283
PARTIAL DERIVATIVES OF HIGHER ORDER 286
HOMOGENEOUS FUNCTIONS 288
Homogeneity of Degree Zero 289
Homogeneity of Degree One 290
Homogeneity of Degrees Higher than One 295

CONTENTS

EULER'S THEOREM | 297
Economic Applications of Euler's Theorem | 299
A Geometric Interpretation of Euler's Theorem and Its Applications | 302
RELATIONSHIP OF CONSTANT RETURNS TO SCALE
  AND MARGINAL PRODUCTIVITY | 304
The Theory of Long-Run Total Cost | 309
Problems | 314

9 MAXIMA AND MINIMA OF FUNCTIONS | 322
FUNCTIONS OF ONE VARIABLE | 322
THEORY OF THE FIRM | 327
Monopoly Output as Half the Competitive Output | 330
Sales Maximization | 333
POINT OF INFLECTION | 336
FUNCTIONS OF SEVERAL VARIABLES | 338
PRICE DISCRIMINATION BY A MONOPOLIST | 339
CONSTRAINED MAXIMUM, LaGRANGE MULTIPLIER | 343
MINIMA | 348
MAXIMA OR MINIMA INVOLVING MORE
  THAN TWO VARIABLES | 349
Maximum | 349
Minimum | 350
A STUDY OF SEVERAL DUOPOLY MODELS | 352
A Generalization of the Cournot Model | 352
Hotelling's Stable Duopoly Model | 354
Some Duopoly Reaction Models, Including Frisch's | 356
  Conjectural Variation
Numerical Examples of Conjectural Variation | 361
MAXIMIZATION OF A TAX ON OUTPUT | 363
PROBLEMS | 367

10 ELEMENTS OF INTEGRAL CALCULUS | 372
SOME TECHNIQUES OF INTEGRATION | 372
INTEGRATION OF TRIGONOMETRIC FORMS | 386
CONSTANT OF INTEGRATION | 392
THE DEFINITE INTEGRAL | 395
Differential of the Area Under a Curve | 395
The Definite Integral | 396
APPROXIMATE INTEGRATION | 406
Trapezoidal Rule | 406
Simpson's Rule (Parabolic Rule) | 409
PROBLEMS | 414

11 DIFFERENCE EQUATIONS | 422
DEFINITIONS | 423
THE GROWTH RATE | 424

THE HARROD GROWTH MODEL   425
Time Path of a Solution   426
Time Path of the Harrod Model   429
NONHOMOGENEOUS FIRST-ORDER LINEAR
   DIFFERENCE EQUATIONS   429
THE COBWEB MODEL   435
SECOND-ORDER LINEAR DIFFERENCE EQUATIONS   440
MULTIPLIER-ACCELERATOR MODEL   443
NONHOMOGENEOUS SECOND-ORDER DIFFERENCE
   EQUATIONS   445
PROBLEMS   448

12 DIFFERENTIAL EQUATIONS   450
ORDINARY AND PARTIAL DIFFERENTIAL EQUATIONS   450
THE ORDER AND DEGREE OF A DIFFERENTIAL
   EQUATION   451
SOLVING A DIFFERENTIAL EQUATION   451
DIFFERENTIAL EQUATIONS OF THE FIRST
   ORDER AND OF THE FIRST DEGREE   454
Separation of Variables   454
Homogeneous Equations   456
Linear Differential Equations   459
Exact Differential Equations   463
ECONOMIC APPLICATIONS OF DIFFERENTIAL
   EQUATIONS   468
The Domar Growth Model   468
The Harrod Growth Model   469
Price-Level Adjustment Over Time   470
Derivation of the Cost Function by Separation of Variables   472
Analysis of a Consumer Indifference Curve by the
   Homogeneous Differential Equation   474
Exact Differential Equation   476
DIFFERENTIAL EQUATIONS OF HIGHER ORDER   477
Second-Order, Linear, Homogeneous Differential Equations
   with Constant Coefficients   477
Complete (Nonhomogeneous) Second-Order Differential Equations
   with Constant Coefficients   484
Method of Undetermined Coefficients   484
Two Special Types of Second-Order Differential Equations   487
DIFFERENTIAL EQUATIONS OF ORDER N 489
ECONOMIC APPLICATIONS OF HIGHER ORDER
   DIFFERENTIAL EQUATIONS   491
National Debt Related to National Income   491
Domar's Burden-of-Debt Model   496
PROBLEMS   497
INDEX   499

1
INTRODUCTION

Mathematics, like other languages, is a tool of analysis and communication. The successful use of a language requires an understanding of its rules, i.e., its grammar. An effective communicator must also be in possession of a viable vocabulary to be fitted onto the skeletal structure of the grammar.

In a similar way the successful use of mathematics as a tool of analysis requires an understanding of the rules of mathematics and the unique modes of expression peculiar to mathematics. In addition to the understanding of the basic rules of mathematics, the successful use of mathematical analysis requires the ability to adapt the rules to meet the special problems encountered in the analysis of the specific question under investigation.

In this book, mathematics is used as a tool for the discussion of economic theory. Mathematics is not an end in itself; rather, it is a vehicle through which the postulates of economic theory can be stated more concisely and consistently, and the logical reasoning process made clear.

Geometry has been used to great advantage by economists through the years. Many relationships of economic theory were appropriately represented by geometric configurations of points, lines, and curves. Geometry, however, has the serious limitation that it cannot be applied to cases involving more than two or three variables. Thus the more complicated economic relationships involving many simultaneous variables cannot be handled by the techniques of geometry. Increasingly, mathematical analysis of economic theory has come to rely on the more powerful tools of calculus and differential equations. The use of these tools of mathematics makes possible the treatment of as many economic variables as economic theory encompasses in any given situation.

The purpose of this book is to introduce the reader to the techniques of elementary mathematical analysis. A systematic and careful development of the mathematical tools is attempted, beginning with the basic concepts of algebra and proceeding through integral calculus. As each concept of mathematics is introduced, economic concepts are used wherever convenient to illustrate its use. Specific applications of the methods of mathematical analysis are incorporated in various parts of the book.

The purpose of Chapter 1 is to provide a few preliminary definitions of some of the widely used concepts of mathematics, to discuss the nature of economic theory, and to show the function of mathematics in the development of economic theory.

SELECTED DEFINITIONS

In any mathematical expression there are three kinds of symbols or notations: constants, variables, and auxiliary symbols. For example, in the equation

$$y = (a + x) - (b + x^2)$$

the symbols a, b, and 2 are constants, x and y are the variables, and the parentheses and the operational signs $(+)$, $(-)$, and $(=)$ are auxiliary symbols.

Constants

A *constant* number in a mathematical expression assumes a given value or magnitude without any possibility of variation. In the equation $y = 10x$, the number 10 is a constant. The number system from which constants are drawn may be represented by a scheme of classification as shown below.

$$\text{the real number system} \begin{cases} \text{rational numbers} \begin{cases} \text{positive integers} \\ \text{positive fractions} \\ \text{zero} \\ \text{negative integers and fractions} \end{cases} \\ \text{irrational numbers} \begin{cases} \text{positive irrational numbers} \\ \text{negative irrational numbers} \end{cases} \end{cases}$$

The positive integers are numbers such as 1, 2, 3, 10, 100, 999, and so on. When integers are added and multiplied, the sum and product are integers. But the reverse process of multiplication, division, sometimes yields fractional numbers. Thus the division of 1 by 2, or $\frac{1}{2}$, is a fraction. When 7 is divided by 3 the result is $2\frac{1}{3}$, a fractional number. Negative integers and negative fractions are similarly described, except in this case the resulting numbers are less than 0 in value. Positive or negative irrational numbers are such numbers as $\sqrt{2}$, $\sqrt[3]{7}$, $\sqrt{-1}$, and π.

The ordered sequence of numbers may be represented by a number scale (see Figure 1-1). The numbers may be represented geometrically as

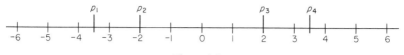

Figure 1-1

points on a straight line. A straight line XX' of unlimited length can be drawn. On the line XX', an arbitrary point can be chosen, and designated as O, or origin. By definition, all points to the right of origin are designated as positive numbers, and all points to the left of origin as negative numbers. The point p_1 represents the negative number -2; p_2 represents $-3\frac{1}{2}$. The point p_3 corresponds to the positive number 2, and p_4 shows the positive fractional number $3\frac{1}{2}$.

The number scale also illustrates two important characteristics of the real number system: an ordered sequence of numbers is both *limitless* and *indefinitely dense*. A number, however large, can be exceeded by other larger numbers. A smaller number can always be identified for any number, however small. This is the property of limitlessness. Between any two numbers on the number scale, we can insert as many numbers as we like. For example, in the range between $\frac{1}{2}$ and 1, we could have fractions $\frac{1}{2}, \frac{2}{3}, \frac{3}{4}, \frac{4}{5}, \frac{5}{6}, \frac{6}{7}, \frac{7}{8}, \frac{8}{9}, \frac{9}{10}, \ldots, 1$. This is the property of indefinite density.

Variables: Continuous and Discrete

A *variable* number is an unspecified number capable of assuming any magnitude from a set of real numbers. It is usually designated by a letter such as x, y, z, u, v, or w. A particular number or magnitude assigned to a variable is called its *value*. The whole set of all possible values of a variable constitutes the *range* of the variable. For example, $a < x < b$ means that x can assume any value greater than a and less than b. The expression $10 \leq y \leq 20$ means that y may assume any value from 10 through 20, including the values 10 and 20.

A *continuous* variable is a variable whose possible values within the range are infinitely dense and without gaps. Thus a continuous variable x with a range of $2 < x < 3$ may assume any values between 2 and 3. Some economic variables which are (for all practical purposes) continuous are quantities of commodities such as wheat or salt, or others which are finely divisible.

A discrete or *discontinuous* variable has a range which is not the entire set of all possible values in the range. Gaps exist between any two values of a discrete variable. A set of integers cannot assume fractional numbers.

In economic terms, population is a discrete variable, fractional persons being a meaningless notion. Quantities of such things as cars, locomotives, factories, and houses are examples of discrete variables. These are things which come in units of 1 or multiples of 1, with fractional quantities having no significance.

Auxiliary Symbols

Many kinds of auxiliary symbols are used in mathematics to facilitate the expression of ideas contained in an equation. They specify the nature of relationships and the operations which are to be performed.

THE NATURE OF ECONOMIC THEORIZING

The purpose of this section is to discuss the nature and significance of a special scientific method which is used in economics. Various names can be used to describe this method: theory, model, a structure, a relationship, a mental image. Whatever the name, economic theory is a widely accepted and used tool of economic analysis. We now turn our attention to some of the salient features of economic theorizing.

Scientific experimentation is a powerful tool in the hands of the natural scientist. In an experiment, the scientist tries to set up a situation in which he is able to control precisely the variables relevant to his problem. Under these laboratory conditions, the scientist is able to allow one variable to change by a measured amount, and observes the effect of this change on the other variables. Such a technique is not available to the economist, because the subject matter of his study involves a large number of variables, none of which is under his precise control.

Instead of scientific experimentation, the economist uses deductive reasoning, or the method of constructing mental images and models. There are four steps in the conception, development, and acceptance of an economic theory: (1) the definition of the problem, including a statement of assumptions; (2) the statement of a hypothesis; (3) the construction of a theory; and (4) empirical verification.

The Definition of the Problem
and the Statement of Assumptions

The problem being chosen for investigation must be clearly stated. The statement of assumptions defines and clarifies the conditions underlying the problem.

Assumptions may be classified into three groups: (a) fundamental assumptions; (b) definitional assumptions; and (c) procedural assumptions. *Fundamental* assumptions are basic and essential for the economic problem under analysis. They are an integral and permanent part of the problem. Such assumptions cannot be dropped in the course of the analysis. For example, the assumptions of scarcity and rationality are fundamental to economic analysis. If scarcity were not an assumed condition of the real economy, problems of choosing among alternatives would not exist. Economics would not be a significant area of study, for its function would be of doubtful use to society. If men and institutions behaved irrationally and unpredictably, no body of principles would be possible, for behavior would no longer be directed toward identifiable objectives.

Definitional assumptions set the boundaries of the problem under investigation. The definition of the problem should include the precise nature of the question proposed for study; the dimensions, components and elements comprising the problem; and the limitations of the problem. If, for example, we are interested in the factors which determine the volume of employment and unemployment in the decade of the 1960s, certain aspects of the problem need to be defined. Definitional assumptions can be used to serve this function. Such questions as the following need to be clarified: Are we interested in the volume of employment in the entire economy, or is the focus of our investigation the nonagricultural sector of the economy? Do we mean by the economy the 50 states which make up the United States, or do we wish to confine our attention to the 48 states occupying a contiguous land mass of the North American continent? Why is one or the other of the definitions chosen? If the proportion of the labor force which may become unemployed during the period is of interest, it is essential to define the total work force of the economy. Is the labor force composed of persons 14 years of age and over? Are both males and females to be included in the labor force? How are students seeking summer employment to be treated in the definition of the labor force? Since the number of people employed and unemployed in the economy varies from day to day and month to month, how are annual employment data to be computed? Would an average of monthly data be an adequate measure?

Definitional assumptions can be used to give a precise and unambiguous understanding of the nature, the dimensions, and the limitations of the problem.

Procedural assumptions define explicitly the types of techniques to be used in the analysis of the problem. In the search for factors contributing to the volume of employment, are we interested in all factors, both economic and noneconomic, direct and indirect, domestic and international? Do we plan to use, initially, a closed-economy model, concentrating our attention on the domestic economic conditions and forces which have an influence on the size of employment in the economy? In the latter stages of analysis, do we plan to drop the assumption of a closed economy and introduce the international trade relationships which may affect domestic employment? How are such noneconomic factors as international political climate and the development of technology to be treated in the analysis?

Procedural assumptions are introduced at succeeding stages of the investigation to mark the explicit transition from one frame of reference in the analytic technique to another. Procedural assumptions are often temporary expedients invoked to set the stage of analysis, as the investigation proceeds from a simplified, skeletal, and ideal set of conditions to more complex, realistic settings.

The Hypothesis

A hypothesis is a tentative proposition, provisionally adopted to serve as the basis of further investigation to establish the relationships among facts and events. A hypothesis is a shrewd conjecture, an educated guess as to the probable relationship among observations. Forethought, imagination, and insight derived from observation of relevant facts and events are essential elements in the development of a plausible hypothesis. At this stage of the game, there is no systematic factual investigation or clear knowledge of the relationships which might exist among economic facts.

Although a hypothesis is an untested and tentative proposition, many of the great unifying conceptions in the modern sciences are working hypotheses. In the same way, working hypotheses serve as the foundation for further investigation in economics.

Some examples of economic hypotheses are: (1) the size of the population, the level of technological achievement, and the capital stock of a society influence its economic growth and development; (2) the quantity demanded of a product may, in part, depend on the income of the consumer; and (3) among other things, the competitive structure of the industry determines the pattern of revenues received by a firm.

Theory

A theory is a general principle, or an ideal construction designed to explain the relationships among economic facts. A sequence of logical reasoning leads from postulated assumptions through intermediate relationships to final conclusions. The implications of the assumptions, the hypothesis, and the relevant facts and observations are explored to construct an internally logical and consistent structure. Such a theoretical structure serves the function of a map, showing the relationships among the elements of a terrain.

Both induction and deduction are needed in the development of a theory. Induction is the logical process of marshalling the relevant facts to reach a specific conclusion. Deduction is the process of reaching the conclusions presaged by the nature of the assumptions. It is an inference about a particular case from a general principle which holds true of all such cases.

A theory is not a general-purpose garment, meeting the requirements of all occasions and situations. A theory is suitable for the analysis of a particular problem only if the assumptions of the theory fit the conditions of the problem. The often-heard lament that "it may be fine in theory, but does not work in practice," is a symptom of misunderstanding of the uses of theory. If the assumptions of the theory fit the conditions of an economic problem, the conclusions of the theory will be logical and correct both in theory and in practice.

Economics, as a social science, has an impressive array of theories addressed to the various branches of the discipline. A rich tradition of rigorous application of deductive and inductive reasoning has enabled economists to develop a sophisticated methodology of economic analysis.

THE FUNCTION OF MATHEMATICS

Mathematical analysis has traditionally made a significant contribution to the development and exposition of economic theories. The variables with which economics deals are capable of either numerical or meaningful conceptual quantification. The use of mathematics almost suggests itself.

The use of mathematics makes it possible to frame the assumptions of economic theory consistently, to carry out the deductive reasoning logically, and to arrive at conclusions consistent with the premises given by the original assumptions. It is widely accepted that mathematics makes an invaluable contribution to the growing precision of exposition and accuracy of prediction of economic theory.

It is important to recognize, however, that the precision of economic exposition and the accuracy of economic prediction are no greater than the precision in the formulation of the basic assumptions of theory and the accuracy of the measurement of economic quantities.

The use of mathematics as a tool of economic theorizing often involves the development of a *model*. An economic model can be represented by a system of mathematical equations, which can be classified as *definitional* equations and *behavioral* equations. A simple example of the mathematical model of an economic theory can be derived from the well-known supply and demand analysis. We might construct the following system of equations:

$$Q_d = 100 - 2p \qquad \text{Demand function (a behavioral equation)}$$

$$Q_s = 10 + 4p \qquad \text{Supply function (a behavioral equation)}$$

$$Q_d = Q_s \qquad \text{Equilibrium (a definitional equation)}$$

In this system of equations, Q_d is the quantity demanded, Q_s the quantity supplied, and p is the price of the good in question.

The demand function specifies the behavior of the demanders for the commodity, responding to the various prices of the good. The supply function indicates the reaction of the suppliers of the commodity to the various prices of the good. Together the demand function and the supply function are the behavioral equations of our model. The third equation is a definitional equation. Equilibrium is defined to be that position of the market at which the quantity demanded will be exactly equal to the quantity supplied. Thus the third equation defines for us an identity relationship which will always exist when equilibrium is achieved.

The solution of this model will yield the equilibrium price of 15. The substitution of $p = 15$ into the demand function shows that the quantity demanded is $Q_d = 70$, and the same operation performed on the supply function results in $Q_s = 70$.

Precise and neat as the solutions may seem in this model, it is important to recognize the impressive body of theoretical literature which stands behind each of the equations. A long history of slow and tedious development is quickly summarized in the simple demand curve we used in this model. An equally long series of development of economic thought and theorizing stands behind the supply function. And the definition of equilibrium is the culmination of the contributions of many minds in the study of economics.

2
REVIEW OF ELEMENTARY MATHEMATICS

It is the purpose of Chapter 2 to review the elements of mathematics. It should be particularly helpful to those readers whose mathematical background may be relatively weak. Even those who are reasonably familiar with the fundamentals of mathematics may find this chapter helpful, in that an effort is made here to summarize the important and useful ideas and rules of elementary mathematics in an organized and systematic way.

BASIC OPERATIONS AND ASSUMPTIONS OF ALGEBRA

There are six basic operations of algebra: addition, subtraction, multiplication, division, raising to power, and the extraction of roots.

In performing the operations of algebra, five fundamental assumptions are made (see below). These assumptions govern the various aspects of algebraic manipulations. They are not subject to proof, but are simply accepted as the foundation of algebraic operations. In this sense, the fundamental assumptions of algebra are similar in nature to the postulates in geometry and the assumptions of economic theory.

1. *Addition is commutative.* The sum of two numbers is the same, whatever the order of addition:

$$a + b = b + a$$
$$3 + 2 = 2 + 3$$

2. *Addition is associative.* The sum of two or more numbers is the same, whatever the manner of grouping:

$$(a + b) + c = a + (b + c)$$
$$(3 + 5) + 8 = 3 + (5 + 8)$$

3. *Multiplication is commutative.* The product of two numbers is the same, whatever the order in which they are multiplied:

$$ab = ba \qquad (50)(64) = (64)(50)$$

4. *Multiplication is associative.* The product of three or more numbers is the same, however the numbers are grouped in the multiplication:

$$a(bc) = (ab)c \qquad 6(3 \cdot 9) = (6 \cdot 3)9$$

5. *Multiplication is distributive with respect to addition.* When one number is to be multiplied by the sum of two or more numbers, the product is the same as the sum of the first number multiplied by each of the numbers of the sum:

$$a(b + c) = ab + ac$$
$$2(7 + 6) = 2 \cdot 7 + 2 \cdot 6$$

LAWS OF SIGNS

The explicit assignment of positive and negative signs enlarges the range of numbers which can be systematically treated. No longer must analysis be confined to positive numbers; negative numbers and quantities can be treated in a uniform and systematic way as well.

1. To add two numbers with identical signs, add their absolute values and assign their common sign:

$$5 + 6 = 11$$
$$(-5) + (-6) = -11$$

2. To add two numbers with dissimilar signs, subtract the smaller absolute value from the larger and use the sign of the number with larger absolute value as the sign of the result:

$$7 + (-4) = 3 \qquad 8 + (-11) = -3$$

3. To subtract two numbers, change the sign of the number to be subtracted, and proceed as in addition:

$$10 - 6 = 10 + (-6) = 4$$
$$8 - (-12) = 8 + (+12) = 20$$

4. To multiply two numbers, multiply their absolute values. If the numbers were of identical sign, the result is positive. If the numbers were of dissimilar signs, the result is negative:

$$(2)(3) = 6 \qquad (-2)(-4) = 8 \qquad (4)(-6) = -24$$

5. To divide two numbers, divide their absolute values. If the numbers were of identical sign, the result is positive. If the numbers were of dissimilar signs, the result is negative.

$$\frac{8}{2} = 4 \qquad \frac{-6}{-3} = 2 \qquad \frac{-1}{4} = -\frac{1}{4} = -0.25$$

LAWS OF EXPONENTS

The concept of exponents makes it possible to use a larger group of numbers, including numbers called *powers*. In the expression

$$2^3 = 2 \cdot 2 \cdot 2 = 8$$

the exponent is 3 and the base 2; or 2 is raised to the third power. Either of these statements means that the number 2 is to be multiplied 3 times.

1. The product of exponential expressions equals the common base raised to a power whose value is the sum of the individual exponents.

$$(x^2)(x^3) = (x)(x)\,(x)(x)(x) = x^{2+3} = x^5$$
$$(2^3)(2^4) = (2)(2)(2)\,(2)(2)(2)(2) = 2^{3+4} = 2^7 = 128$$

2. An exponential expression raised to a power equals the base of that expression raised to a power whose value is the product of the exponents.

$$(x^2)^4 = (x^2)(x^2)(x^2)(x^2) = (x)(x)\,(x)(x)\,(x)(x)\,(x)(x)$$
$$= x^{(2)(4)} = x^8$$

The expression $(x^2)^4$ indicates that (x^2) is raised to the fourth power. The result is that x is raised to the $((2)(4) = 8)$ eighth power.

3. An exponential expression whose base is a product is equal to that product whose factors are the factors of the base, each raised to the power represented by the exponent.

$$(xy)^3 = (xy)(xy)(xy) = (x \cdot x \cdot x)(y \cdot y \cdot y) = x^3y^3$$

Consider, however, an exponential expression whose base is the sum of two numbers: $(x + y)^2$. This expression cannot be written as $x^2 + y^2$. Rather, the whole expression $(x + y)$ must be raised to the second power. Therefore,

$$(x + y) = (x + y)(x + y) = x^2 + 2xy + y^2$$

The second power of the sum of two numbers will provide an example:

$$(2 + 4)^2 = 6^2 = 36$$

$$(2 + 4)^2 \neq 2^2 + 4^2 = 4 + 16 = 20$$

The expression $(2 + 4)^2$ can be expanded in the following manner to get the correct answer of 36:

$$(2 + 4)^2 = (2 + 4)(2 + 4) = 2^2 + (2)(2)(4) + 4^2 = 4 + 16 + 16 = 36$$

4. An exponential expression whose base is a fraction is equal to that fraction whose numerator is the numerator of the base raised to the power

represented by the exponent and whose denominator is the denominator of the base raised to the same power.

$$\left(\frac{x}{y}\right)^2 = \left(\frac{x}{y}\right)\left(\frac{x}{y}\right) = \frac{x^2}{y^2}$$

When a fraction x/y is raised to the second or any other power, the result is the ratio of the numerator raised to the desired power over the denominator raised to the same desired power.

5. The quotient of two exponential expressions equals the common base raised to a power whose value is the result of subtracting the exponent of the denominator from the exponent of the numerator.

$$\frac{x^3}{x^2} = \frac{xxx}{xx} = x^{(3-2)} = x$$

When a base, for example x, is raised to any power, and it is to be divided by that same base raised to any power, the result is the base x raised to the power corresponding to the difference of the power of the numerator minus the power of the denominator.

The reason for rule 5 is illustrated by the example above. In that example, two of the x's in the numerator cancel the two x's in the denominator. There is one x left in the numerator, while the denominator becomes 1. The result is $x/1$, which is x.

Consider another example of the use of rule 5. Suppose the function we are interested in to be the function

$$\frac{x^3}{x^5} = \frac{xxx}{xxxxx} = \frac{1}{x^2} = x^{(3-5)} = x^{-2}$$

In this example, there are three x's in the numerator and five x's in the denominator. The three x's in the numerator cancel three of the x's in the denominator. The numerator cancels out to 1 and the denominator cancels out to x^2. The result is $1/x^2$, which is the same as

$$x^{(3-5)} = x^{-2}$$

The *negative exponent* of a number means the reciprocal of that number raised to the same power. For example:

$$x^{-3} = \frac{1}{x^3} \qquad x^{-1} = \frac{1}{x} \qquad x^{-4} = \frac{1}{x^4}$$

6. An expression whose exponent is fractional equals the nth root of the base, where n is the reciprocal of the exponent.

$$x^{1/2} = \sqrt{x}$$

If $x^{\frac{1}{2}}$ were multiplied by $x^{\frac{1}{2}}$, the result would be

$$x^{(\frac{1}{2}+\frac{1}{2})} = x^1$$

The relationship is

$$x^{\frac{1}{2}}x^{\frac{1}{2}} = x$$

Taking the square root of both sides yields

$$x^{\frac{1}{2}} = \sqrt{x}$$

Similarly, it can be shown that

$$x^{\frac{1}{3}} = \sqrt[3]{x}$$

Extending rule 6, consider the expression $x^{\frac{2}{3}}$.

$$x^{\frac{2}{3}} = x^{\frac{1}{3}}x^{\frac{1}{3}} = (x^2)^{\frac{1}{3}} = \sqrt[3]{x^2}$$

The expression $x^{\frac{2}{3}}$ means the third root of the square of x.

7. The value of an expression whose exponent is 0 equals 1.

$$\frac{x^2}{x^2} = \frac{xx}{xx} = x^{2-2} = x^0 = 1$$

Since the numerator and the denominator cancel to unity, the fraction becomes 1. Put another way, since the difference of the exponent of the numerator and the exponent of the denominator is 0, the result is x^0, and any number raised to zero power is 1. Therefore, the expression results in 1.

LOGARITHMS

The logarithm of any positive number N to any positive base b is the power to which the base b must be raised to equal the number N. In the equation

$$N = b^x$$

the number x is the logarithm of the number N to the base b. An identical statement of equality can be made, therefore, in logarithmic form

$$\log_b N = x$$

It is obvious that a system of logarithms could be constructed using any base whatever. That is to say, b might be equal to any number, and a corresponding logarithmic system could be developed. In more advanced works of mathematics, logarithms of negative and imaginary numbers are defined. For the purposes of this text, b is restricted to $b > 0$ and $b \neq 1$. If $b = 0$, then $b^x = 0$ for whatever value of x. A negative value cannot be assigned to b, for then certain numbers would not have logarithms within the real number system. For example, if $b = -2$, the number 8 would have no logarithm, because $8 = (-2)^x$ cannot be satisfied by any real number x. It is for these reasons that the conditions $b > 0$ and $b \neq 1$ are imposed. The consequence is that the logarithmic system developed on the base b is a system of logarithms for positive numbers.

The methods of determining the values of logarithms of numbers from logarithmic tables will not be discussed in this section. The techniques of determining the characteristics and the mantissas of numbers are discussed in many college textbooks in algebra. The purpose of this section is to discuss the properties of logarithms and the use of logarithms in calculations.

The following pairs of equations are identical statements, the first in exponential form and the second in corresponding logarithmic form:

1. $4^3 = 64$ or $\log_4 64 = 3$

2. $6^2 = 36$ or $\log_6 36 = 2$

3. $9^{3/2} = 27$ or $\log_9 27 = 3/2$

4. $8^{-2} = 1/64$ or $\log_8 1/64 = -2$

5. $5^0 = 1$ or $\log_5 1 = 0$

6. $\dfrac{Y}{A} = b^x$ or $\log_b \dfrac{Y}{A} = x$

7. $10^3 = 1000$ or $\log_{10} 1000 = 3$

8. $2.71828^2 = 7.389$ or $\log_{2.71828} 7.389 = 2$

These examples illustrate the fact that logarithms are simply another set of rules by which numbers and quantities may be represented. Too often beginning students in mathematics view logarithms as a set of mystifying tricks. It is helpful for the student to try his hand at making up his own set of equations in exponential form and in corresponding logarithmic form. Having written out the equations, he can verbalize the corresponding pairs of equations. For example, the first pair of equations above may be verbalized. The exponential form says the number 4 raised to the third power is equal to 64. The logarithmic version of this statement says the logarithm of the number 64 to the base 4 is equal to 3.

Laws of Logarithmic Operations

Logarithms are exponents. Because of this fact, there are laws governing manipulations of logarithmic numbers analogous to the laws relating to exponents.

1. The logarithm of the product of two or more numbers is equal to the sum of the logarithms of the factors, all logarithms being expressed in relation to the same base. For example,

$$\log_b (KL) = \log_b K + \log_b L$$

To prove this law, proceed by the following steps:

(*a*) Let $x = \log_b K$ and $y = \log_b L$

(*b*) Write in exponential form

$$K = b^x \quad \text{and} \quad L = b^y$$

(*c*) Multiply K by L

$$KL = b^x \cdot b^y = b^{x+y}$$

(*d*) Write in logarithmic form

$$\log_b (KL) = x + y$$

(*e*) Substitute for x and y their values

$$\log_b (KL) = \log_b K + \log_b L$$

Some illustrations of the applications of this law are:

(*a*) $\log_2 (18) = \log_2 (3 \cdot 6) = \log_2 3 + \log_2 6$

(*b*) $\log_{10} (x^2 + x)(12x - 8) = \log_{10} (x^2 + x) + \log_{10} (12x - 8)$

(*c*) $\log_6 (216) = \log_6 (36 \cdot 6) = \log_6 36 + \log_6 6 = 2 + 1 = 3$

Law 1 can be applied to the product of any number of factors, such as

$$\log_b (JKL) = \log_b [(JK)L] = \log_b (JK) + \log_b L$$
$$= \log_b J + \log_b K + \log_b L$$

2. The logarithm of a quotient is equal to the difference of the logarithm of the dividend minus the logarithm of the divisor, both logarithms being expressed in relation to the same base. This is to say

$$\log_b \frac{K}{L} = \log_b K - \log_b L$$

To prove this law, proceed as follows:

(*a*) Let $x = \log_b K$ and $y = \log_b L$

(*b*) Write in exponential form

$$K = b^x \quad L = b^y$$

(c) Divide K by L

$$\frac{K}{L} = \frac{b^x}{b^y} = b^{x-y}$$

(d) Write the result of step c in logarithmic form

$$\log_b \frac{K}{L} = x - y$$

(e) Substitute for x and y their respective values

$$\log_b \frac{K}{L} = \log_b K - \log_b L$$

Illustrations of Law 2:

(a) $\log_4 (^{18}/_8) = \log_4 18 - \log_4 8$

(b) $\log_5 (^{125}/_{25}) = \log_5 125 - \log_5 25 = 3 - 2 = 1$

(c) $\log_{10} (^{1000}/_{10}) = \log_{10} 1000 - \log_{10} 10 = 3 - 1 = 2$

(d) $\log_{10} \dfrac{3x^2 - x - 18}{4x^4 - x^3 + 2x^2 - x + 5} = \log_{10} (3x^2 - x - 18)$

$$- \log_{10} (4x^4 - x^3 + 2x^2 - x + 5)$$

(e) $\log_{10} \dfrac{16(x + y)(x - y)}{(x^3 - x)(8x + 6y^2)}$

$$= \log_{10} 16 + \log_{10} (x + y) + \log_{10} (x - y)$$
$$- [\log_{10} (x^3 - x) + \log_{10} (8x + 6y^2)]$$
$$= \log_{10} 16 + \log_{10} (x + y) + \log_{10} (x - y)$$
$$- \log_{10}(x^3 - x) - \log_{10} (8x + 6y^2)$$

3. The logarithm of a number raised to a given power is equal to the exponent multiplied by the logarithm of the number. That is,

$$\log_b K^p = (p) \log_b K$$

To prove this law, proceed as follows:

(a) Let $x = \log_b K$

(b) Write in exponential form

$$K = b^x$$

(c) Raise both sides of the equation in step b to the pth power

$$K^p = (b^x)^p = b^{px}$$

(d) Write the equation of step c in logarithmic form

$$\log_b K^p = px$$

(e) Substitute for x its value

$$\log_b K^p = (p) \log_b K$$

Illustrations of Law 3:

(a) $\log_3 (6)^2 = 2 \log_3 (6)$
(b) $\log_{10} 16^2 = 2 \log_{10} 16$
(c) $\log_{10} (16x^2 - x)^4 = 4 \log_{10} (16x^2 - x)$

4. The logarithm of the nth root of a number is equal to the logarithm of the number divided by n.

$$\log_b \sqrt[n]{K} = \frac{1}{n} \log_b K$$

To prove Law 4, proceed as follows:

(a) Let $x = \log_b K$

(b) Write in exponential form

$$K = b^x$$

(c) Take the nth root of both sides of the equation in step b

$$\sqrt[n]{K} = \sqrt[n]{b^x}$$

(d) Remember that

$$\sqrt[n]{K} = (K)^{1/n} \quad \text{and} \quad \sqrt[n]{b^x} = (b^x)^{1/n}$$

Thus

$$(K)^{1/n} = (b^x)^{1/n} = b^{x/n}$$

(e) Take the logarithm of both sides of the equation in step d

$$\log_b (K)^{1/n} = \frac{x}{n}$$

(f) Substitute for x its value

$$\log_b (K)^{1/n} = \frac{\log_b K}{n} = \frac{1}{n} \log_b K$$

Illustrations of Law 4:

(a) $\log_2 \sqrt[3]{16} = \frac{1}{3} \log_2 16$
(b) $\log_{10} \sqrt[4]{200} = \frac{1}{4} \log_{10} 200$
(c) $\log_{10} \sqrt[18]{x^2 + x + 10} = \frac{1}{18} \log_{10} (x^2 + x + 10)$

The following illustration uses all the laws of logarithmic manipulation:

$$\log_b \sqrt[3]{\frac{(5x^2 + x)^2(x^3 - x^2 + x - 5)}{(18x + 10)^3(x + 5)^p}}$$
$$= \frac{1}{3} \log_b \left[\frac{(5x^2 + x)^2(x^3 - x^2 + x - 5)}{(18x + 10)^3(x + 5)^p} \right]$$
$$= \frac{1}{3}[2 \log_b (5x^2 + x) + \log_b (x^3 - x^2 + x - 5)$$
$$- 3 \log_b (18x + 10) - (p) \log_b (x + 5)]$$

Bases of Logarithms

Logarithms are simply a set of rules for representing numbers and quantities. A logarithmic system may be developed to whatever base one may choose with the only condition being that the base be positive and not equal to 1.

There are two widely used bases for logarithmic systems: the common logarithm (or Briggsian), with the base 10; and the natural (or Napierian) logarithm, whose base is an irrational number with a value to five decimal places of 2.71828.

The common logarithm of a number is written $\log K$. Note that the base is omitted. When the logarithm of a number is given without the specification of the base, it is to be understood that the base is 10.

The logarithmic base of 10 is a convenient device. It has the properties that $\log 1 = 0$, $\log 10 = 1$, $\log 100 = 2$, and $\log 1000 = 3$. For a number $0 < N < 10$, the common logarithm is between 0 and 1, i.e., $0 < \log N < 1$. For any number M such that $10 < M < 100$, the logarithm is between 1 and 2, i.e., $1 < \log M < 2$. For any number K whose value lies between 100 and 1000, the logarithm has a value between 2 and 3. Using symbols, this is written: if $100 < K < 1000$, then $2 < \log K < 3$.

The natural logarithm of any number is computed to the base $e \approx 2.71828$. The natural logarithm of a number N is written $\ln N$. The importance of the natural logarithmic base e cannot be over-emphasized. It has many applications in many branches of mathematics and the sciences.

As an economic application of the number e, suppose that one were to invest a sum of money P_0 at an interest rate i compounded annually. At the end of t years, the value of the initial investment would have grown to

$$P_t = P_0(1 + i)^t$$

If one were to add the growth to the principal k times per year and at a rate i/k per $1/k$ year, the growth would be at the rate

$$P_t = P_0\left(1 + \frac{i}{k}\right)^{kt}$$

If the interest rate were assumed to be 100% so that $i = 1$, the value of the investment would be

$$P_t = P_0\left(1 + \frac{1}{k}\right)^{kt}$$

The expression $(1 + 1/k)^k$ will tend toward the value $e = 2.71828$ as k tends toward infinity. Substituting several values for k and evaluating the expression $(1 + 1/k)^k$ yields the following results:

When $k = 1$ $(1 + \frac{1}{1})^1 = 2$
When $k = 2$ $(1 + \frac{1}{2})^2 = (1.5)^2 = 2.25$
When $k = 3$ $(1 + \frac{1}{3})^3 = (1.33)^3 = 2.358$
When $k = 4$ $(1 + \frac{1}{4})^4 = (1.25)^4 = 2.441$
When $k = 5$ $(1 + \frac{1}{5})^5 = (1.2)^5 = 2.488$
When $k = 6$ $(1 + \frac{1}{6})^6 = (1.166)^6 = 2.512$
When $k = 7$ $(1 + \frac{1}{7})^7 = (1.142)^7 = 2.547$
When $k = 8$ $(1 + \frac{1}{8})^8 = (1.125)^8 = 2.565$
When $k = 9$ $(1 + \frac{1}{9})^9 = (1.111)^9 = 2.575$
When $k = 10$ $(1 + \frac{1}{10})^{10} = (1.1)^{10} = 2.593$

Thus if P_0 dollars were invested at 100% interest, the investment would grow in one year's time to $2P_0$ dollars if compounded annually; to $2.25P_0$ dollars if compounded semiannually; to $2.441P_0$ dollars if compounded quarterly; and to $2.71828 \cdots P_0$ dollars if compounded continuously through the year. If interest were compounded continuously, the initial investment would grow as a function of time t,

$$P_t = P_0 e^t$$

If interest were to be i percent instead of 100%, the growth would be

$$P_t = P_0 e^{(i)t}$$

This is an exponential rate of growth.

The use of the number e gives rise to the most important cases of exponential and logarithmic functions. When an exponential or a logarithmic function has the base e, it is called a *natural exponential* or a *natural logarithmic* function. Examples of such functions are

$$y = e^x \quad \text{and} \quad y = \ln x$$

The Relation between Common and Natural Logarithms

For a natural exponential expression

$$y = e^x$$

the natural logarithm is

$$\ln y = x$$

The natural logarithm of y is equal to x. In that same exponential expression

$$y = e^x$$

taking the common logarithm of both sides of the equation yields

$$\log y = \log e^x$$

which is

$$\log y = x \log e$$

The common log of y is equal to the natural log of y times the common log of the number e.

ALGEBRAIC EXPRESSIONS

An algebraic expression is a combination of *explicit* (exact) numbers and *literal* (letter) numbers according to the rules of the fundamental operations of algebra. Examples of algebraic expressions are

$$6xy \tag{1}$$
$$x - y \tag{2}$$
$$4x^2 + y^2 - 18 \tag{3}$$

In the examples above, the numbers 6, 4, 2, and 18 are called explicit numbers, and the letters x and y are literal numbers which represent explicit numbers.

When an algebraic expression is composed of several distinct parts connected by plus or minus signs, each part together with the sign preceding it is called a term of the expression. When an algebraic expression is made up of only one such term, it is called a *monomial*; otherwise, it is a *polynomial*. Of polynomials, an expression containing two terms is called a *binomial* expression, as for example the expression $x - y$ above, or $(2x^2 + 3y^2)$; a polynomial made up of three terms is a *trinomial*, illustrated by

$$4x^2 + y^2 - 18 \quad \text{or} \quad 2xy + 6y^2 + xyz$$

An algebraic expression is said to be *integral and rational* in certain of its literal numbers if it is composed of positive integral powers of those literal numbers. For example, the expression $-6x^2 + x - \sqrt{7}$ is integral and rational in x. The expression $2x^2y^3 + x^3y^2 + y^3$ is integral and rational in x and y. The polynomial $(6/x\,2) + x$ is not integral in x, but it is rational in x. The binomial $-6\sqrt{x} + (2/x)$ is neither integral nor rational in x.

EQUATIONS AND IDENTITIES

A statement of equality between two algebraic expressions establishes that those expressions are equal to each other. Each such expression in the equality relationship is called a member of the equality. Equalities are of two kinds, *identical equalities* or simply *identities*, and *conditional equalities* or simply *equations*.

When two members of an equality are equal for all values of the literal numbers, the equality is an *identity*. Examples of identities are:

$$(a + b)^2 \equiv a^2 + 2ab + b^2$$
$$(x + y)(x - y) \equiv x^2 - y^2$$
$$\frac{x^2 + 3x - 4}{x - 1} \equiv x + 4$$

(the left-hand member of the last equality is undefined for $x = 1$).

In each of the equalities shown above, whatever values are assigned to the literal numbers a, b, x, and y, the two members of the equality will always be equal. Identities exist between an algebraic expression and the product of its factors. Identities also result when an algebraic expression is simplified, for the equality between the simplified form of the expression and the original expression will be an identity. Sometimes the symbol $\equiv$ (read "is identically equal to") is used to emphasize that the equality is an identity.

If the members of an equality are equal for only certain values of the literal numbers but not for all values, the equality is called a *conditional equality* or an *equation*. Only one value of x (-4) will satisfy the equation

$$2x + 8 = 0$$

There are two values of x (0 or -16) which will satisfy the equation

$$x^2(2x + 1) = 2x(x^2 - 8)$$

which can be rewritten as

$$x^2 + 16x = 0$$

Substitution of 0 or -16 for x shows that these values will satisfy the equation. No other values of x will satisfy the equation. These are examples of equations, for they meet the definition in that only a limited number of values of the unknown will satisfy the conditional equality.

The distinction between an identity and an equation is that any value whatever of the unknown literal number or numbers will satisfy an identity, whereas the values of the unknown that will satisfy an equation are particular and unique. The search for the value or values of the unknown satisfying an equation is the process of *solution* of the equation.

SOLUTION OF EQUATIONS

Linear Equations

An equation of the form

$$ax + b = 0$$

is a first degree equation, for the highest degree of the unknown is 1. The solution of this equation is

$$x = -\frac{b}{a}$$

The substitution of $-(b/a)$ into the original equation for x will yield

$$a\left(-\frac{b}{a}\right) + b = -b + b = 0$$

Some examples of the solution of linear equations are:

1. $x + 4 = 10$
   $x = 10 - 4 = 6$

2. $3(3x - 5) = 3(x - 1)$
   $9x - 15 = 3x - 3$
   $9x - 3x = 15 - 3$
   $6x = 12$
   $x = 2$

3. Solve: $\dfrac{8}{4x - 10} - \dfrac{28}{5x - 8} = 0$

Solution: Clear fractions by multiplying every term by the lowest common denominator $(4x - 10)(5x - 8)$:

$$8(5x - 8) - 28(4x - 10) = 0$$

Multiply the terms:

$$40x - 64 - 112x + 280 = 0$$

After simplifying, the equation becomes:

$$-72x + 216 = 0$$

Transposing the term not containing x to the right-hand side of the equation and solving for x gives the desired solution for x.

$$-72x = -216$$

$$x = \frac{-216}{-72} = 3$$

To check for the correctness of the solution, substitute $x = 3$ into the original equation to see if the equation is satisfied.

$$\frac{8}{4(3) - 10} - \frac{28}{5(3) - 8} = 0$$

$$\frac{8}{12 - 10} - \frac{28}{15 - 8} = \frac{8}{2} - \frac{28}{7} = 4 - 4 = 0$$

Some nonlinear equations can be changed to a linear form to be solved for the unknown by the method discussed in this section.

4. Solve: $\dfrac{x - 3}{x + 3} - \dfrac{x + 3}{x - 3} = 1 - \dfrac{x^2 + 3}{x^2 - 9}$

Solution: First clear the fractions by multiplying each member by the lowest common denominator of the fraction, namely, $(x + 3)(x - 3)$:

$$(x - 3)^2 - (x + 3)^2 = (x^2 - 9) - x^2 - 3$$

Expand the terms:

$$x^2 - 6x + 9 - x^2 - 6x - 9 = x^2 - 9 - x^2 - 3$$

Collecting terms and transposing yields

$$-12x = -12$$
$$x = 1$$

Substituting $x = 1$ into the original equation, check to determine whether the solution satisfies the equation:

$$\frac{1 - 3}{1 + 3} - \frac{1 + 3}{1 - 3} = 1 - \frac{1 + 3}{1 - 9}$$

$$\frac{-2}{4} - \frac{4}{-2} = 1 - \frac{4}{-8}$$

$$-\tfrac{1}{2} + 2 = 1 + \tfrac{1}{2}$$

$$1\tfrac{1}{2} = 1\tfrac{1}{2}$$

Quadratic Equations

An equation of the form

$$ax^2 + bx + c = 0$$

where a, b, and c are constants, is called the general quadratic equation in the unknown x. If b, the coefficient of x, is zero, the equation becomes $ax^2 + c = 0$, and is called a pure quadratic equation. If $b \neq 0$, the quadratic equation is called a complete quadratic equation. In a quadratic equation either b or c, or both b and c, may be zero. But a, the coefficient of x^2, may not be zero, for then the equation will no longer be quadratic, but linear, of the form

$$bx + c = 0$$

with the solution

$$x = -\frac{c}{b}$$

In the solution of a quadratic equation, it is helpful first to reduce the given equation to the form of the standard quadratic equation. For example, the equation

$$(px + q)^2 = mx^2 + nx + q$$

can be reduced to the form of

$$ax^2 + bx + c = 0$$

To do so, first expand $(px + q)^2$:

$$p^2x^2 + 2pqx + q^2 = mx^2 + nx + q$$

Next transpose all the terms to the left-hand side of the equation, which results in

$$p^2x^2 - mx^2 + 2pqx - nx + q^2 - q = 0$$

Now combine like terms:

$$(p^2 - m)x^2 + (2pq - n)x + (q^2 - q) = 0$$

In this final standard form

$$a = (p^2 - m)$$
$$b = (2pq - n)$$
$$c = (q^2 - q)$$

Consider another example: Reduce to standard form

$$(3x + 4)(2x - 5) = (x - 1)^2$$

Solution: Expand the terms on both sides of the equation:

$$6x^2 - 7x - 20 = x^2 - 2x + 1$$

Transpose the terms:

$$6x^2 - x^2 - 7x + 2x - 20 - 1 = 0$$

Combine like terms:

$$5x^2 - 5x - 21 = 0$$

$$a = 5 \qquad b = -5 \qquad c = -21$$

Any equation which can be reduced to the standard form

$$ax^2 + bx + c = 0$$

is a quadratic equation. A quadratic equation will have at most two solutions or roots.

Solution of Pure Quadratic Equations

A pure quadratic equation is an equation of the form

$$ax^2 + bx + c = 0$$

in which $b = 0$, thus reducing the equation to the form

$$ax^2 + c = 0$$

The solution of the equation

$$ax^2 - c = 0$$

is achieved by transposing c to the right-hand side of the equation, dividing both members by a, and taking the square root of both members of the equation:

$$ax^2 - c = 0$$

$$ax^2 = c$$

$$x^2 = \frac{c}{a}$$

$$x = \pm\sqrt{\frac{c}{a}}$$

In this case the two roots will have the same numerical value, $\sqrt{c/a}$, but of opposite signs. Further, since c/a is positive, the roots are real numbers.
If the original equation had been

$$ax^2 + c = 0$$

the solutions would have been

$$x = \pm\sqrt{-\frac{c}{a}}$$

The roots are imaginary numbers. A discussion of imaginary numbers will be deferred to a later section.

Some examples of the solution of pure quadratic equations are given below:

1. Solve: $2x^2 - 50 = 0$

Solution:

$$2x^2 = 50$$
$$x^2 = 25$$
$$x = \pm\sqrt{25}$$
$$x = \pm5$$

Check:

$$2(5^2) - 50 = 0$$
$$2(-5^2) - 50 = 0$$

2. Solve: $3x^2 = 12$

Solution:

$$x^2 = 4$$
$$x = \pm\sqrt{4}$$
$$x = \pm2$$

Substitution of either $x = 2$ or $x = -2$ will satisfy the equation.

3. Solve: $x(x + 6) = 6(x + 6)$

Solution: Expanding both members gives

$$x^2 + 6x = 6x + 36$$

Transpose and simplify:

$$x^2 = 36$$
$$x = \pm\sqrt{36}$$
$$x = \pm6$$

Check: Substitute $x = \pm6$ into the original equation to find that both roots satisfy the equation.

Solution of Complete Quadratic Equations

In a complete quadratic equation a, the coefficient of x^2, and b, the coefficient of x, are both nonzero. The constant c may or may not be zero.

The solution of such a quadratic equation may be achieved in several ways: by factoring, by completing the square, and by the use of the quadratic formula.

Solution by factoring is particularly expedient if the equation to be solved is factorable. Not all quadratic equations are factorable, however, and as a result, this method is somewhat limited in its application. Consider some examples of solution by factoring.

1. If $c = 0$ in the standard form of the quadratic equation

$$ax^2 + bx + c = 0$$

the equation reduces to

$$ax^2 + bx = 0$$

To solve for the roots of this equation, factor out the x and write

$$x(ax + b) = 0$$

For the product

$$x(ax + b) = 0$$

to be true, either $x = 0$ or $ax + b = 0$. The solutions then follow immediately:

$$x = 0 \quad \text{and} \quad x = -\frac{b}{a}$$

These roots may be checked by substitution into the equation. If $x = 0$, the product $x(ax + b)$ will be equal to zero whatever value $ax + b$ may assume. Substituting

$$x = -\frac{b}{a}$$

into the equation yields

$$-\frac{b}{a}\left[a\left(-\frac{b}{a}\right) + b\right] = -\frac{b}{a}[-b + b] = 0$$

The solution checks. The two roots of the equation, therefore, are

$$x = 0 \quad \text{and} \quad x = -\frac{b}{a}$$

2. Solve: $2x^2 + 8x = 0$

Solution:

$$x(2x + 8) = 0$$
$$x = 0$$
$$2x + 8 = 0$$
$$x = -4$$

Check:

$$x = 0$$
$$2(0^2) + 8(0) = 0$$
$$x = -4$$
$$2(-4^2) + 8(-4) = 32 - 32 = 0$$

Now consider some quadratic equations in which a, b, and c are all of nonzero value.

1. Solve: $x^2 + 6x + 8 = 0$

Solution: Factor the equations:

$$(x + 4)(x + 2) = 0$$

Set $x + 4 = 0$ and $x + 2 = 0$ to get $x = -4$ and $x = -2$.

Check:

$$x = -4; \ (-4^2) + 6(-4) + 8 = 16 - 24 + 8 = 0$$
$$x = -2; \ (-2^2) + 6(-2) + 8 = \ 4 - 12 + 8 = 0$$

2. Solve: $3x^2 + 7x + 2 = 0$

Solution: Factor the equation:

$$(3x + 1)(x + 2) = 0$$

Set $3x + 1 = 0$ and $x + 2 = 0$ to get $x = -\frac{1}{3}$ and $x = -2$.

Check:

$$x = -\tfrac{1}{3}; \ 3(-\tfrac{1}{3})^2 + 7(-\tfrac{1}{3}) + 2 = \tfrac{3}{9} - \tfrac{21}{9} + 2 = 0$$
$$x = -2; \ 3(-2)^2 + 7(-2) + 2 = 12 - 14 + 2 = 0$$

3. Solve: $6x^2 - x - 12 = 0$

Solution: Note that

$$6x^2 - x - 12 = (2x - 3)(3x + 4)$$

Since the original equation shows that the left member

$$6x^2 - x - 12 = 0$$

set the product of the factors equal to zero:

$$(2x - 3)(3x + 4) = 0$$

For this equation to hold, either

$$2x - 3 = 0 \qquad x = \tfrac{3}{2}$$

or

$$3x + 4 = 0 \qquad x = -\tfrac{4}{3}$$

Check:

$$x = \tfrac{3}{2}; \ 6(\tfrac{3}{2})^2 - (\tfrac{3}{2}) - 12 = \tfrac{54}{4} - \tfrac{6}{4} - \tfrac{48}{4} = 0$$
$$x = -\tfrac{4}{3}; \ 6(-\tfrac{4}{3})^2 - (-\tfrac{4}{3}) - 12 = \tfrac{96}{9} + \tfrac{12}{9} - \tfrac{108}{9} = 0$$

These examples show the application of the technique of factoring to solve quadratic equations. As indicated earlier, this technique is sometimes difficult or impossible to apply. In such cases the method of completing the square of the quadratic equation can be applied to solve the equation. This method of solution can be used on all quadratic equations whether or not solutions could be achieved by factoring. The following several paragraphs will develop the solutions of several quadratic equations by the method of completing the square. Then this solution technique will be applied to the general standard form of the quadratic equation to develop the so-called quadratic formula used in the solution of all quadratic equations.

The process of completing the square relies upon the fact that any binomial expression of the form $ax^2 + bx$ can be made into a perfect square by (1) dividing both terms by the coefficient of x^2, namely a, and (2) adding the square of one-half of b/a, i.e., $(b/2a)^2$:

$$x^2 + \frac{b}{a}x + \left(\frac{b}{2a}\right)^2 = x^2 + \frac{b}{a}x + \frac{b^2}{4a^2} = \left(x + \frac{b}{2a}\right)^2$$

To complete the square of the binomial expression $x^2 - 6x$, add $(-\frac{6}{2})^2$ or $(\frac{36}{4}) = 9$; thus the perfect square becomes

$$x^2 - 6x + 9 = (x - 3)^2$$

This technique of completing the square can be used to solve any quadratic equation. The following examples will illustrate its use.

1. Solve by completing the square:

$$2x^2 + 8x = 0$$

Solution: Divide by the coefficient of x^2, i.e., 2:

$$x^2 + 4x = 0$$

Add to both sides of the equation the square of one-half of the coefficient of x, i.e., $(\frac{1}{2} 4)^2$:

$$x^2 + 4x + 4 = 4 \qquad (x + 2)^2 = 4$$

Find the square roots:

$$x + 2 = \pm\sqrt{4}$$

Solve for x:

$$x + 2 = 2 \qquad x = 0$$
$$x + 2 = -2 \qquad x = -4$$

The two roots of the quadratic equation are therefore $x = 0$ and $x = -4$.

2. Solve by completing the square:

$$x^2 + 6x + 8 = 0$$

Solution: Transpose the constant term

$$x^2 + 6x = -8$$

Divide by the coefficient of x^2. Add the square of one-half the coefficient of x, i.e., $(\frac{6}{2})^2$ or 9:

$$x^2 + 6x + 9 = -8 + 9$$
$$(x + 3)^2 = 1$$

Extract the square roots:

$$x + 3 = \pm\sqrt{1}$$

Solve for x:

$$x + 3 = 1 \qquad x = -2$$
$$x + 3 = -1 \qquad x = -4$$

The roots are $x = -2$ and $x = -4$.

3. Solve by completing the square:

$$x^2 - 2x - 8 = 0$$

Solution: Transpose the constant term

$$x^2 - 2x = 8$$

Divide by the coefficient of x^2. Add the square of one-half the coefficient of x:

$$x^2 - 2x + 1 = 9$$
$$(x - 1)^2 = 9$$

Extract the square roots:

$$x - 1 = \pm\sqrt{9}$$

Solve for x:

$$x - 1 = 3 \qquad x = 4$$
$$x - 1 = -3 \qquad x = -2$$

The roots are $x = 4$ and $x = -2$.

In the examples above, the technique of completing the square was used to solve specific quadratic equations. By applying this technique to the general quadratic equation, one can develop the general formula for the solution of all quadratic equations. Begin with the general quadratic equation

$$ax^2 + bx + c = 0$$

Transpose the constant term to the right-hand side of the equation:

$$ax^2 + bx = -c$$

Divide every term of this equation by the coefficient of x^2, i.e., a:

$$x^2 + \frac{b}{a}x = -\frac{c}{a}$$

When the square of one-half of the coefficient of x is added to both sides of the equation, the left-hand side of the equation becomes a perfect square:

$$x^2 + \frac{b}{a}x + \left(\frac{b}{2a}\right)^2 = -\frac{c}{a} + \left(\frac{b}{2a}\right)^2$$

or

$$x^2 + \frac{b}{a}x + \frac{b^2}{4a^2} = -\frac{c}{a} + \frac{b^2}{4a^2}$$

$$x^2 + \frac{b}{a}x + \frac{b^2}{4a^2} = \frac{b^2 - 4ac}{4a^2}$$

which is

$$\left(x + \frac{b}{2a}\right)^2 = \frac{b^2 - 4ac}{4a^2}$$

Extract the square root of both sides:

$$x + \frac{b}{2a} = \frac{\pm\sqrt{b^2 - 4ac}}{2a}$$

Subtract $b/2a$ from both sides of the equation:

$$x = \frac{-b \pm \sqrt{b^2 - 4ac}}{2a}$$

This is the quadratic formula which can be used to solve any second-degree equation in one unknown. If $b^2 > 4ac$, the expression under the radical sign is positive and the roots of the equation are real numbers. If $b^2 < 4ac$, the difference $b^2 - 4ac$ is negative and the roots are complex numbers.

With the use of this formula, the solution of any quadratic equation is a simple matter of substituting the appropriate values into the equation to derive the desired solutions. For example, solve:

$$2x^2 - 7x - 15 = 0$$

Here $a = 2$, $b = -7$, and $c = -15$:

$$x = \frac{7 \pm \sqrt{7^2 - 4(2)(-15)}}{2(2)} = \frac{7 \pm \sqrt{49 + 120}}{4} = \frac{7 \pm \sqrt{169}}{4} = \frac{7 \pm 13}{4}$$

$$x = \frac{7 + 13}{4} = 5 \quad \text{or} \quad x = \frac{7 - 13}{4} = -\frac{6}{4} = -\frac{3}{2}$$

The Character of the Roots of Quadratic Equations

When seeking solutions of quadratic equations it is often instructive to know something about the nature of the solutions which will emerge. For example, it is helpful to be able to estimate in advance whether the roots will be real or imaginary; whether they will be equal or unequal; and whether they will be rational or irrational.

If r_1 and r_2 are the two roots of the standard quadratic equation, they must have the values

$$r_1 = \frac{-b + \sqrt{b^2 - 4ac}}{2a} \qquad \text{and} \qquad r_2 = \frac{-b - \sqrt{b^2 - 4ac}}{2a}$$

The expression under the radical sign ($b^2 - 4ac$) is called the *discriminant* of the quadratic equation. The numerical character of the roots will depend on the value of the discriminant. If

$$b^2 - 4ac > 0$$

the roots will be real numbers. Further, in this case the 2 roots will be unequal in value. If

$$b^2 - 4ac = 0$$

the roots will be real numbers and equal in magnitude. If

$$b^2 - 4ac < 0$$

the roots will be complex numbers and unequal in magnitude. If

$$b^2 - 4ac = \text{a perfect square}$$

the solutions will be rational numbers; if

$$b^2 - 4ac \neq \text{a perfect square}$$

the solutions will be irrational numbers.

Another interesting point to be noted about the roots of quadratic equations emerges upon taking their sum and their product. The sum of r_1 and r_2 is

$$r_1 + r_2 = \frac{-b + \sqrt{b^2 - 4ac}}{2a} + \frac{-b - \sqrt{b^2 - 4ac}}{2a} = \frac{-2b}{2a} = -\frac{b}{a}$$

The product of the two roots is

$$r_1 \cdot r_2 = \frac{-b + \sqrt{b^2 - 4ac}}{2a} \cdot \frac{-b - \sqrt{b^2 - 4ac}}{2a}$$

$$= \frac{(-b)^2 - (b^2 - 4ac)}{4a^2} = \frac{4ac}{4a^2} = \frac{c}{a}$$

These results show that the sum of the two roots of any quadratic equation will be the negative of the ratio of the coefficient of x to the coefficient of x^2, i.e., $-(b/a)$, while their product will be the positive ratio of the constant term to the coefficient of x^2, i.e., c/a.

In one of the quadratic equations solved earlier, the roots of the equation

$$2x^2 + 8x = 0$$

were shown to be

$$x_1 = 0 \quad \text{and} \quad x_2 = -4$$

The preceding discussion suggests that their sum must be equal to

$$x_1 + x_2 = -\frac{b}{a} = -\frac{8}{2} = -4$$

Note from the known values of x_1 and x_2 that

$$x_1 + x_2 = 0 + (-4) = -4$$

Further, the product of x_1 and x_2 must be equal to

$$x_1 \cdot x_2 = \frac{c}{a} = \frac{0}{2} = 0$$

From the values of x_1 and x_2, it is apparent that the product of those two roots is

$$x_1 \cdot x_2 = 0 \cdot (-4) = 0$$

These relationships are highly useful in suggesting possible solutions of quadratic equations. As an illustration, solve the equation

$$2x^2 - 5x + 3 = 0$$

The roots x_1 and x_2 will hold the following relationships

$$x_1 + x_2 = -\frac{b}{a} = -\frac{-5}{2} = \frac{5}{2} \qquad x_1 \cdot x_2 = \frac{c}{a} = \frac{3}{2}$$

The set of values of x_1 and x_2 satisfying these relations is

$$x_1 = \tfrac{3}{2} \quad \text{and} \quad x_2 = 1$$

These then are the roots of the equation. This is essentially the method of factoring.

COMPLEX NUMBERS

In the solution of the quadratic equation

$$x^2 + 1 = 0$$

the two roots are

$$x = \pm\sqrt{-1}$$

Inasmuch as the square of either a positive or a negative number is positive, the number $\sqrt{-1}$ cannot be a member of the real number system. The number $\sqrt{-1}$ is called an *imaginary* unit. It is designated by i. The number i has the property that

$$i^2 = (\sqrt{-1})^2 = -1$$

The number i is assumed to have algebraic properties such that it can be manipulated as any other literal number. Then, for any positive real number N,

$$\sqrt{-N} = \sqrt{i^2 N} = i\sqrt{N}$$

Any number such as $\pm i\sqrt{N}$ where N is a positive real number is called an *imaginary number*.

A number of the form $a \pm bi$ is called a *complex number*, where a and b are real numbers. The number a is called the real part and the number bi is called the imaginary part of the complex number.

Equality of complex numbers follows the definition of equality of real numbers. Complex numbers are equal if and only if their real parts are equal and their imaginary parts are equal. This is to say that the two imaginary numbers $a + bi$ and $c + di$ are equal if and only if $a = c$ and $b = d$.

Two complex numbers which differ only in the sign of their imaginary parts are called *conjugate complex numbers*. Either is the conjugate of the other. For example, $a + bi$ and $a - bi$ are conjugate complex numbers. One may say either that $a + bi$ is the conjugate of $a - bi$, or that $a - bi$ is the conjugate of $a + bi$. The numbers bi and $-bi$ are also conjugate complex numbers.

Algebraic Operations with Complex Numbers

Addition and Subtraction. When adding or subtracting two complex numbers, add or subtract the real parts and the imaginary parts separately.

Illustrations:

1. $(a + bi) + (c + di) = (a + c) + (bi + di) = (a + c) + (b + d)i$
2. $(a + bi) - (c + di) = (a - c) + (b - d)i$
3. $(6 + 2i) + (6 + 3i) = (6 + 6) + (2 + 3)i = 12 + 5i$
4. $(3 + 2i) - (5 + 4i) = (3 - 5) + (2 - 4)i = -2 - 2i$
5. $(a + bi) + (a - bi) = (a + a) + (b - b)i = 2a$

Note that the sum of two conjugate complex numbers is that real number which is twice the real part.

Multiplication.   Multiplication of complex numbers is achieved by following the usual algebraic rules for multiplying real numbers and substituting $i^2 = -1$.

Illustrations:

1. $(a + bi)(c + di) = ac + bci + adi + bdi^2$
$$= ac + (bc + ad)i - bd$$
$$= (ac - bd) + (bc + ad)i$$

2. $(3 + 2i)(4 + 3i) = 12 + 8i + 9i + 6i^2 = 12 + 17i - 6 = 6 + 17i$

3. $(a + bi)(a - bi) = a^2 + abi - abi - b^2i^2 = a^2 + b^2$

Note that the product of conjugate complex numbers is a real number.

Division.   To divide one complex number by another complex number, multiply both the numerator and the denominator by the conjugate of the denominator.

Illustrations:

1. $$\frac{a + bi}{c + di} = \frac{(a + bi)(c - di)}{(c + di)(c - di)} = \frac{ac + bci - adi - bdi^2}{c^2 + cdi - cdi - d^2i^2}$$
$$= \frac{ac + (bc - ad)i + bd}{c^2 + d^2} = \frac{(ac + bd) + (bc - ad)i}{c^2 + d^2}$$

2. $$\frac{3 + 4i}{4 - 2i} = \frac{(3 + 4i)(4 + 2i)}{(4 - 2i)(4 + 2i)} = \frac{12 + 16i + 6i + 8i^2}{16 - 8i + 8i - 4i^2}$$
$$= \frac{12 + 22i - 8}{16 + 4} = \frac{4 + 22i}{16 + 4} = \frac{4 + 22i}{20}$$

After this brief review of the fundamental algebraic operations involving complex numbers, it is time to examine particular solutions of quadratic equations involving complex numbers. When using the quadratic formula for solution, if the given equation is such that $b^2 < 4ac$, the solution will contain conjugate complex numbers $-b + i\sqrt{N}$ and $-b - i\sqrt{N}$ where $N = -(b^2 - 4ac)$.

The solutions of the following equations will result in either imaginary or complex numbers:

1. $x^2 + 1 = 0$

   $x = \pm\sqrt{-1} = \pm\sqrt{i^2} = \pm i$

2. $x^2 + 5 = 0$

   $x = \pm\sqrt{-5} = \pm\sqrt{(-1)5} = \pm\sqrt{i^25} = \pm i\sqrt{5}$

3. $4x^2 - 5x + 5 = 0$

   $$x = \frac{5 \pm \sqrt{(-5)^2 - 4(4)(5)}}{2(4)} = \frac{5 \pm \sqrt{25 - 80}}{8} = \frac{5 \pm \sqrt{-55}}{8}$$

   $$= \frac{5 \pm \sqrt{(-1)55}}{8} = \frac{5 \pm \sqrt{i^255}}{8} = \frac{5 \pm i\sqrt{55}}{8} = \frac{5}{8} \pm \frac{1}{8}i\sqrt{55}$$

The solutions are, therefore,

$$x = \tfrac{5}{8} + \tfrac{1}{8}i\sqrt{55} \qquad \text{and} \qquad x = \tfrac{5}{8} - \tfrac{1}{8}i\sqrt{55}$$

These two solutions are conjugate complex numbers where

$$a = \tfrac{5}{8} \qquad \text{and} \qquad b = \pm\tfrac{1}{8}\sqrt{55}$$

Solutions involving complex numbers are sometimes meaningful; at other times such solutions cannot be given any specific meaning in terms of the problem being solved. This statement applies not only to complex roots of equations but to roots taking other forms as well. For example, if the problem is to find the equilibrium prices, negative quantities will be rejected, unless special interpretations of such negative prices are provided elsewhere. Similarly, complex roots of equations have meaning in some specific problems of economic theory such as location analyses and second-order difference equations. It is sufficient at this point to know the nature of imaginary numbers and complex numbers, and a few of the operational techniques involving complex numbers. The subject of complex numbers is a vast one, and its complete treatment is not part of the purpose of this book.

Graphic Solution of Quadratic Equations

If a rectangular coordinate system is used to plot a function such as

$$f(x) = ax^2 + bx + c$$

a parabola will result. When $f(x)$ is equal to zero, the roots of

$$ax^2 + bx + c = 0$$

can be found. The roots can be found graphically by plotting the function and finding the values of x at which the function crosses the x-axis.

There are three possibilities when such a curve is plotted: (1) the curve may cross the x-axis at two distinct points, in which case the roots of $f(x) = 0$ will be real and unequal; (2) the curve may touch the x-axis at some one point but not cross it, in which case the roots of $f(x) = 0$ are real and equal; (3) the curve may neither cross nor touch the x-axis, in which case the roots of the function $f(x) = 0$ are imaginary.

$$f_1(x) = x^2 - 2x - 2$$

x	-2	-1	0	1	2	3	4
$f_1(x)$	6	1	-2	-3	-2	1	6

$$f_2(x) = x^2 - 2x + 1$$

x	-2	-1	0	1	2	3	4
$f_2(x)$	9	4	1	0	1	4	9

$$f_3(x) = x^2 - 2x + 3$$

x	-2	-1	0	1	2	3	4
$f_3(x)$	11	6	3	2	3	6	11

The three possibilities above are illustrated in Figure 2-1. The graph shows that $f_1(x) = 0$ has roots $x = -0.7$ and $x = 2.7$ approximately. The algebraic solution of $f_1(x)$ shows the roots to be

$$x = \frac{2 \pm \sqrt{12}}{2} \qquad x = -0.73 \qquad \text{or} \qquad x = 2.73$$

to two decimal places. Since the discriminant of this quadratic equation is 12, the roots are real, unequal, and irrational.

An examination of the curve traced by $f_2(x)$ shows that $f_2(x) = 0$ occurs at $x = 1$. Algebraically, the solutions of $f_2(x) = 0$ are

$$x = \frac{2 \pm \sqrt{(-2)^2 - 4(1)(1)}}{2} = \frac{2 \pm \sqrt{0}}{2} = 1$$

Since the discriminant of the quadratic equation $f_2(x)$ is 0, the roots of the equation are real, equal, and rational.

Figure 2-1 shows that $f_3(x)$ does not touch or cross the x-axis anywhere, suggesting that $f_3(x) = 0$ has no real roots. Algebraically, we find that

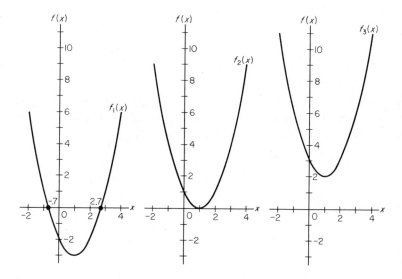

Figure 2-1   Roots of Equations

$f_3(x) = 0$ has the solutions:

$$x = \frac{2 \pm \sqrt{(-2)^2 - 4(1)(3)}}{2} = \frac{2 \pm \sqrt{-8}}{2}$$

$$x = \frac{2 \pm i\sqrt{8}}{2}$$

$$x = 1 + \frac{\sqrt{8}}{2}i \quad \text{or} \quad x = 1 - \frac{\sqrt{8}}{2}i$$

SYSTEMS OF EQUATIONS

This section is devoted to the solution of linear simultaneous equations involving two and three unknowns, and simultaneous equations involving quadratics.

Systems of Linear Equations

In a system of two linear equations with two unknowns, say x and y, the technique of solution is to eliminate one of the unknowns, say x, and solve for y. After the value of y has been established, it is substituted into one of the original equations to solve for the value of the remaining un-known, x. There are three basic methods of solving linear equations involving two or three unknowns, which can be generalized to solve for any number of unknowns. The three methods are (1) elimination by addition or subtraction, (2) elimination by substitution, and (3) solution by using determinants.

Elimination by Addition or Subtraction. As the first illustration of this method of solution, suppose that six pounds of bacon and ten dozen eggs cost $21, and that four pounds of bacon and five dozen eggs cost $12. What are the prices of bacon and eggs?

This is a situation involving two unknowns. If the statement had been only "six pounds of bacon and ten dozen eggs cost $21," an infinite number of combinations of bacon and egg prices would have satisfied the condition. It would have been impossible to find a unique solution. The addition of the second statement, "4 pounds of bacon and 5 dozen eggs cost $12," makes the solution unique. Only one combination of prices will satisfy both conditions.

Let x be the price of bacon and y the price of eggs. The two statements can be translated into two equations:

$$6x + 10y = 21 \qquad (1)$$
$$4x + 5y = 12 \qquad (2)$$

The problem is then to find the values of x and y which will satisfy both equations.

Solution:

Multiply (2) by 2:	$8x + 10y = 24$	(3)
Rewrite (1):	$6x + 10y = 21$	(4)
Subtract (4) from (3):	$2x \quad\quad = 3$	(5)
Solve (5) for x:	$x = {}^{3}\!/_{2} = 1.5$	
Substitute		
$x = 1.5$ into (1):	$6(1.5) + 10y = 21$	(6)
Solve (6) for y:	$y = 1.2$	

Substitution of $x = 1.5$ and $y = 1.2$ into the two original equations satisfies both:

$$6(1.5) + 10(1.2) = 21$$
$$4(1.5) + 5(1.2) = 12$$

A second example illustrates the solution for x and y of a system of two equations linear in $1/x$ and $1/y$:

$$\frac{6}{x} - \frac{4}{y} + 2 = 0 \tag{1}$$

$$\frac{14}{x} - \frac{12}{y} + 4 = 0 \tag{2}$$

Multiply (1) by 3:

$$\frac{18}{x} - \frac{12}{y} + 6 = 0 \tag{3}$$

Rewrite (2):

$$\frac{14}{x} - \frac{12}{y} + 4 = 0 \tag{4}$$

Subtract (4) from (3):

$$\frac{4}{x} \qquad + 2 = 0 \tag{5}$$

Solve (5) for x:

$$\frac{4}{x} = -2 \qquad 4 = -2x \qquad x = -2$$

Substitute $x = -2$ into (1):

$$\frac{6}{-2} - \frac{4}{y} + 2 = 0 \tag{6}$$

Solve (6) for y:

$$-3 - \frac{4}{y} + 2 = 0$$

$$y = -4$$

Substitution of $x = -2$ and $y = -4$ into (1) and (2) can be used to check the solutions:

$$\frac{6}{-2} - \frac{4}{-4} + 2 = -3 + 1 + 2 = 0$$

$$\frac{14}{-2} - \frac{12}{-4} + 4 = -7 + 3 + 4 = 0$$

An alternative technique of solution of this problem is to let $u = 1/x$ and $v = 1/y$ and proceed with the solutions for u and v first. When the values of u and v are found, their reciprocals will be the values of x and y respectively. The original equations to be solved become

$$6u - 4v + 2 = 0 \tag{1}$$
$$14u - 12v + 4 = 0 \tag{2}$$

Multiply (1) by 3: $\qquad 18u - 12v + 6 = 0 \tag{3}$

Rewrite (2): $\qquad 14u - 12v + 4 = 0 \tag{4}$

Subtract (4) from (3): $\qquad 4u \qquad\quad + 2 = 0 \tag{5}$

Solve (5) for u: $\qquad\qquad\qquad u = -\frac{1}{2}$

Substitute

$u = -(\frac{1}{2})$ into (1): $6(-\frac{1}{2}) - 4v + 2 = 0$ $\qquad\qquad$ (6)

Solve (6) for v: $\qquad\qquad -3 - 4v + 2 = 0$

$$-4v = 1$$
$$v = -\frac{1}{4}$$

Since

$u = -\dfrac{1}{2}$ $\quad$ and $\quad$ $u = \dfrac{1}{x}$ $\quad$ then $\quad$ $\dfrac{1}{x} = -\dfrac{1}{2}$ $\quad$ $x = -2$

$v = -\dfrac{1}{4}$ $\quad$ and $\quad$ $v = \dfrac{1}{y}$ $\quad$ then $\quad$ $\dfrac{1}{y} = -\dfrac{1}{4}$ $\quad$ $y = -4$

As a third example of solutions of simultaneous equations, examine the solution for three unknowns in a system of three linear equations. Suppose there are three linear equations in three unknowns, x, y, and z. The technique of solution is to eliminate one of the unknowns, say x, from the first two of the original equations. The same unknown is then eliminated from the second two of the original equations. This results in two equations in two unknowns, y and z. Solve these equations for y and z. The substitution of the solutions of y and z into one of the original equations yields the solution for x.

$$2x + 3y + z = -1 \qquad\qquad (1)$$
$$x - y + 2z = 7 \qquad\qquad (2)$$
$$3x + 2y - z = 1 \qquad\qquad (3)$$

Multiply (1) by 2: $\qquad 4x + 6y + 2z = -2 \qquad\qquad (4)$

Rewrite (2): $\qquad\qquad x - y + 2z = 7 \qquad\qquad (5)$

Subtract (5) from (4): $\qquad 3x + 7y = -9 \qquad\qquad (6)$

Multiply (3) by 2: $\qquad 6x + 4y - 2z = 2 \qquad\qquad (7)$

Rewrite (2): $\qquad\qquad x - y + 2z = 7 \qquad\qquad (8)$

Add (7) and (8): $\qquad 7x + 3y = 9 \qquad\qquad (9)$

Equations (6) and (9) are in the unknowns x and y.

Rewrite (6): $\qquad\qquad 3x + 7y = -9 \qquad\qquad (10)$

Rewrite (9): $\qquad\qquad 7x + 3y = 9 \qquad\qquad (11)$

Multiply (10) by 3: $\qquad 9x + 21y = -27 \qquad\qquad (12)$

Multiply (11) by 7: $\qquad \overline{49x + 21y = 63} \qquad\qquad (13)$

Subtract (12)

from (13): $\qquad\qquad 40x = 90 \qquad\qquad (14)$

Solve (14) for x: $\qquad\qquad x = {}^{90}\!/_{40} = 2.25$

Substitute $x = 2.25$

into (10): $3(2.25) + 7y \qquad = -9$ (15)

Solve (15) for y: $y \qquad = -2.25$

Substitute $x = 2.25$ and $y = -2.25$ into (2):

$$2.25 - (-2.25) + 2z = \quad 7$$
$$z = \ 1.25$$

To check the solutions, substitute $x = 2.25$, $y = -2.25$, and $z = 1.25$ into the original three equations:

$$2(2.25) + 3(-2.25) + 1.25 = -1$$
$$2.25 - (-2.25) + 2(1.25) = 7$$
$$3(2.25) + 2(-2.25) - 1.25 = 1$$

The solutions check, confirming that they satisfy all three equations.

Elimination by Substitution. Again we begin our discussion by first examining the solution of systems of linear equations in two unknowns. Return to the problem involving prices of bacon and eggs, in which x was the unknown price of bacon and y was the unknown price of eggs. The solution consists of taking one of the equations and solving it for, say, x in terms of y, and substituting this expression of x in terms of y into the remaining equation to obtain the solution for y. Then the substitution of this value of y into one of the original equations yields the solution for x:

$$6x + 10y = 21 \qquad (1)$$
$$4x + 5y = 12 \qquad (2)$$

Solve (1) for x: $x = \dfrac{21}{6} - \dfrac{10y}{6}$ (3)

Substitute (3) into (2): $4\left(\dfrac{21}{6} - \dfrac{10y}{6}\right) + 5y = 12$ (4)

$$\frac{42}{3} - \frac{20y}{3} + 5y = 12$$

Multiply every term by 3: $42 - 20y + 15y = 36$
$$y = 1.2$$

Substitute $y = 1.2$

into (1): $6x + 10(1.2) = 21$ (5)

Solve (5) for x: $x \qquad = 1.5$

These answers agree with the answers previously derived.

As a second illustration of the method of substitution, solve again

$$\frac{6}{x} - \frac{4}{y} + 2 = 0 \tag{1}$$

$$\frac{14}{x} - \frac{12}{y} + 4 = 0 \tag{2}$$

Solve (1) for $1/y$:
$$-\frac{4}{y} = -2 - \frac{6}{x} \tag{3}$$

Multiply both sides of the equation by $-(\frac{1}{4})$:

$$\frac{1}{y} = \frac{1}{2} + \frac{3}{2x} \tag{4}$$

Substitute (4) into (2):
$$\frac{14}{x} - 12\left(\frac{1}{2} + \frac{3}{2x}\right) + 4 = 0 \tag{5}$$

Solve (5) for x:
$$\frac{14}{x} - \frac{12}{2} - \frac{18}{x} + 4 = 0$$

$$-\frac{4}{x} = 2$$

$$x = -2$$

Substitute $x = -2$ into (2):
$$\frac{14}{-2} - \frac{12}{y} + 4 = 0$$

$$-7 + 4 = \frac{12}{y}$$

$$y = -4$$

The solutions by the substitution method again agree with the answers previously derived.

Now consider a system of three linear equations in three unknowns, x, y, and z. The approach to this system is simply an expansion of the technique already illustrated. Solve the first equation for z and substitute this expression for z into the second equation. The result is an equation in two unknowns, x and y. Substitute this expression for z in terms of x and y into the third original equation to obtain a second equation in x and y. The two new equations in terms of x and y form a system that can be solved simultaneously. Substitute the solutions of x and y into any of the original equations to find the solution of z:

$$2x + 3y + z = -1 \tag{1}$$

$$x - y + 2z = 7 \tag{2}$$

$$3x + 2y - z = 1 \tag{3}$$

Solve (1) for z:
$$z = -1 - 2x - 3y \tag{4}$$

Substitute (4)
  into (2): $x - y + 2(-1 - 2x - 3y) = 7$

$$x - y - 2 - 4x - 6y = 7$$

$$-3x - 7y = 9 \qquad\qquad (5)$$

Substitute (4)
  into (3): $3x + 2y - (-1 - 2x - 3y) = 1$

$$3x + 2y + 1 + 2x + 3y = 1$$

$$5x + 5y = 0 \qquad\qquad (6)$$

Solve (6) for x: $x = -y \qquad\qquad (7)$

Substitute (7)
  into (5): $(-3)(-y) - 7y = 9$

$$-4y = 9$$

$$y = -2.25$$

Substitute $y = -2.25$ into (6) and solve for x:

$$5x + 5(-2.25) = 0$$

$$5x - 11.25 = 0$$

$$x = 2.25$$

Substitute $x = 2.25$ and $y = -2.25$ into (3) and solve for z:

$$3(2.25) + 2(-2.25) - z = 1$$

$$6.75 - 4.5 - 1 = z$$

$$z = 1.25$$

The solutions found by the substitution method agree with the solutions previously obtained.

Solution by Using Determinants. Take the system of two linear equations in two unknowns, x and y,

$$a_1x + b_1y = k_1 \qquad a_1x + b_2y = k_2$$

and use either the addition-subtraction method or the substitution method to solve for the values of x and y:

$$x = \frac{k_1b_2 - b_1k_2}{a_1b_2 - a_2b_1} \qquad y = \frac{a_1k_2 - a_2k_1}{a_1b_2 - a_2b_1}$$

provided $a_1b_2 - a_2b_1 \neq 0$. The denominators of the two solutions are identical. The following new symbol

$$\begin{vmatrix} a_1 & b_1 \\ a_2 & b_2 \end{vmatrix}$$

is defined as a *determinant*. The value of the determinant is by definition

$$\begin{vmatrix} a_1 & b_1 \\ a_2 & b_2 \end{vmatrix} = a_1 b_2 - a_2 b_1$$

which is the value of the common denominator of the expressions for x and y. This determinant has two rows and two columns, and is called a determinant of the *second order*. A determinant with three rows and three columns is called a third-order determinant. An $N \times N$ determinant is an Nth-order determinant. The numbers $a_1 b_2$ comprise the *principal diagonal*, while the numbers b_1 and a_2 make up the *secondary diagonal*.

By definition, the value of a second-order determinant is given by the product of the principal diagonal minus the product of the secondary diagonal.

The solutions of x and y can now be rewritten in the form of determinants:

$$x = \frac{\begin{vmatrix} k_1 & b_1 \\ k_2 & b_2 \end{vmatrix}}{\begin{vmatrix} a_1 & b_1 \\ a_2 & b_2 \end{vmatrix}} = \frac{b_2 k_1 - b_1 k_2}{a_1 b_2 - a_2 b_1}$$

$$y = \frac{\begin{vmatrix} a_1 & k_1 \\ a_2 & k_2 \end{vmatrix}}{\begin{vmatrix} a_1 & b_1 \\ a_2 & b_2 \end{vmatrix}} = \frac{a_1 k_2 - a_2 k_1}{a_1 b_2 - a_2 b_1}$$

The solutions of a system of two linear equations in two unknowns can be found by the use of second-order determinants. For example, the equations

$$6x + 10y = 21 \qquad 4x + 5y = 12$$

will have the solutions

$$x = \frac{\begin{vmatrix} 21 & 10 \\ 12 & 5 \end{vmatrix}}{\begin{vmatrix} 6 & 10 \\ 4 & 5 \end{vmatrix}} = \frac{(21)(5) - (10)(12)}{(6)(5) - (10)(4)} = \frac{105 - 120}{30 - 40} = \frac{-15}{-10} = 1.5$$

$$y = \frac{\begin{vmatrix} 6 & 21 \\ 4 & 12 \end{vmatrix}}{\begin{vmatrix} 6 & 10 \\ 4 & 5 \end{vmatrix}} = \frac{(6)(12) - (21)(4)}{(6)(5) - (10)(4)} = \frac{72 - 84}{30 - 40} = \frac{-12}{-10} = 1.2$$

Determinants of Nth Order

Determinants can be of great value. Since the solution of second-order equations may be somewhat cumbersome in dealing with, say, five equations in five unknowns, the complexity of substitution or elimination demands the relative simplicity of determinants.

The determinant of Nth order is defined by a square array of N columns and N rows

$$
\begin{array}{c}
N \text{ Columns} \rightarrow \\[4pt]
N \text{ Rows} \downarrow \quad
\begin{vmatrix}
a_1 & b_1 & c_1 & \cdots & s_1 \\
a_2 & b_2 & c_2 & \cdots & s_2 \\
a_3 & b_3 & c_3 & \cdots & s_3 \\
\cdot & \cdot & \cdot & & \cdot \\
\cdot & \cdot & \cdot & & \cdot \\
\cdot & \cdot & \cdot & & \cdot \\
a_n & b_n & c_n & \cdots & s_n
\end{vmatrix}
\end{array}
$$

The matrix thus defined represents the sum of each of the products, derived (1) by using as factors one, and only one, element from each row and column, and (2) by determining the sign of each product by the rule that left-hand products are negative and right-hand products are positive. Right-hand and left-hand products are found as follows: Given the determinant $|D|$ (shorthand for determinant),

$$
\begin{vmatrix}
a_1 & b_1 & c_1 \\
a_2 & b_2 & c_2 \\
a_3 & b_3 & c_3
\end{vmatrix}
$$

rewrite columns 1 and 2 to facilitate the collection of factors:

$$
\left|
\begin{array}{ccc}
a_1 & b_1 & c_1 \\
a_2 & b_2 & c_2 \\
a_3 & b_3 & c_3
\end{array}
\right|
\begin{array}{cc}
a_1 & b_1 \\
a_2 & b_2 \\
a_3 & b_3
\end{array}
$$

Beginning with the element a_1, multiply downward and to the right, taking one element in each row until each element in row 1 has been used once.

These products are

$$a_1b_2c_3 + b_1c_2a_3 + c_1a_2b_3$$

The left-hand products are similarly obtained

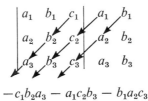

and are

$$-c_1b_2a_3 - a_1c_2b_3 - b_1a_2c_3$$

Thus the value implied by

$$\begin{vmatrix} a_1 & b_1 & c_1 \\ a_2 & b_2 & c_2 \\ a_3 & b_3 & c_3 \end{vmatrix}$$

is, by definition

$$a_1b_2c_3 + b_1c_2a_3 + c_1a_2b_3 - c_1b_2a_3 - a_1c_2b_3 - b_1a_2c_3$$

It is now obvious that if any or several of the elements are zero, the labor of evaluation is greatly reduced. Therefore, it is time to consider some properties of determinants which will assist in making elements of a given determinant equal to zero.

Law 1. The value of a determinant is not altered by interchanging corresponding rows and columns.

$$\begin{vmatrix} a_1 & b_1 & c_1 \\ a_2 & b_2 & c_2 \\ a_3 & b_3 & c_3 \end{vmatrix} = \begin{vmatrix} a_1 & a_2 & a_3 \\ b_1 & b_2 & b_3 \\ c_1 & c_2 & c_3 \end{vmatrix}$$

This property is offered without proof, since the proof is lengthy and outside the scope of this book. The interested student may check the proof of Law 1 in any good college algebra text.

Law 1 is offered to indicate that subsequent laws given for columns apply also to rows.

Law 2. A determinant in which any column of elements each equal zero has a value of zero.

$$\begin{vmatrix} a_1 & b_1 & 0 \\ a_2 & b_2 & 0 \\ a_3 & b_3 & 0 \end{vmatrix} = 0$$

Proof of this law follows from the definition of the determinant, that is, one, and only one, element from each row and each column is a factor of each product. Thus zero would appear as a factor in each product.

Law 3. The sign of the value changes if two columns are interchanged.

$$\begin{vmatrix} a_1 & b_1 & c_1 \\ a_2 & b_2 & c_2 \\ a_3 & b_3 & c_3 \end{vmatrix} = - \begin{vmatrix} a_1 & c_1 & b_1 \\ a_2 & c_2 & b_2 \\ a_3 & c_3 & b_3 \end{vmatrix}$$

Law 4. If the corresponding elements of two columns are equal, the value of the determinant is zero.

$$\begin{vmatrix} a_1 & b_1 & a_1 \\ a_2 & b_2 & a_2 \\ a_3 & b_3 & a_3 \end{vmatrix} = 0 \qquad \text{Column 1} = \text{column 3}$$

Proof of Law 4 follows from Law 3. If columns 1 and 3 are interchanged, the value of the determinant changes sign, say from v to $-v$. Since the determinants are still identical, then

$$v = -v \qquad 2v = 0 \qquad v = 0$$

Law 5. If a column of a determinant is represented by a sum of two terms, the determinant can be expressed as the sum of two determinants, as shown below:

$$\begin{vmatrix} a_{11} + a_{21} & b_1 & c_1 \\ a_{12} + a_{22} & b_2 & c_2 \\ a_{13} + a_{23} & b_3 & c_3 \end{vmatrix} = \begin{vmatrix} a_{11} & b_1 & c_1 \\ a_{12} & b_2 & c_2 \\ a_{13} & b_3 & c_3 \end{vmatrix} + \begin{vmatrix} a_{21} & b_1 & c_1 \\ a_{22} & b_2 & c_2 \\ a_{23} & b_3 & c_3 \end{vmatrix}$$

The value of the left member is determined by:

$$(a_{11} + a_{21})b_2c_3 + \cdots$$

The value of the right member is

$$(a_{11}b_2c_3 + \cdots) + (a_{21}b_2c_3 + \cdots)$$

Removing brackets and grouping the above yields

$$(a_{11}b_2c_3 + a_{21}b_2c_3) + \cdots$$

Factor to get

$$(a_{11} + a_{21})b_2c_3 + \cdots$$

which is the expansion of the left-hand member.

Law 6. If a column of a determinant is multiplied by a constant, k, the value of the determinant is multiplied by k:

$$\begin{vmatrix} a_1 & kb_1 & c_1 \\ a_2 & kb_2 & c_2 \\ a_3 & kb_3 & c_3 \end{vmatrix} = k \begin{vmatrix} a_1 & b_1 & c_1 \\ a_2 & b_2 & c_2 \\ a_3 & b_3 & c_3 \end{vmatrix}$$

Law 7. The value of a determinant remains unchanged if all the elements of a column are multiplied by a constant, k, and added to the corresponding elements of some other column.

$$\begin{vmatrix} a_1 & b_1 + kc_1 & c_1 \\ a_2 & b_2 + kc_2 & c_2 \\ a_3 & b_3 + kc_3 & c_3 \end{vmatrix} = \begin{vmatrix} a_1 & b_1 & c_1 \\ a_2 & b_2 & c_2 \\ a_3 & b_3 & c_3 \end{vmatrix}$$

We illustrate the proof thus:

$$\begin{vmatrix} a_1 & b_1 + kc_1 & c_1 \\ a_2 & b_2 + kc_2 & c_2 \\ a_3 & b_3 + kc_3 & c_3 \end{vmatrix} = \begin{vmatrix} a_1 & b_1 & c_1 \\ a_2 & b_2 & c_2 \\ a_3 & b_3 & c_3 \end{vmatrix} + \begin{vmatrix} a_1 & kc_1 & c_1 \\ a_2 & kc_2 & c_2 \\ a_3 & kc_3 & c_3 \end{vmatrix} \qquad \text{by Law 5}$$

$$= \begin{vmatrix} a_1 & b_1 & c_1 \\ a_2 & b_2 & c_2 \\ a_3 & b_3 & c_3 \end{vmatrix} + k \begin{vmatrix} a_1 & c_1 & c_1 \\ a_2 & c_2 & c_2 \\ a_3 & c_3 & c_3 \end{vmatrix} \qquad \text{by Law 6}$$

$$= \begin{vmatrix} a_1 & b_1 & c_1 \\ a_2 & b_2 & c_2 \\ a_3 & b_3 & c_3 \end{vmatrix} + k(0) \qquad \text{by Law 4}$$

$$= \begin{vmatrix} a_1 & b_1 & c_1 \\ a_2 & b_2 & c_2 \\ a_3 & b_3 & c_3 \end{vmatrix}$$

For illustration, two methods of evaluating the following determinant will be shown; the first by summing the products, the second by simplification.

$$\begin{vmatrix} -33 & 17 & 5 \\ -6 & 3 & 1 \\ -28 & 15 & 9 \end{vmatrix}$$

The solution is as follows:

1. To assist in obtaining the correct factors and signs for the products, rewrite the determinant and columns 1 and 2:

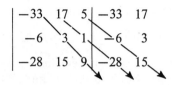

2. Draw product lines for right-hand and left-hand products:

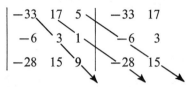

Indicated right-hand products are

$$+(-33)(3)(9) + (17)(1)(-28) + (5)(-6)(15)$$

$$\begin{vmatrix} -33 & 17 & 5 \\ -6 & 3 & 1 \\ -28 & 15 & 9 \end{vmatrix} \begin{matrix} -33 & 17 \\ -6 & 3 \\ -28 & 15 \end{matrix}$$

Indicated left-hand products are

$$-(5)(3)(-28) - (-33)(1)(15) - (17)(-6)(9)$$

3. Evaluate the products:

$$+(-891) + (-476) + (-450) - (-420) - (-495) - (-918)$$

4. Add terms:
$$-1817 + 1833 = 16$$

This is the value of the determinant. The value can also be obtained by simplification, as follows:

1. Write the determinant:

$$\begin{vmatrix} -33 & 17 & 5 \\ -6 & 3 & 1 \\ -28 & 15 & 9 \end{vmatrix}$$

2. Multiply column 2 by 2 and add the result to column 1:

$$\begin{vmatrix} -33+34 & 17 & 5 \\ -6+6 & 3 & 1 \\ -28+30 & 15 & 9 \end{vmatrix} = \begin{vmatrix} 1 & 17 & 5 \\ 0 & 3 & 1 \\ 2 & 15 & 9 \end{vmatrix}$$

3. Multiply row 2 by -5 and add to rows 1 and 3:

$$\begin{vmatrix} 1+0 & 17-15 & 5-5 \\ 0 & 3 & 1 \\ 2+0 & 15-15 & 9-5 \end{vmatrix} = \begin{vmatrix} 1 & 2 & 0 \\ 0 & 3 & 1 \\ 2 & 0 & 4 \end{vmatrix}$$

4. Evaluate the determinant arrived at in (3) above:

$$\begin{vmatrix} 1 & 2 & 0 \\ 0 & 3 & 1 \\ 2 & 0 & 4 \end{vmatrix} \begin{matrix} 1 & 2 \\ 0 & 3 \\ 2 & 0 \end{matrix} = (1)(3)(4) + (2)(1)(2) + (0)(0)(0)$$
$$- (0)(3)(2) - (1)(1)(0) - (2)(0)(4)$$

5. All but the first two terms of (4) are zero because each contains zero as a factor. Thus the determinant's value is

$$(1)(3)(4) + (2)(1)(2) = 12 + 4 = 16$$

This is the same as the value previously determined.

The *laws* given above work for all determinants $|D|$; however, the *methods* employed fail for evaluation of $|D|$ with degree >3.

Systems of Equations Involving Quadratics

In order to solve a system of quadratic equations in two unknowns, one usually must solve a fourth-power equation in one of the unknowns. Since solution techniques for equations of powers higher than second are beyond the scope of this text, the systems discussed here have been chosen to be special cases whose solutions lead to quadratic equations only.

1. To illustrate the solution of a system of equations in which one of the given equations is linear, solve the following system of equations:

$$2x^2 + 2y^2 + x - 4y = 10 \qquad (1)$$
$$x + y = -2 \qquad (2)$$

One method of solution is to solve (2) for one of the unknowns, say x, and substitute the result into (1). Solve (2) for x:

$$x = -2 - y \qquad (3)$$

Substitute (3) in (1)

$$2(-2 - y)^2 + 2y^2 + (-2 - y) - 4y = 10$$
$$8 + 8y + 2y^2 + 2y^2 - 2 - y - 4y = 10$$
$$4y^2 + 3y - 4 = 0 \qquad (4)$$

Solve (4) by the quadratic formula

$$y = -1.443 \qquad y = 0.693$$

Substitute in (3)

$$x = -2 - (-1.443) = -2 + 1.443 = -0.557$$
$$x = -2 - 0.693 = -2.693$$

As a second example of the technique of substitution, consider the following system of equations:

$$xy = 12 \qquad (1)$$
$$x^2 + y^2 = 25 \qquad (2)$$

In this case, neither equation is of linear form. It is nevertheless possible to use the technique of substitution illustrated in the previous example. In this case, some modification is necessary to solve for the values of x and y. Solve (1) for x:

$$x = \frac{12}{y} \qquad (3)$$

Substitute (3) in (2):

$$\left(\frac{12}{y}\right)^2 + y^2 = 25$$

Clearing of fractions gives

$$y^4 - 25y^2 + 144 = 0 \qquad (4)$$

Equation (4) is a quadratic in y^2. Therefore the next step is to solve (4) for y^2:

$$y^2 = \frac{25 \pm \sqrt{(-25)^2 - 4(1)(144)}}{2}$$
$$y^2 = 16 \qquad \text{or} \qquad y^2 = 9$$
$$y = \pm 4 \qquad \text{or} \qquad y = \pm 3$$

Substituting in (3) gives

$$x = \pm 3 \qquad \text{or} \qquad x = \pm 4$$

There are four pairs of solutions:

$$(x = 3, y = 4) \qquad (x = -3, y = -4)$$
$$(x = 4, y = 3) \qquad (x = -4, y = -3)$$

2. In solving a system of equations in which each equation is of the form

$$ax^2 + by^2 + c = 0$$

each equation may be regarded as being linear in x^2 and y^2. Elimination by addition or subtraction may be used to reduce the system to a single equation in either x^2 or y^2. To illustrate, solve the following system of equations:

$$x^2 + y^2 = 61 \tag{1}$$
$$4x^2 - y^2 = 64 \tag{2}$$

Add the two equations:

$$5x^2 = 125 \tag{3}$$

Divide (3) by 5:

$$x^2 = 25$$

Extract the square root:

$$x = \pm 5$$

Substitute in (1):

$$y^2 = 36 \qquad y = \pm 6$$

THEORY OF EQUATIONS

Equations of higher order than the linear and quadratic forms already discussed can also be solved either algebraically or graphically. Various techniques by which roots of equations can be successively approximated are available. In particular, equations of cubic or quartic power can be solved algebraically, but equations of powers higher than the fourth usually cannot. Students who wish to pursue the techniques of equation solution further are referred to any of numerous texts in college algebra or theory of equations. Several selected topics from the theory of equations, which will prove useful in later discussions, are considered in this section.

Fundamental Theorem of Algebra

The fundamental theorem of algebra states that every polynomial equation in a single variable has at least one root. The corollary to this theorem is that every polynomial equation in a single variable of degree n can be broken into n linear factors. This implies that a polynomial equation of degree n in a single variable has n roots, some of which may not be distinct.

To prove the theorem and its corollary, consider the equation

$$f(x) = a_1 x^n + a_2 x^{n-1} + a_3 x^{n-2} + \cdots + a_n x + a_{n+1}$$

By the fundamental theorem, this equation has at least one root. Let that root be x_1. Then $(x - x_1)$ is a factor of $f(x)$, and $f(x)$ can be rewritten in the following form:

$$f(x) = (x - x_1)Q_1(x)$$

where $Q_1(x)$ is the quotient of $f(x)/x - x_1$. It is apparent that $Q_1(x)$ is a polynomial of x of $(n - 1)$ degree. This is to say that the highest degree in which x appears is now one less than in the original equation.

Since $Q_1(x)$ is a function of x it has at least one root, which can be designated x_2. $Q_1(x)$ can now be written in the form

$$Q_1(x) = (x - x_2)Q_2(x)$$

The original equation $f(x)$ can now be written as the product of the two factored functions and the quotient:

$$f(x) = (x - x_1)(x - x_2)Q_2(x)$$

Observe that $Q_2(x)$ is in turn a polynomial in x of $(n - 2)$ degree with yet another root.

Continuing this process successively, the original equation $f(x)$ can be broken down into n linear factors and a term free of the unknown x, with the result

$$f(x) = (x - x_1)(x - x_2)(x - x_3) \cdots (x - x_n)Q_n(x)$$

where $Q_n(x)$ is a constant with x reduced to zero-power, $x^{(n-n)}$. Now for $f(x) = 0$, the roots are $x_1, x_2, x_3, \ldots, x_n$. These roots may not be distinct.

To illustrate the theorem that has just been discussed in general terms, consider a specific numerical example with the equation

$$f(x) = x^3 + 8x^2 + 17x + 10 = 0$$

If it is given that one root of this equation is $x = -1$, then $(x + 1)$ is a factor of $f(x)$. Dividing $f(x)$ by $(x + 1)$ gives

$$\frac{f(x)}{x + 1} = x^2 + 7x + 10$$

The term $f(x)$ can therefore be expressed as

$$f(x) = (x + 1)(x^2 + 7x + 10)$$

The factor $x^2 + 7x + 10$ can be written in its factored form as

$$x^2 + 7x + 10 = (x + 5)(x + 2)$$

It is now possible to express the original equation $f(x)$ as the product of the three linear factors:

$$f(x) = x^3 + 8x^2 + 17x + 10 = (x + 1)(x + 5)(x + 2)$$

There are three distinct, real, and rational roots for $f(x)$:

$$x_1 = -1 \qquad x_2 = -5 \qquad x_3 = -2$$

Another important application of this theorem is that it may be used to form a polynomial whose roots are given. Given the information that the roots of a polynomial in x are -2, 3, and -4, if the problem is to find the polynomial, proceed as follows:

$$f(x) = (x + 2)(x - 3)(x + 4)$$
$$f(x) = (x^2 - x - 6)(x + 4)$$
$$f(x) = x^3 + 3x^2 - 10x - 24$$

The equation

$$f(x) = x^3 + 3x^2 - 10x - 24$$

has the three roots

$$x_1 = -2 \qquad x_2 = 3 \qquad \text{and} \qquad x_3 = -4$$

and no others. It is therefore shown that

$$x^3 + 3x^2 - 10x - 24$$

is the required polynomial.

The polynomial whose roots are the conjugate complex numbers $2 - 4i$ and $2 + 4i$ is

$$f(x) = [x - (2 - 4i)][x - (2 + 4i)]$$
$$f(x) = x^2 - 4x + 20$$

To check the result, set

$$x^2 - 4x + 20 = 0$$

and solve for the values of x by the quadratic formula:

$$x = 2 \pm \frac{8i}{2} = 2 \pm 4i$$

Remainder Theorem

When any polynomial $f(x)$ is divided by $(x - x_1)$, the remainder is equal to $f(x_1)$. For example, let

$$f(x) = 3x^4 - 5x^3 + 3x^2 + x + 10$$

be divided by $(x + 2)$:

$$\frac{3x^4 - 5x^3 + 3x^2 + x + 10}{x + 2} = (3x^3 - 11x^2 + 25x - 49) + \frac{108}{x + 2}$$

Multiplying both members of the equation by $(x + 2)$ gives

$$3x^4 - 5x^3 + 3x^2 + x + 10 = (x + 2)(3x^3 - 11x^2 + 25x - 49) + 108$$

Here the factored term is $(x + 2)$ and the quotient is $3x^3 - 11x^2 + 25x - 49$ with a remainder of 108. The remainder theorem states that if $f(x_1)$ is calculated from the original $f(x)$, the result should be equal to the remainder, 108:

$$f(-2) = 3(-2)^4 - 5(-2)^3 + 3(-2)^2 - 2 + 10$$
$$= 48 + 40 + 12 - 2 + 10$$
$$= 108$$

This important theorem can be used to determine whether a number is a root of an equation. Suppose that x_1 is a root of the equation $f(x)$. Then $f(x_1)$ will be equal to zero, and $(x - x_1)$ will be a factor of the function $f(x)$. This means that

$$f(x) = (x - x_1)Q(x) + f(x_1)$$

But x_1 is a root of $f(x) = 0$, and $f(x_1) = 0$. Thus

$$f(x) = (x - x_1)Q(x)$$

which establishes that $(x - x_1)$ is a factor of $f(x)$.

This theorem can be used to determine whether a given number x_1 is a root of a given equation. For example, in the equation

$$f(x) = x^3 + 4x^2 + x - 6$$

the question is whether or not $x_1 = 1$ is a root. Here $x_1 = 1$, and a possible factor of $f(x)$ is $(x - 1)$. To determine whether $(x - 1)$ is indeed a factor of the function $f(x)$, substitute $x_1 = 1$ into $f(x)$:

$$f(1) = 1^3 + 4(1)^2 + 1 - 6 = 0$$

This shows that $x_1 = 1$ is a root of the equation. Next, test $x_2 = -3$ to see if it is a root of the equation. If -3 is a root of the equation, then $x + 3$ must be a factor of $f(x)$. Substituting -3 for x in $f(x)$ gives

$$f(-3) = (-3)^3 + 4(-3)^2 + (-3) - 6$$
$$= -27 + 36 - 3 - 6 = 0$$

Thus -3 is a root of the equation. At this point $f(x)$ can be written in its factored form as

$$f(x) = (x - 1)(x + 3)Q(x)$$

To find $Q(x)$, the remaining factor of $f(x)$, observe that

$$\frac{f(x)}{(x - 1)} = (x + 3)Q(x)$$

By long division,

$$\frac{x^3 + 4x^2 + x - 6}{(x - 1)} = x^2 + 5x + 6$$

which is to say

$$(x + 3)Q(x) = x^2 + 5x + 6$$

Now it appears that

$$Q(x) = \frac{x^2 + 5x + 6}{x + 3} = x + 2$$

Therefore $f(x)$ can be written in its three linear factors

$$f(x) = (x - 1)(x + 3)(x + 2)$$

and the three roots of the equation $f(x) = 0$ are

$$x_1 = 1 \qquad x_2 = -3 \qquad x_3 = -2$$

PARTIAL FRACTIONS

A fraction such as x^2/x is an *improper fraction*, for

$$\frac{x^2}{x} = x$$

is not really a fraction. A fraction such as

$$\frac{2x^3 + x^2 - x + 5}{x + 5}$$

is also an improper fraction, since the numerator is a polynomial in x which contains powers of x greater than the highest power of x appearing in the denominator. The fraction

$$\frac{2x^3 + x^2 - x + 5}{x + 5} = 2x^2 - 9x + 44 - \frac{215}{x + 5}$$

turns out to be a polynomial whose last term only is a true fraction.
Expressions such as

$$\frac{x^2 + x + 5}{x^3 + x^2 + 6} \qquad \frac{x}{x^2} = \frac{1}{x} \qquad \frac{5}{x + 5}$$

are examples of *proper fractions*, since the numerators are expressions
containing terms of x of lower degrees than the denominators. The process
of finding partial fractions applies only to proper fractions. The ability to
reduce a given proper fraction into its partial fractions is particularly useful
in integral calculus, where the integrals of complex fractions are difficult to
derive, but the integrals of the partial fractions may be found easily. Several
theorems govern the method by which a proper fraction may be reduced
to its partial fractions. Their use is illustrated in this section.

Theorem I

If the denominator of a given proper fraction is composed of distinct linear
factors such as $(ax + b)$, $(cx + d)$, the partial fraction will have the form

$$\frac{A}{ax + b} + \frac{B}{cx + d}$$

where A and B are constants. For example:

$$\frac{4x - 2}{(x + 1)(x + 3)} = \frac{A}{x + 1} + \frac{B}{x + 3}$$

Note that this relationship is an identity. It is now necessary to find the
values of A and B satisfying this identity. Clearing fractions gives

$$4x - 2 = A(x + 3) + B(x + 1)$$
$$4x - 2 = Ax + 3A + Bx + B$$
$$4x - 2 = (A + B)x + (3A + B)$$

Since this is an identity, the coefficients of like-powered terms of x are
equal in both members of the identity. Two equations can therefore be
established:

$$A + B = 4 \qquad 3A + B = -2$$

Solving these two simultaneous equations gives

$$A = -3 \qquad B = 7$$

The partial fractions can now be written as

$$\frac{4x - 2}{(x + 1)(x + 3)} = \frac{-3}{x + 1} + \frac{7}{x + 3} = \frac{7}{x + 3} - \frac{3}{x + 1}$$

The terms

$$\frac{7}{x + 3} - \frac{3}{x + 1}$$

are the partial fractions of the proper fraction

$$\frac{4x - 2}{(x + 1)(x + 3)}$$

The results can be checked by performing the necessary subtraction.

Theorem 2

When the denominator is made up of linear factors some of which are repeated, the partial fractions are of the form

$$\frac{A}{(ax + b)^k} = \frac{A_1}{(ax + b)} + \frac{A_2}{(ax + b)^2} + \cdots + \frac{A_k}{(ax + b)^k}$$

For example, resolve

$$\frac{x^2 + 2x - 5}{(x - 2)^3}$$

into partial fractions. By theorem 2, this fraction is equal to the sum of the partial fractions

$$\frac{x^2 + 2x - 5}{(x - 2)^2} = \frac{A_1}{x - 2} + \frac{A_2}{(x - 2)^2} + \frac{A_3}{(x - 2)^3}$$

where A_1, A_2, and A_3 are the unknown constants to be determined. Clearing of fractions and expanding gives

$$x^2 + 2x - 5 = A_1(x - 2)^2 + A_2(x - 2) + A_3$$
$$x^2 + 2x - 5 = A_1 x^2 - (4A_1 - A_2)x + (4A_1 - 2A_2 + A_3)$$

Since the coefficients of the like-powered terms of x are equal on both sides of the equation, the three equations can be set up as

$$A_1 \qquad\qquad = 1$$
$$-4A_1 + A_2 \qquad = 2$$
$$4A_1 - 2A_2 + A_3 = -5$$

The solution of these simultaneous equations gives the values of A_1, A_2, and A_3:

$$A_1 = 1 \qquad A_2 = 6 \qquad A_3 = 3$$

Hence

$$\frac{x^2 + 2x - 5}{(x-2)^3} = \frac{1}{x-2} + \frac{6}{(x-2)^2} + \frac{3}{(x-2)^3}$$

Theorem 3

When the denominator is composed of exactly one distinctly quadratic factor, the partial fractions will be of the form

$$\frac{f(x)}{ax^2 + bx + c} = \frac{Ax + B}{ax^2 + bx + c}$$

Example I. Resolve

$$\frac{x + 5}{3x^2 + 2x + 3}$$

into partial fractions. This is a rather trivial case, but it may highlight quite clearly the implications of theorem 3. From theorem 3, establish the identity

$$\frac{x + 5}{3x^2 + 2x + 3} = \frac{Ax + B}{3x^2 + 2x + 3}$$

where, as usual, A and B are the constants to be determined. It is obvious that, for this equality to hold, $A = 1$ and $B = 5$. In this case the proper fraction in the left member of the equation is its own partial fraction.

Example 2. Resolve

$$\frac{3x + 7}{(x + 1)(2x^2 + 5x - 6)}$$

into partial fractions. The denominator is composed of one linear factor and one quadratic factor. Using theorems 1 and 3, write

$$\frac{3x + 7}{(x + 1)(2x^2 + 5x - 6)} = \frac{A}{x + 1} + \frac{Bx + C}{2x^2 + 5x - 6}$$

Clearing of fractions gives

$$3x + 7 = A(2x^2 + 5x - 6) + (Bx + C)(x + 1)$$

Expanding and collecting terms gives

$$3x + 7 = (2A + B)x^2 + (5A + B + C)x + (-6A + C)$$

Since there is no term containing x^2 on the left-hand side, the coefficient of x^2 on the left is zero. Again equating the coefficients of like-powered terms of x, three equations in three unknowns are established:

$$2A + B = 0 \qquad 5A + B + C = 3 \qquad -6A + C = 7$$

Solving these three equations simultaneously gives the values of A, B, and C:

$$A = -\tfrac{4}{9} \qquad B = \tfrac{8}{9} \qquad C = \tfrac{39}{9}$$

The desired partial fractions are therefore

$$\frac{3x + 7}{(x + 1)(2x^2 + 5x - 6)} = -\frac{4}{9(x + 1)} + \frac{8x + 39}{9(2x^2 + 5x - 6)}$$

By performing the subtraction of the first partial fraction from the second in the right-hand member of the equation, the original proper fraction on the left-hand side would be obtained, thus confirming that the correct partial fractions have been found.

Theorem 4

If a proper fraction contains in its denominator a repeated quadratic factor, the partial fractions will be of the form

$$\frac{f(x)}{(ax^2 + bx + c)^k} = \frac{A_1x + B}{ax^2 + bx + c}$$
$$+ \frac{A_2x + B}{(ax^2 + bx + c)^2} + \cdots + \frac{A_kx + B}{(ax^2 + bx + c)^k}$$

For example, resolve

$$\frac{x^3 + x - 5}{x(x^2 - 3x - 1)^2}$$

into its partial fractions. By theorem 1 and theorem 4, the partial fractions are

$$\frac{x^3 + x - 5}{x(x^2 - 3x - 1)^2} = \frac{A}{x} + \frac{Bx + C}{x^2 - 3x - 1} + \frac{Dx + E}{(x^2 - 3x - 1)^2}$$

Clearing of fractions gives

$$x^3 + x - 5 = A(x^2 - 3x - 1)^2 + (Bx + C)x(x^2 - 3x - 1) + (Dx + E)x$$

After terms are expanded and collected, the equation is

$$x^3 + x - 5 = (A + B)x^4 + (-6A - 3B + C)x^3$$
$$+ (7A - B - 3C + D)x^2$$
$$+ (6A - C + E)x + A$$

The like-powered terms of x have equal coefficients on both sides of the equation. Thus there are five simultaneous equations in the five unknowns:

$$
\begin{aligned}
A + B &&&&= 0 \\
-6A - 3B + C &&&&= 1 \\
7A - B - 3C + D &&&= 0 \\
6A \quad\quad - C \quad + E &&= 1 \\
A &&&&= -5
\end{aligned}
$$

Solving this system of simultaneous equations yields the values of the five undetermined constants:

$$
\begin{aligned}
A &= -5 \\
B &= 5 \\
C &= -14 \\
D &= -2 \\
E &= 17
\end{aligned}
$$

The partial fractions of the proper fraction can now be written as the algebraic sum of the right-hand member of the equation

$$\frac{x^3 + x - 5}{x(x^2 - 3x - 1)^2} = \frac{-5}{x} + \frac{5x - 14}{x^2 - 3x - 1} - \frac{2x - 17}{(x^2 - 3x - 1)^2}$$

As usual, the indicated algebraic operations can be performed on the right-hand side of the equation to get the fraction on the left.

The various techniques of resolving given proper fractions into appropriate partial fractions have been discussed in this section. Note that these techniques apply only to fractions whose denominators can be decomposed into rational, integral, linear, or quadratic factors. It is not always possible to do this. The discussion has been confined to those fractions whose denominators either are given in the appropriate factored forms or can easily be factored.

PROBLEMS

1. Give examples to show that the five assumptions about algebraic operations are true. What is true about subtraction and division when applied to the assumptions? Give examples to illustrate the conclusions.

2. Show that the following equations are identities:

(a) $\dfrac{x^2 + x + 1}{x + 1} \equiv x + \dfrac{1}{x + 1}$ (c) $(x + 1)^3 \equiv x^3 + 3x^2 + 3x + 1$

(b) $\dfrac{2x}{x^2 - 1} \equiv \dfrac{1}{x - 1} + \dfrac{1}{x + 1}$ (d) $\dfrac{2x + 1}{x^2 + x} \equiv \dfrac{1}{x} + \dfrac{1}{x + 1}$

3. Solve for x and check:

(a) $6x - 9 = 3x$ (f) $\dfrac{1}{x} + \dfrac{5}{3x} = 1$

(b) $7(x + 5) = 5(5 - x) - 2$ (g) $\dfrac{2}{3x} + \dfrac{5}{12} = \dfrac{3}{2x} + \dfrac{5}{4}$

(c) $3(4 - 5x) - 2(x + 4) = 4$ (h) $\dfrac{x + 1}{x} + \dfrac{4}{x^2 - x} = \dfrac{x + 1}{x - 1}$

(d) $\dfrac{3x - 4}{6} + \dfrac{5 + 2x}{3} = 0$ (i) $\dfrac{x^2 + 1}{x^2 - x - 2} = \dfrac{-3}{x + 1} + 1$

(e) $\dfrac{2x + 7}{4} - \dfrac{x + 1}{6} = \dfrac{5 - x}{3}$

4. Solve for x and check:
   (a) $4x^2 - 64 = 0$ (d) $a^2x^2 - c^2 = 0$
   (b) $9x^2 + 72 = 0$ (e) $x(x + 1) = x + 9$
   (c) $a^2x^2 + c = 0$ (f) $x(x^2 + 3x) = x^3 - 12$

5. Solve for x and check:
   (a) $-4x^2 - 4x = 0$ (d) $a^2x^2 - a^2x = 0$
   (b) $16x^2 = 4x$ (e) $x^2 + 6x + 9 = 3x + 9$
   (c) $a^2x^2 + ax = 0$ (f) $a^2x^2 - ax - 6x = 0$

6. Solve for x by using the methods of completing the square, the quadratic formula, and factoring (if possible), and check:
   (a) $6x^2 - 6x - 12 = 0$ (f) $3x^2 - x - 10 = 0$
   (b) $x^2 - 7x + 12 = 0$ (g) $x^2 + 4ix - 4 = 0$
   (c) $-2x^2 - x + 1 = 0$ (h) $abx^2 + a^2x - 2abx$
   $\qquad\qquad\qquad\qquad\qquad + b^2x - a^2 + 2ab - b^2 = 0$
   (d) $ax^2 + bx + acx + bc = 0$ (i) $x^2 - 2ax + a^2 - b^2 = 0$
   (e) $x^2 + x + 4 = 0$ (j) $ix^2 + 5ix + 6i = 0$

7. Without solving, find the sums and products of the roots of the following equations:

(a) $x^2 - 3x - 10 = 0$ (b) $2x^2 + x - 3 = 0$

8. Write the quadratic equations, given the following roots:

(a) $r_1 = 2$ $r_2 = -\frac{1}{2}$
(b) $r_1 = -1 + 3i$ $r_2 = -1 - 3i$

9. Without solving, find the quadratic equation whose roots are the squares of the roots of
$$x^2 - 3x + 2 = 0$$

10. Without solving, find a quadratic equation whose roots are reciprocals of the roots of
$$x^2 - 3x + 2 = 0$$

11. Perform the indicated operations:

(a) $(2 + 2i) + (3 + 3i)$ (g) $(1 + i)(2 + i)$

(b) $(2 - i) + (-3 - i)$ (h) $\dfrac{2 + 5i}{4 - i}$

(c) $(-1 + i) - (-5 - 3i)$ (i) $\dfrac{2 + 5i}{4 + i}$

(d) $(-2 - i) - (6 + 7i)$ (j) $\dfrac{1 + i}{i}$

(e) $(2 + 2i)(1 - i)$ (k) $\dfrac{-1 - i}{2i}$

(f) $(-2 + i)(-1 + 2i)$

12. Solve the equations for x and check:

(a) $x^2 - ix + 2 = 0$ (c) $x^2 - ix - 2x + i + 1 = 0$
(b) $ix^2 + 7x - 12i = 0$

13. Find the solutions graphically and check by another method:

(a) $f(x) = x^2 - 1$ (c) $f(x) = x^2 + 6x + 9$
(b) $f(x) = x^2 + 2x + 4$ (d) $f(x) = 2x^2 - 6x + 4$

14. Solve the following systems of equations by the processes of elimination, substitution, and determinants and check:

(a) $3x + y = 4$ $2x - y = 1$

(b) $4x + 3y = 2$ $3x + 4y = 12$

(c) $x - y = 1$ $x + y = 1$

(d) $\dfrac{3}{x} - \dfrac{5}{y} = 2$ $\dfrac{1}{y} - \dfrac{2}{x} = 1$

(e) $\dfrac{1}{2x} + \dfrac{3}{4y} = 2$ $\dfrac{5}{3x} - \dfrac{1}{y} = -1$

[Hint for (d) and (e) by determinants: Substitute $u = 1/x$, $v = 1/y$]

15. Solve $2x + y = 3$, $4x + 2y = 10$ by the three methods. Graph the functions. What conclusions can be drawn?

16. Solve the following equations by substitution and by elimination and check:

(a) $2x - y + 2z = 3$
    $3x + y - 2z = 2$
    $x + y + z = 1$

(b) $x + 4y + 5z = -2$
    $x + 3y + z = 6$
    $2x - 3y + 2z = 2$

(c) $\dfrac{3}{x} + \dfrac{4}{y} + \dfrac{1}{z} = 8$

$\dfrac{6}{x} + \dfrac{2}{y} + \dfrac{1}{z} = 7$

$\dfrac{1}{x} - \dfrac{2}{y} - \dfrac{3}{z} = 2$

17. Solve the following equations by substitution and elimination. What conclusions can be drawn?

$$x + 2y - z = 6$$
$$3x + 2y + z = 1$$
$$3x + 6y - 3z = 18$$

18. Solve by using the quadratic formula and factoring:

(a) $x^4 - 6x^2 + 9 = 0$ (c) $x^4 - x^2 - 12 = 0$

(b) $x - 3x^{1/2} - 10 = 0$

19. Solve for the intersection of the two curves:

(a) $x^2 - 5x - y + 4 = 0$ $x - y = 1$

(b) $4x^2 + 9y^2 - 48x + 72y + 144 = 0$ $3y + 2x = -12$

(c) $x^2 + y^2 = 4$ $4x^2 + 9y^2 = 36$

(d) $x^2 + y^2 - 2x - 2y - 14 = 0$
    $x^2 + y^2 - 4x - 6y + 12 = 0$

20. Find the other roots, given the one root of the equation:

   (a) $x = 1$ $f(x) = x^3 - 6x^2 + 11x - 6$
   (b) $x = 1$ $f(x) = x^3 - x^2 - x + 1$

21. Given the following roots, find the equation:

   (a) $x = 2$ $x = -1$ $x = 1$
   (b) $x = i$ $x = i$ $x = 1$

22. Perform the indicated operations:

   (a) $\log_2 (32) =$
   (b) $\log_{10} [(x + 1)(x + 1)] =$
   (c) $\log_2 (256/2) =$
   (d) $\log_{10} \left[\dfrac{x}{x + 1} \right] =$
   (e) $\log_{10} \left[\dfrac{1}{x^2} \right] =$
   (f) $\log_{10} \dfrac{(x + y)^2(x - y)}{4(x^2 - y)(x^2)} =$
   (g) $\log_3 (81)^3 =$
   (h) $\log_2 4\sqrt{16} =$
   (i) $\log_{10} \left[x^2 \dfrac{\sqrt{(x + y)(x - y)}}{2(x - 1)^2(y - x)} \right] =$

23. Solve for x:

   (a) $3^x = 27$

   (b) $e^x + 4e^{-x} = 4$
         (by quadratic formula)
   (c) $\log x - \frac{1}{2} \log 4 = \log 32$

   (d) $\log (x + 2) - \log x = \log 11$

   (e) $x = \log_4 32$

   (f) $e^x - e^{-x} = 0$

24. Expansion of a binomial to any positive integral power can be obtained from the binomial formula:

$$(a + b)^n = a^n + na^{(n-1)}b + \frac{n(n - 1)}{2!} a^{(n-2)}b^2$$

$$+ \frac{n(n - 1)(n - 2)}{3!} a^{(n-3)}b^3 + \cdots + b^n$$

where $n! = 1 \cdot 2 \cdot 3 \cdots n$ (called factorial n). Expand by the binomial formula:

(a) $(1 + x)^4$ (b) $(2 + b)^5$ (c) $(1 + 0.1)^4$

25. The definition of e is

$$e = \lim_{\kappa \to \infty} \left(1 + \frac{1}{\kappa}\right)^\kappa$$

Show that another definition is

$$e = \lim_{h \to 0} (1 + h)^{1/h}$$

Expand

$$\left(1 + \frac{1}{\kappa}\right)^\kappa$$

by the binomial theorem and factor each term so that κ only exists in the denominator. Then take the limit of each term as $\kappa \to \infty$ so that terms such as n/κ become 0. Verify the remaining series and compute e so that

$$e = 1 + 1 + \frac{1}{2!} + \frac{1}{3!} + \cdots + \frac{1}{n!} \cdots \simeq 2.71828 \cdots$$

26. Find the compounded amount of money at the end of 10 years on an original principal of $500 at 5% compounded annually.

27. If $500 were invested for 10 years at 6%, compounded quarterly, what would be the result?

28. Given $\log e = 0.4343$, solve for y by logarithms:

(a) $y = e^2$ (b) $y = e^0$

29. (a) Let $f(x) = x^3 + 9x^2 + 9x + 3$ be divided by $x - x_1$ where $x_1 = 3$.
(b) Let $f(x) = x^4 - 4x^3 + 3x^2 - 3x + 3$ be divided by $x - x_1$ where $x_1 = 1$. Calculate $f(x)$ to verify the remainder.

30. Verify that $x = 1$ is the only distinct root of

$$f(x) = x^4 - 4x^3 + 6x^2 - 4x + 1$$

31. Resolve into partial fractions:

(a) $\dfrac{x - 5}{(x + 1)(x - 4)}$ (c) $\dfrac{x + 5}{(x - 4)^2}$

(b) $\dfrac{8x + 8}{x^3 - 2x^2 - 8x}$ (d) $\dfrac{2x^2 - 2x - 1}{(x + 2)(x - 1)^2}$

(e) $\dfrac{x^2 + 6x + 12}{(x + 1)(x^2 - 3x + 1)}$

(f) $\dfrac{x^3 + x + 1}{(x + 1)(x^2 + x + 1)^2}$ (g) $\dfrac{e^x}{e^{2x} + 2e^x + 1}$

32. The principle of mathematical induction involves proving that a statement is valid for all n integers. The steps are: (1) Prove true for the case $n = 1$, (2) Assume to be true for the case $n = k$, (3) Prove true for the case $n = k + 1$. Prove by mathematical induction:

(a) $1 + 2 + 3 + \cdots + n = \frac{1}{2} n(n + 1)$

(b) $a + ar + ar^2 + ar^3 + \cdots + ar^n = \dfrac{a - ar^{n+1}}{1 - r}$

33. Solve the systems of equations in problem 16 by determinants.

34. The sum of two numbers is 22 and the product of the two numbers is 85. Find the numbers.

35. Find the length, width, perimeter, and area of a rectangle whose dimensions are such that the difference of length and width equals 2, and the sum of the length and width is 10.

36. A man has $3.00 in nickels, dimes, and quarters. If he adds 50¢ to the nickels and dimes, they will have the same total value as the quarters. How many of each coin does he have?

37. The product of two consecutive odd integers is 399. Find the numbers.

38. If a right triangle has sides whose lengths are $(7 - x)$, $(14 - x)$, and $(15 - x)$, find the value of x.

3
TYPES OF FUNCTIONS

Analytic geometry is the study of relationships between algebraic equations and their geometric representations. A mathematical equation may be shown geometrically as a line, a curve, or a surface. Both the mathematical and the geometric methods of expressing the effect of one variable upon another are extremely useful in many fields of study. Economic theory is replete with applications of mathematical and geometric representations to relationships existing among economic variables.

It is the purpose of this chapter to discuss certain selected topics from analytic geometry which are particularly useful for economic analysis. The linear, quadratic, and higher-powered algebraic functions will be considered. As these function types are developed, examples from economic theory will be used to show their applications.

LINEAR FUNCTION, STRAIGHT LINE

An equation of the first degree in both the dependent and the independent variables will define a straight line whose locus coordinates will show the relationship between the variables. The general equation of a straight line is

$$y = a + bx$$

where a and b are constants.

One way of visualizing the particular straight line defined by the equation is to find the point at which the line will intersect the y-axis—called the *y-intercept*—and the point on the x-axis at which the line crosses the abscissa—called the *x-intercept*. Since the line will cross the y-axis when the value of the independent variable, x, is equal to zero, the y-intercept is found by substituting into

$$y = f(x) = a + bx$$

the value $x = 0$:

$$y = f(0) = a + b(0) = a \qquad \text{or} \qquad y = a$$

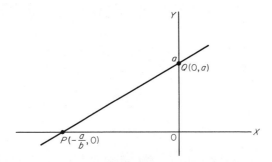

FIGURE 3-1   Axis Intercepts of a Straight Line

The x-intercept will be found when the value of the function, i.e., the value of y, is equal to zero. To identify such a point, set the function equal to zero and solve for x.

$$a + bx = 0 \qquad x = -\frac{a}{b}$$

These two points are shown in Figure 3-1. The coordinates of the x-intercept are

$$x = -\frac{a}{b} \qquad \text{and} \qquad y = 0$$

and the coordinates of the y-intercept are

$$x = 0 \qquad \text{and} \qquad y = a$$

Slope

The concept of the *slope* of a function is important and much used. The slope of a straight line is defined as the amount of increment in y divided by the amount of the increment in x between any two points on the straight line. To measure the slope of the line between the points P and Q in Figure 3-1, find

$$m = \frac{a - 0}{0 - \left(-\dfrac{a}{b}\right)} = \frac{a}{\dfrac{a}{b}} = a\left(\frac{b}{a}\right) = b$$

where m is the slope of the line. It appears, therefore, that the slope of a straight line defined by the function

$$y = a + bx$$

is equal to the coefficient of the independent variable, namely the constant b. This makes sense, for the slope of the function is the amount by which the value of the dependent variable changes per unit change in the value of the independent variable. In the relation $y = a + bx$, every time x increases by 1, y will increase by $b(1)$ or b, which is the rate of increase of y or the slope of the function.

Another way of calculating the slope of a straight line is to designate the coordinates of P as x_1 and y_1 and to designate the coordinates of Q as x_2 and y_2. Then,

$$y_1 = f(x_1) = a + bx_1$$
$$y_2 = f(x_2) = a + bx_2$$

The slope of the line between P and Q may be expressed as the ratio

$$m = \frac{y_2 - y_1}{x_2 - x_1} = \frac{(a + bx_2) - (a + bx_1)}{x_2 - x_1}$$
$$= \frac{a + bx_2 - a - bx_1}{x_2 - x_1} = \frac{bx_2 - bx_1}{x_2 - x_1} = \frac{b(x_2 - x_1)}{x_2 - x_1} = b$$

This formulation shows that the measure of the slope of a straight line is the ratio

$$m = \frac{y_2 - y_1}{x_2 - x_1}$$

It is clear that if $y_2 = y_1$ so that $y_2 - y_1 = 0$, the slope of the straight line will be zero. The situation in which $y_2 = y_1$ would arise if the straight line were horizontal. This situation is depicted in Figure 3-2. Here the value of y at $A(= y_1)$ is equal to the value of y at $B(= y_2)$ and the difference between y_2 and y_1 is equal to zero. The numerical value of the slope is zero. The equation of the horizontal line is therefore $y = k$.

When a straight line is positioned vertically ($x_2 = x_1$), the denominator of the slope ratio is $x_2 - x_1 = 0$ and the slope of the line is undefined. Such a line is shown in Figure 3-3. The equation of the line in Figure 3-3 is $x = n$.

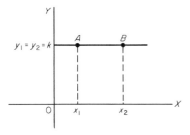

FIGURE 3-2   Horizontal Straight Line

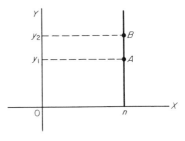

FIGURE 3-3   Vertical Straight Line

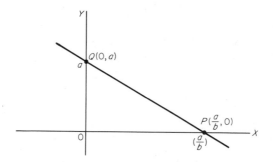

FIGURE 3-4   Slope of a Straight Line

Now take the equation $y = a + bx$ and replace b with $-b$, resulting in the equation

$$y = a - bx$$

The y-intercept will remain a, but the x-intercept will become a/b, as illustrated in Figure 3-4. The measure of the slope will be

$$m = \frac{0 - a}{\dfrac{a}{b} - 0} = \frac{-a}{\dfrac{a}{b}} = -a\left(\frac{b}{a}\right) = -b$$

The slope of this function is $m = -b$. Again the slope of the straight line shown in Figure 3-4 is the coefficient of the independent variable x.

So far the literal numbers a and b have been used to develop the general equations of straight lines. These equations were used to identify the intercepts and the slopes. Now a and b can be replaced by explicit numbers to develop a family of straight lines. To do this, first hold constant the value of a, the y-intercept, and change the value of b to introduce different slopes. Next hold the slope constant and change the y-intercept.

Consider the following family of equations:

$$y = 2 + 2x$$
$$y = 2 + x$$
$$y = 2 + 0x$$
$$y = 2 - x$$
$$y = 2 - 2x$$

These equations are plotted in Figure 3-5. All of the straight lines in Figure 3-5 have one point in common: the point $(0, 2)$. These lines differ in the

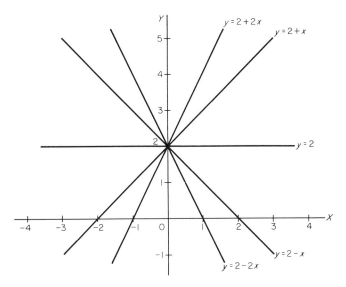

FIGURE 3-5 **Straight Lines with Common *y*-Intercept and Different Slopes**

measure of their slopes, with the values of the slopes being 2, 1, 0, −1, and −2.

Now consider another family of linear equations:

$$y = 2 + x$$
$$y = 1 + x$$
$$y = x$$
$$y = -1 + x$$
$$y = -2 + x$$

These equations are plotted in Figure 3-6. Notice that the five lines in Figure 3-6 have the same slope but different *y*-intercepts and different *x*-intercepts. The *y*-intercept of

$$y = 2 + x$$

is at $y = 2$ and its *x*-intercept occurs when

$$2 + x = 0 \qquad \text{or} \qquad x = -2$$

For the equation

$$y = -1 + x$$

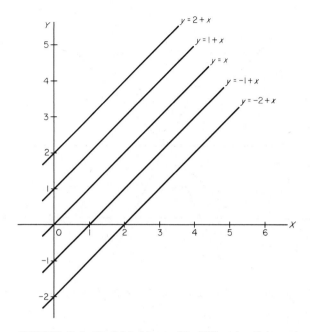

FIGURE 3-6 Straight Lines with Different y-Intercept and Constant Slope

the y-intercept will be at $y = -1$ and the x-intercept will be at

$$-1 + x = 0 \quad \text{or} \quad x = 1$$

These lines are parallel because of their identical slope measure, each having a slope of $m = 1$.

Equations of Straight Lines

As indicated by the previous discussion, a straight line can be identified from either (1) two points on that line, or (2) one point and the slope of the line.

First consider the case in which two points are known and the problem is to determine the equation of the line passing through those two points. Let $P_1(x_1, y_1)$ and $P_2(x_2, y_2)$ be the points on the line. Next designate $P(x, y)$ as any other point on the line. The points are illustrated in Figure 3-7. Since this is assumed to be a straight line whose slope is constant throughout its entire range, the slope of the line segment from P to P_1

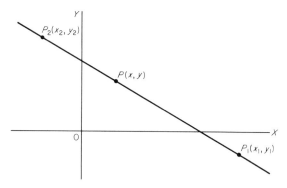

FIGURE 3-7   Derivation of a Straight Line from Two Points

must be the same as the slope of the line segment from P_2 to P_1. So the equation can be set up

$$\frac{y - y_1}{x - x_1} = \frac{y_2 - y_1}{x_2 - x_1}$$

Multiplying both sides of the equation by $x - x_1$ gives

$$y - y_1 = \frac{y_2 - y_1}{x_2 - x_1}(x_2 - x_1)$$

in which $(y_2 - y_1)/(x_2 - x_1)$ is the slope of the line.

Consider a numerical example. The problem is to write the equation of the line passing through the points $(-1, 2)$ and $(3, 4)$. If the points are designated $P_1(-1, 2)$ and $P_2(3, 4)$, the slope of the line will be

$$m = \frac{4 - 2}{3 - (-1)} = \frac{2}{4} = \frac{1}{2}$$

The equation will be

$$y - 2 = \tfrac{1}{2}(x + 1)$$

Upon simplification, the equation of the line becomes

$$y = 2\tfrac{1}{2} + \tfrac{1}{2}x$$

Substituting $x = -1$ into the equation of the line gives

$$y = 2\tfrac{1}{2} + (\tfrac{1}{2})(-1) = 2\tfrac{1}{2} - \tfrac{1}{2} = 2$$

The coordinates $x = -1$ and $y = 2$ are the coordinates of P_1. Similar substitution of $x = 3$ into the equation yields $y = 4$; these are the co-ordinates of P_2.

Suppose that two points of a linear demand function are known to be $A(q_1 = 2, p_1 = 4)$ and $B(q_2 = 6, p_2 = 3)$, and the equation of the function is to be derived. The slope of the demand curve will be

$$m = \frac{3 - 4}{6 - 2} = -\frac{1}{4} = -0.25$$

From the general formula, the equation of the demand function is

$$p - p_1 = m(q - q_1)$$

Substituting the known values for p_1, m_1, and q_1 gives

$$p - 4 = -0.25(q - 2)$$

After terms are simplified and collected, the equation of the demand function becomes

$$p = 4.5 - 0.25q$$

Figure 3-8 shows this demand curve. As is customary, prices are plotted on the ordinate and quantities on the abscissa.

Sometimes a given point on a line and the slope of the line may be known. From these pieces of information, the equation of the line is to be developed. The general method of deriving an equation from such information is to designate the known point as $P_1(x_1, y_1)$. Let $P(x, y)$ be any other point on the line. Then

$$\frac{y - y_1}{x - x_1} = m$$

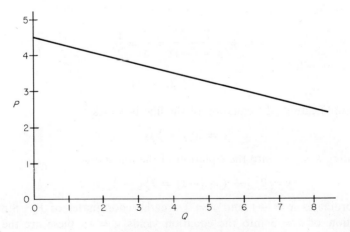

FIGURE 3-8   A Demand Curve

m being the known slope of the line. This equation can be rewritten

$$y - y_1 = m(x - x_1)$$

As a numerical illustration, determine the equation of a straight line which goes through the point $P_1(3, 4)$ with a slope $m = -2$. From the given information, set up the equation

$$y - 4 = -2(x - 3)$$

which is

$$y = 10 - 2x$$

Note that the equation $y = 10 - 2x$ will satisfy the conditions of the problem. The slope of the locus of the equation will be $m = -2$ and the substitution of $x = 3$ into the equation will give

$$y = 10 - 2(3) = 4$$

The line passes through the point $P_1(3, 4)$.

Suppose that a given supply curve is known to be linear with a slope of $m = 0.5$, and that the supply curve passes through the point $P_1(q_1 = -4000, p_1 = 8)$. Again using economic convention, prices will be plotted on the vertical axis and quantities on the horizontal axis. The point-slope form of the equation will be

$$\frac{p - p_1}{q - q_1} = m$$

$$p - p_1 = m(q - q_1)$$

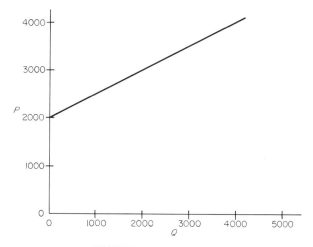

FIGURE 3-9 A Supply Curve

Substituting the known values of p_1, m_1, and q_1 gives

$$p - 8 = 0.5(q + 4000)$$

Rearranged, this becomes

$$p = 2008 + 0.5q$$

This supply equation is plotted as a straight line in Figure 3-9.

Distance Between Two Points

For later discussions it will be important to be able to measure the distance between two points on a line segment. Suppose the distance from point A to point B of Figure 3-10 is to be measured. Draw a line parallel to the y-axis through point A, and a line parallel to the x-axis through point B. These lines will intersect at the point $M(x_1, y_2)$. The triangle AMB is a right triangle whose hypotenuse is AB. Hence the line segment AB is of the length

$$\overline{AB}^2 = \overline{MA}^2 + \overline{MB}^2 = (y_2 - y_1)^2 + (x_2 - x_1)^2$$

When the square roots of both sides of the equation are taken,

$$\overline{AB} = \sqrt{(y_2 - y_1)^2 + (x_2 - x_1)^2}$$

On a linear demand curve whose equation is $p = 100 - 2q$ the length of the line between $q_1 = 10$ and $q_2 = 20$ is to be measured. Corresponding to q_1 and q_2 are the prices

$$p_1 = 100 - 2q_1 = 100 - 2(10) = 80$$
$$p_2 = 100 - 2q_2 = 100 - 2(20) = 60$$

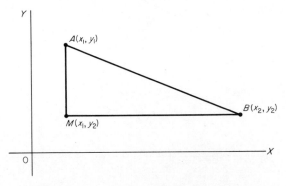

FIGURE 3-10   Distance Between Points A and B

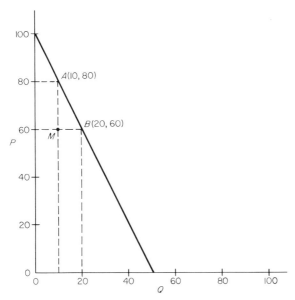

FIGURE 3-11   Distance Between Points A and B on a Demand Curve

The points on the demand curve between which the distance is to be found are shown in Figure 3-11 as points A and B. Construct a straight line AM parallel to the price axis and a straight line MB parallel to the quantity axis. Then

$$AB^2 = (80 - 60)^2 + (20 - 10)^2 = 400 + 100 = 500$$

and

$$AB = \sqrt{500} = 22.36$$

QUADRATIC EQUATIONS, CONIC SECTIONS

Quadratic equations and their graphs are the subject matter of this section. Graphs of quadratic equations form plane sections of a right circular cone with two *nappes*. Consider the three-dimensional figure shown in Figure 3-12. It represents the cone generated by a line passing through the *vertex*, G, and the circle AC. Along the edges of the figure are straight lines such as AB and CD. Cutting a plane section such as E produces an *ellipse*. Cutting a plane section perpendicular to the *axis* of the cone, MN, such as F in the bottom of Figure 3-12, yields a *circle*. In Figure 3-13, a plane is taken parallel to CD. The resulting curve is a *parabola*. In Figure 3-14, a

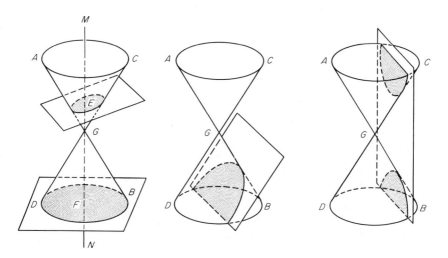

FIGURE 3-12   Conics   FIGURE 3-13   A Parabola   FIGURE 3-14   Hyperbolas

plane is taken so that it cuts both nappes of the cone. The resulting curves in the nappes are *hyperbolas*.

The next eight subsections are devoted to developing the equations for these curves and examining their economic applications.

The Circle

A circle is the locus of a point which moves at a constant distance from a fixed point. The fixed point is called the *center* of the circle, and the constant distance is the *radius* of the circle. The radius of the circle is then the linear distance from the given point on the circle to the center. If the center of a circle is at $x = h$ and $y = k$, a given point on the circle is $P(x, y)$, and the radius is r, the equation of the circle is

$$CP = \sqrt{(x - h)^2 + (y - k)^2} = r$$

If the center of the circle is at the origin of the coordinate system, $h = k = 0$ and the equation can be reduced to

$$r = \sqrt{x^2 + y^2}$$

The standard forms of the equation are, therefore,

$$r^2 = x^2 + y^2 \qquad (1)$$

for a circle with the center at origin, and

$$r^2 = (x - h)^2 + (y - k)^2 \qquad (2)$$

for a circle with the center $C(h, k)$.

Expansion of (2) yields

$$x^2 + y^2 - 2hx - 2ky + h^2 + k^2 - r^2 = 0 \qquad (3)$$

If the center is at origin, (3) reduces to

$$x^2 + y^2 - r^2 = 0$$

Equation (3) is often rewritten in the form

$$x^2 + y^2 + Ax + By + C = 0$$

where $A = -2h$, $B = -2k$, and $C = h^2 + k^2 - r^2$.

Figure 3-15 shows a circle with center $C(h, k)$ and radius r. If in the circle shown in Figure 3-15, $h = 3$ and $k = 2$, the center will be $C(3, 2)$. Further assume that the radius is $r = 5$. These conditions specifying the values of the arbitrary constants h, k, and r define one specific circle, whose equation is

$$5 = \sqrt{(x - 3)^2 + (y - 2)^2}$$

Squaring both sides of the equation gives

$$25 = (x - 3)^2 + (y - 2)^2$$

Expanding and collecting terms gives

$$x^2 + y^2 - 6x - 4y + (9 + 4 - 25) = 0$$

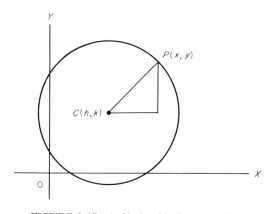

FIGURE 3-15   A Circle with Center at (h, k)

which is in the standard form

$$x^2 + y^2 + Ax + By + C = 0$$

with $A = -6 = -2h$, $B = -4 = -2k$, $C = 9 + 4 - 25 = h^2 + k^2 - r^2$.

To define any circle, three conditions must be given to determine the values of the constants. The circle can be specified, as above, by identifying the center coordinates and assigning a value to the radius. If the center is given, the variations of r will generate a system of concentric circles, the circles becoming larger as the value of r increases.

A circle can also be defined by three points on the circle. If, for example, three points of the circle are $P_1(8, 4)$, $P_2(2, 4)$, and $P_3(5, 1)$, by substituting the values of the three sets of coordinates into

$$x^2 + y^2 + Ax + By + C = 0$$

three simultaneous equations are established:

$$80 + 8A + 4B + C = 0$$
$$20 + 2A + 4B + C = 0$$
$$26 + 5A + B + C = 0$$

The solution of this system of simultaneous equations yields

$$A = -10 \qquad B = -8 \qquad C = 32$$

Since

$$A = -2h \qquad B = -2k \qquad C = h^2 + k^2 - r^2$$

substitution gives the equations

$$-10 = -2h \qquad h = 5$$
$$-8 = -2k \qquad k = 4$$
$$32 = 5^2 + 4^2 - r^2 \qquad r^2 = 9 \qquad r = 3$$

Therefore, the circle in question has its center at $C(5, 4)$ and the radius $r = 3$. The equation of the circle is then

$$(x - 5)^2 + (y - 4)^2 = 3^2$$

As another example, three points on a circle are given: $P_1(3, 4)$, $P_2(4, 3)$, and $P_3(-5, 0)$. Again direct substitution of the coordinates of the three points into the general equation of the circle yields three simultaneous equations

$$25 + 3A + 4B + C = 0$$
$$25 + 4A + 3B + C = 0$$
$$25 - 5A + C = 0$$

The solution of this system of simultaneous equations yields

$$A = 0 \qquad B = 0 \qquad C = -25$$

Therefore, $h = k = 0$, and $C = -r^2$. Thus

$$-25 = -r^2 \qquad r^2 = 25 \qquad r = 5$$

Since the coordinates of the center of this circle are $C(0, 0)$, the center is located at the origin. This circle has a radius of $r = 5$. The equation of the circle is therefore

$$x^2 + y^2 = 25$$

It is helpful in visualizing a given circle to be able to identify the extreme values of the function, i.e., to know at what value of x the values of y will be the greatest or least, and at what value of y the values of x will be the greatest or least. The equation of a circle with center at origin and radius r is

$$x^2 + y^2 = r^2 \qquad \text{or} \qquad y^2 = r^2 - x^2$$

Taking the square root of both sides of the equation,

$$y = \overset{\pm}{\sqrt{r^2 - x^2}}$$

It is clear that x cannot assume any value greater than r, for then the right-hand member of the equation will be an imaginary number for which no locus can be defined. Therefore the extreme values x may assume are $x = r$ and $x = -r$. When x is equal to r, $r^2 - x^2 = 0$, and $y = 0$. The circle will cut the x-axis at $x = -r$ and again at $x = r$.

For y to have its greatest positive or negative value, the difference $r^2 - x^2$ under the radical sign must be at its greatest. Obviously, the difference $r^2 - x^2$ will be maximum when $x = 0$. Then y will be

$$y = \overset{\pm}{\sqrt{r^2}} = \pm r$$

Thus y will be at a maximum value of $y = r$ and at a minimum value of $y = -r$ when $x = 0$.

Assign a numerical value to the radius r so that $r = 5$, and place the center at origin, $C(0, 0)$. In this case the equation of the circle is

$$x^2 + y^2 = 5^2$$

or

$$y = \overset{\pm}{\sqrt{25 - x^2}}$$

Clearly, x may not assume any value greater than 5 or less than -5, so the permissible range of values of x is

$$-5 \le x \le 5$$

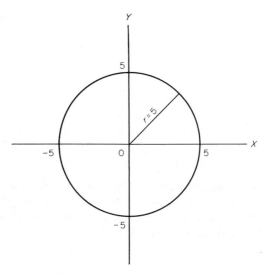

FIGURE 3-16   A Circle with Radius of 5

When $x = 5$ and $x = -5$, the expression under the radical will be zero, and y will be zero.

For y to be maximum, the expression under the radical sign must be at a maximum. The quantity $25 - x^2$ will be at its maximum when x is equal to zero. The values of y when $x = 0$ are

$$y = \overset{\pm}{\sqrt{25}} = \pm 5$$

This is the circle illustrated in Figure 3-16.

If the circle has its center at $C(h, k)$ with a radius of r, from the equation of such a circle

$$(x - h)^2 + (y - k)^2 = r^2$$

and rearranging,

$$(y - k)^2 = r^2 - (x - h)^2$$

or

$$y - k = \overset{\pm}{\sqrt{r^2 - (x - h)^2}}$$

For this circle to have a locus, $(x - h)^2$ must not be greater than r^2. If $(x - h)^2 > r^2$, the number under the radical sign will be negative. But when $(x - h)^2 = r^2$, the difference $r^2 - (x - h)^2$ will be zero, and the equation of the circle will reduce to $y = k$. Therefore, $y = k$ when x assumes the maximum permissible values of

$$(x - h)^2 = r^2 \quad \text{or} \quad x - h = \overset{\pm}{\sqrt{r^2}} = \pm r$$

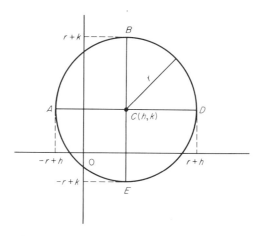

**FIGURE 3-17   Maximum and Minimum Values of
X and Y on a Circle with Radius r**

and

$$x = r + h \qquad \text{or} \qquad x = -r + h$$

In Figure 3-17, the extreme values of x are shown at points A and D on the circle. At point A the coordinates are $x = -r + h$ and $y = k$. At point D the coordinates are $x = r + h$ and $y = k$. The extreme values of y are seen to be at points B and E on the circle with the coordinates $x = h$, $y = r + k$ and $x = h$, $y = -r + k$ respectively.

The circle with center $C(3, 5)$ and radius $r = 6$ has the equation

$$(y - 5)^2 = 6^2 - (x - 3)^2 \qquad \text{or} \qquad y - 5 = \overset{\pm}{\sqrt{6^2 - (x - 3)^2}}$$

This circle is illustrated in Figure 3-18. The maximum and minimum values of x are defined by the relation

$$6^2 - (x - 3)^2 = 0$$

which is to say, $x = -3$ or $x = 9$. Since the center of the circle is $C(3, 5)$, $h = 3$ and $k = 5$. The maximum and minimum values are given also by the relations

$$x_{\max} = r + h = 6 + 3 = 9$$

$$x_{\min} = -r + h = -6 + 3 = -3$$

Note also that when $x = 9$ and $x = -3$, the expression under the radical becomes zero, and the value of y will therefore be

$$y - 5 = 0 \qquad \text{or} \qquad y = 5$$

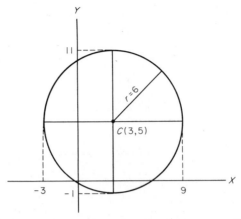

FIGURE 3-18   A Circle with Radius 6 and C
(3, 5)

For y to be either the maximum or the minimum, we must have

$$x - 3 = 0$$

that is, y will assume its extreme values when $x = 3$. The corresponding values of y are

$$y - 5 = \overset{\pm}{\sqrt{6^2 - (3 - 3)^2}}$$

$$y - 5 = \pm 6$$

$$y = 11 \quad \text{or} \quad y = -1$$

As defined earlier, the relationships which will specify the extreme values of y are

$$y_{\text{max}} = r + k = 6 + 5 = 11$$

$$y_{\text{min}} = -r + k = -6 + 5 = -1$$

Economic Applications of The Circle

Consider a simplified problem of plant location. The following assumptions are made:

1. The plant needs one raw material for its productive activity.
2. The plant needs one type of labor.
3. The raw material and the workers are located at one point, O.
4. One worker uses exactly one unit of raw material.

5. The cost of transportation of one worker or one unit of raw material over one unit of distance is one dollar.
6. The transportation budget of the plant is M.

The problem, depicted in Figure 3-19, is to define the permissible range of locations of the plant so as to make the total transportation cost exactly equal to the budget.

The circle C_1 is such that every point on it is exactly equidistant from the center O, the location of the raw material and the labor force. The distance from O to any point on the circle is d_1. Similarly every point on circle C_2 has a distance d_2 from O. As is evident, d_2 is greater than d_1. The distance d from any point on any circle C from O is defined by the relation

$$d = \sqrt{x^2 + y^2}$$

If Q units of raw material and Q men must be transported to the plant, the total number of units to transport is $2Q$. Since each unit of raw material or labor costs \$1 to transport over one unit of distance, the transportation cost is

$$\$2Q\sqrt{x^2 + y^2}$$

Now set this expression for the cost of transportation equal to the budget of the plant, giving

$$M = 2Q\sqrt{x^2 + y^2}$$

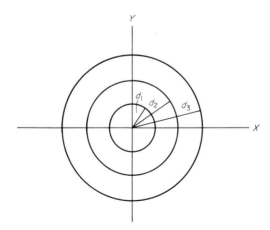

FIGURE 3-19   Three Circles with Varying Radii

Squaring both sides of the equation gives

$$M^2 = 4Q^2(x^2 + y^2)$$

Divide both sides of the equation by $4Q^2$, and write

$$\frac{M^2}{4Q^2} = x^2 + y^2$$

This is the equation of a circle with its center at origin and the radius

$$r = \frac{M}{2Q}$$

Note that the greater the transportation budget M of the plant, the greater will be the radius of the circle around O, along which the plant can be located. Also, given the amount of the budget M, the greater the quantity of raw material and men to be transported, Q, the shorter must be the distance

$$r = \frac{M}{2Q}$$

at which the plant can be located.

A portion of a circle may be used to represent some economic functions. One might plot on the abscissa the quantity demanded of some good, and on the ordinate the various possible prices of the good. The demand function of the good, then, may assume the form

$$p^2 + q^2 = k^2$$

where k is a constant. This is an equation of a circle in the $p - q$ plane with center at origin and radius k. The demand curve may be plotted from

$$p = \sqrt{k^2 - q^2}$$

Since economic theory of demand is normally concerned with positive quantities and prices, the values of p and q will be restricted to positive magnitudes. The price-axis intercept of this demand curve will be at the point where $q = 0$. When $q = 0$, $p = k$. The quantity-axis intercept will occur when price is equal to zero, or when

$$\sqrt{k^2 - q^2} = 0$$

Squaring yields

$$k^2 - q^2 = 0 \qquad q = k$$

Such a demand curve will shift if the value of k changes. Thus a family of demand functions may be shown as

$$p = \sqrt{2^2 - q^2} = \sqrt{4 - q^2}$$

$$p = \sqrt{3^2 - q^2} = \sqrt{9 - q^2}$$

$$p = \sqrt{4^2 - q^2} = \sqrt{16 - q^2}$$

The Ellipse

If a point moves in such a way that the sum of its distances from two fixed points is constant, the path of the point is an *ellipse*. The two fixed points are called the *foci* and the mid-point between the *foci* is called the *center* of the ellipse.

Let $F(c, O)$, $F'(-c, O)$ be the foci, and $P(x, y)$ be the representative point on the ellipse, as shown in Figure 3-20. The constant sum of the distance from P to F and from P to F' is designated $2a$. Then from the definition of the ellipse, the equation of this ellipse is

$$FP + F'P = 2a$$

or

$$\sqrt{(x + c)^2 + y^2} + \sqrt{(x - c)^2 + y^2} = 2a$$

Transposing the second radical, squaring, and reducing gives

$$cx - a^2 = -a\sqrt{(x - c)^2 + y^2}$$

Squaring again and reducing yields

$$x^2(a^2 - c^2) + a^2 y^2 = a^2(a^2 - c^2)$$

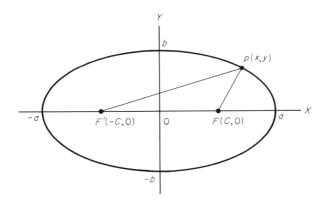

FIGURE 3-20   An Ellipse with Major Axis along x-Axis

Now let $b^2 = a^2 - c^2$. Making this substitution, write

$$b^2 x^2 + a^2 y^2 = a^2 b^2$$

Dividing both sides of the equation by $a^2 b^2$ gives

$$\frac{x^2}{a^2} + \frac{y^2}{b^2} = 1 \tag{1}$$

This is the equation of the ellipse whose foci are $(c, 0)$ and $(-c, 0)$.
  Solving (1) for y yields

$$y = \pm \frac{b}{a} \sqrt{a^2 - x^2} \tag{2}$$

Note that for this function to have a locus, x may only assume values such that $x^2 \leq a^2$. When $x = \pm a$, the expression under the radical will become zero and y will become zero. The ellipse crosses the x-axis when $x = -a$ and $x = a$. To find the y-axis intercepts, set $x = 0$. When $x = 0$, the expression becomes

$$y = \pm \frac{b}{a} \sqrt{a^2 - 0^2} = \pm \frac{b}{a} \sqrt{a^2} = \pm \frac{b}{a} a = \pm b$$

The ellipse crosses the y-axis where $y = b$ and where $y = -b$. From the development of the equation of the ellipse, remember that

$$b^2 = a^2 - c^2 \qquad \text{and} \qquad b = \pm \sqrt{a^2 - c^2}$$

It is apparent that $|b| < |a|$, and the numerical value of b is less than the numerical value of a, as is apparent in Figure 3-20.
  If the foci are taken on the y-axis, so that the foci are $(0, c)$ and $(0, -c)$, the equation of the ellipse will be

$$\frac{x^2}{b^2} + \frac{y^2}{a^2} = 1 \tag{3}$$

which, when solved for y, is

$$y = \pm \frac{a}{b} \sqrt{b^2 - x^2} \tag{4}$$

Real values of y exist only for those values of x such that $x^2 \leq b^2$. If $x = \pm b$

$$b^2 - x^2 = 0 \qquad \text{and} \qquad y = 0$$

The ellipse cuts the x-axis at $x = b$ and $x = -b$. To find the values of y

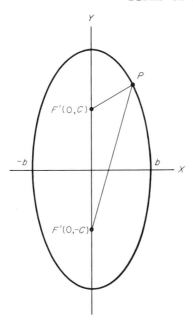

FIGURE 3-21 An Ellipse with Major Axis along the y-Axis

at which the function will cross the y-axis, set $x = 0$ and find

$$y = \pm \frac{a}{b} \sqrt{b^2 - 0^2} = \pm \frac{a}{b} \sqrt{b^2} = \pm \frac{a}{b} b = \pm a$$

The function cuts the y-axis at $y = a$ and $y = -a$. Since the absolute value of $a > b$, this is an ellipse with the shape shown in Figure 3-21.

Consider an ellipse whose equation is

$$\frac{x^2}{25} + \frac{y^2}{9} = 1$$

Solving it for y gives

$$y = \pm \tfrac{3}{5}\sqrt{25 - x^2}$$

The permissible range of the values of x is

$$-5 \leq x \leq 5$$

When $x = \pm 5$,

$$y = \pm \tfrac{3}{5}\sqrt{25 - (\pm 5)^2} = \pm \tfrac{3}{5}\sqrt{0} = 0$$

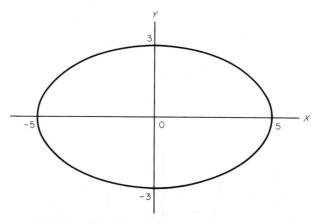

FIGURE 3-22   Ellipse with Extreme Values Identified

The x-axis intercepts are at the points

$$x = -5 \quad y = 0 \quad \text{and} \quad x = 5 \quad y = 0$$

The y-axis intercepts are found where $x = 0$. Therefore

$$y = \pm\tfrac{3}{5}\sqrt{25 - 0^2} = \pm\tfrac{3}{5}\sqrt{25} = \pm\tfrac{3}{5}5 = \pm 3$$

The y-axis intercepts will have the coordinates $(0, 3)$ and $(0, -3)$. Figure 3-22 illustrates this ellipse.

Given the following equation of an ellipse:

$$\frac{x^2}{4} + \frac{y^2}{16} = 1$$

one can write

$$y = \pm 2\sqrt{4 - x^2}$$

The x-intercepts are $(2, 0)$ and $(-2, 0)$, and the y-intercepts are $(0, 4)$ and $(0, -4)$, as seen in Figure 3-23. If the center of the ellipse were at some point other than the origin, the equation of the ellipse would become

$$\frac{(x - h)^2}{a^2} + \frac{(y - k)^2}{b^2} = 1$$

For an ellipse with the center at (h, k), as shown in Figure 3-24, the critical

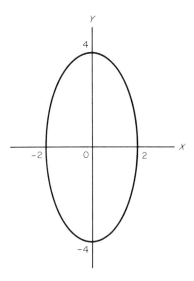

FIGURE 3-23   Ellipse with Extreme Values Identified

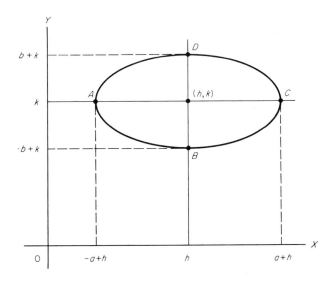

FIGURE 3-24   Ellipse with Center at (h, k)

values of the ellipse are

$$A = x_{\min} = -a + h$$

$$C = x_{\max} = a + h$$

$$B = y_{\min} = -b + k$$

$$D = y_{\max} = b + k$$

Examine an ellipse with center $(3, 6)$, whose equation is

$$\frac{(x - 3)^2}{9} + \frac{(y - 6)^2}{4} = 1$$

Rewriting the equation gives

$$(y - 6)^2 = \tfrac{4}{9}[9 - (x - 3)^2]$$

or

$$y - 6 = \pm\tfrac{2}{3}\sqrt{9 - (x - 3)^2}$$

The maximum and minimum values which x may assume are defined by the expression under the radical such that

$$9 - (x - 3)^2 = 0 \quad \text{or} \quad x = 0 \quad \text{or} \quad x = 6$$

When $x = 0$ and $x = 6$, the expression under the radical becomes zero and $y - 6 = 0$. Therefore $y = 6$. The coordinates of the extreme values of x are $(0, 6)$ and $(6, 6)$. For y to be either a maximum or a minimum, the difference $x - 3$ must equal zero. That is to say, the extreme values of y will occur when $x = 3$. At $x = 3$, we have

$$y - 6 = \pm\tfrac{2}{3}\sqrt{9}$$

$$y - 6 = \pm 2$$

$$y = 8 \quad \text{or} \quad y = 4$$

The coordinates of the extreme values of y are $(3, 8)$ and $(3, 4)$.

Economic Applications of The Ellipse

A firm's revenue and cost conditions are such that its total profit function is defined by the equation

$$\pi = 20 - 2(x - 3)^2 - 4(y - 5)^2$$

where π is the total profit; x and y are the two factors of production used by the firm; the number 2 is the price of the resource x, and the number 4 is the price of the resource y.

An examination of the profit function shows that the firm's maximum profit is 20, employing 3 units of x and 5 units of y. When the firm employs 3 units of x, the second term of the profit expression is zero, and nothing need be subtracted from the maximum profit of 20. Likewise at the optimum employment of 5 units of resource y, the third term of the profit expression is zero, subtracting nothing from the maximum attainable profit of 20. Now if y is held at 5 units, but 4 units of x are employed, it is readily seen that

$$\pi = 20 - 2(4 - 3)^2 - 4(5 - 5)^2$$
$$= 20 - 2 - 0 = 18$$

It can be shown that the employment of any quantity of x other than 3, or any quantity of y other than 5, will decrease total profit.

The profit function can be rewritten in the form

$$\pi - 20 = -2(x - 3)^2 - 4(y - 5)^2$$

Multiplying every term by -1 gives

$$20 - \pi = 2(x - 3)^2 + 4(y - 5)^2$$

Dividing both sides of the equation by $20 - \pi$ gives

$$\frac{2(x - 3)^2}{20 - \pi} + \frac{4(y - 5)^2}{20 - \pi} = 1$$

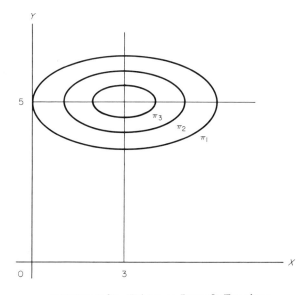

FIGURE 3-25   Ellipses as Isoprofit Functions

Multiplying the numerator and the denominator of the first term by $\frac{1}{2}$, and those of the second term by $\frac{1}{4}$, we have

$$\frac{(x-3)^2}{\frac{1}{2}(20-\pi)} + \frac{(y-5)^2}{\frac{1}{4}(20-\pi)} = 1$$

This expression is clearly the equation of an ellipse, with its center at (3, 5), and

$$a^2 = \frac{1}{2}(20-\pi) \qquad b^2 = \frac{1}{4}(20-\pi)$$

Changing the value of π develops a family of concentric ellipses, as shown in Figure 3-25. The maximum profit of 20 is shown to correspond to the single point at the center. Each ellipse is an iso-profit curve, with profits decreasing as each successive ellipse gets larger and moves away from the center point.

The Parabola

A *parabola* is the locus of a point whose movement is such that it is equidistant from a fixed point and a fixed line. The fixed point is called the *focus* of the parabola and the fixed line is the *directrix* of the parabola.

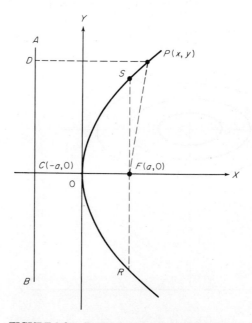

FIGURE 3-26   Derivation of a General Parabola

In Figure 3-26, the vertical straight line AB is the directrix. The point F is the focus. A line is drawn through F perpendicular to the directrix AB, intersecting AB at point C. The mid-point O between C and F is a point on the parabola since it is equidistant from the directrix and from the focus. Choosing the point O as origin, let the horizontal line through C and F be the x-axis. The focus of the parabola F has the coordinates $(a, 0)$ and the point C on the directrix has the coordinates $(-a, 0)$. The equation of the directrix is $x = -a$. Let $P(x, y)$ be any point on the parabola. Draw PF and DP. By definition,

$$PF = DP$$

From the diagram it can be seen that

$$PF = \sqrt{(x - a)^2 + y^2}$$

and

$$DP = x + a$$

Hence by the definition of the parabola, the equation of the parabola is

$$\sqrt{(x - a)^2 + y^2} = x + a$$

Squaring both sides of this equation yields

$$(x - a)^2 + y^2 = (x + a)^2$$

Expanding and collecting terms yields

$$y^2 = 4ax \tag{1}$$

or

$$y = \pm 2\sqrt{ax} \tag{2}$$

Equations (1) and (2) are the standard equations of the parabola. If a is positive, then x must be positive for y to be a real number. The parabola for $a > 0$ therefore corresponds only to positive values of x. If a is negative, then x must be negative to yield real numbers for values of y; hence if $a < 0$ the parabola may be drawn only for negative values of x. For each value of x, there are two corresponding values of y equal in magnitude but opposite in sign. The parabola is symmetrical with respect to the x-axis. The line of symmetry of the parabola is called the *axis* of the parabola. The point on the axis of the parabola at which the parabola intersects the axis is called the *vertex* of the parabola.

The equation

$$y = \pm \sqrt{12x}$$

will generate a parabola with vertex at the origin. Some of the points of the parabola are

$$x = 0$$
$$y = \sqrt{(12)(0)} = 0$$
$$x = 1$$
$$y = \pm\sqrt{12} = \pm 2\sqrt{3}$$
$$x = 2$$
$$y = \pm\sqrt{24} = \pm 2\sqrt{6}$$
$$x = 3$$
$$y = \pm\sqrt{36} = \pm 6$$

Translation of Axes. The discussions of various function types have implied that axes are chosen for convenience in the problem to be analyzed. It is sometimes necessary to change the positions of the axes. Translation of the axes is the movement of the axes parallel to their original positions. Figure 3-27 illustrates such a translation. Let OX and OY be the original axes and $O'X'$ and $O'Y'$ be the new axes. The origin of the new axes, O', has the coordinates (h, k) in relation to the old axes. The coordinates of any point P in relation to the old axes are (x, y) and in relation to the new axes are (x', y'). Then it is evident that the relationship between the old

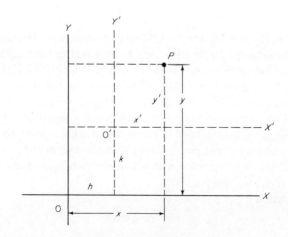

FIGURE 3-27   Shifting of Axes

coordinate values and the new coordinate values of any point P is

$$x = x' + h$$
$$y = y' + k$$

Parabola, Vertex Not at Origin. Armed now with the technique of translation of axes, consider some parabolas whose vertices are not at the origin. The parabola in Figure 3-28 has its vertex at (h, k) in reference to the OX and OY axes. Introducing the new axes $O'X'$ and $O'Y'$, the parabola has its vertex at O' and the axis $O'X'$. In relation to these new axes the equation of the parabola is

$$(y')^2 = 4ax'$$

Substituting the values of y' and x' in reference to the original axes,

$$(y - k)^2 = 4a(x - h)$$

becomes the equation of the parabola in reference to the original axes. Note that there are four classes of parabolas:

1. $(y - k)^2 = 4a(x - h)$, a parabola with the axis parallel to OX, and the curve opening to the right.
2. $(y - k)^2 = -4a(x - h)$, a parabola with the axis parallel to OX, and the curve opening to the left.
3. $(x - h)^2 = 4a(y - k)$, a parabola with the axis parallel to OY, and the curve opening to the top.

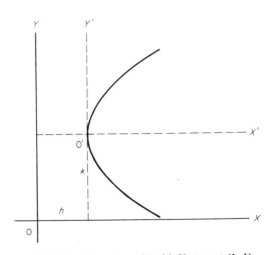

FIGURE 3-28   Parabola with Vertex at (h, k)

4. $(x - h)^2 = -4a(y - k)$, a parabola with the axis parallel to OY and the curve opening downward.

Economic Applications of The Parabola

A parabola traces out a curve which contains a positively sloped and a negatively sloped portion. The vertex of the parabola is at the point where the curve changes from a positive slope to a negative slope, or from a negative to a positive slope. Having these properties, the parabola is a curve with possible applications in many fields. In economics, parabolic functions of many types can be used to represent economic data. Consider a few examples.

1. The supply function $p = \sqrt{2Q + 4}$ may be rearranged into

$$p^2 = 2Q + 4 \qquad \text{or} \qquad p^2 = 2(Q + 2)$$

This is a parabola fitting form (1) in the previous section. It is a parabola with the axis parallel to OQ and the vertex at $(-2, 0)$, as shown in Figure 3-29. The supply curve portrayed turns out to be a portion of the positively sloped segment of the parabola. The supply curve may take the form

$$p^2 = 2Q$$

which will trace out a parabola whose axis is OQ and whose vertex is at origin. This is the curve shown in Figure 3-30.

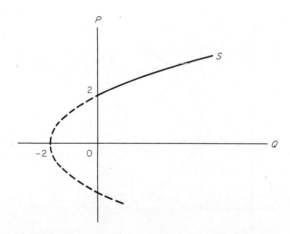

FIGURE 3-29   Portion of a Parabola as a Supply Curve

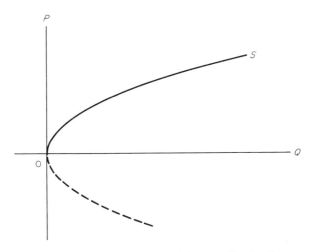

FIGURE 3-30   Portion of a Parabola as a Supply Curve

2. The demand function $Q = 2(50 - p^2)$, which can be written in the equivalent form

$$p = \sqrt{50 - 0.5Q}$$

is a parabola with the vertex at $(p = 0, Q = 100)$, the axis of the parabola being OQ. This is clearly a parabola of the second form, as illustrated in Figure 3-31.

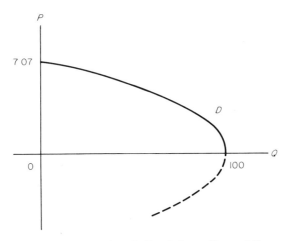

FIGURE 3-31   Portion of a Parabola as a Demand Curve

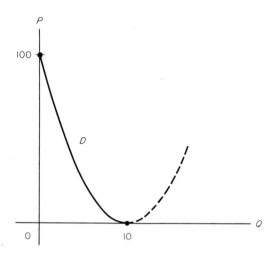

**FIGURE 3-32   Portion of a Parabola as a Demand
Curve**

3. The demand function $p = Q^2 - 20Q + 100$ can be written as

$$p = (Q - 10)^2$$

which is seen to be a parabola of type (3) which opens upward with the axis
of the parabola parallel to OP. This parabola is shown in Figure 3-32.
The vertex of the parabola is at the point $(Q = 10, p = 0)$. At a price of
100, quantity demanded will be zero. The p-axis intercept is at the point
$(Q = 0, p = 100)$.

4. The total revenue curve of a firm operating in an industry of less
than perfect competition is given by this equation:

$$R = 10Q - Q^2$$

where R is the total revenue and Q is the quantity sold. Rearranging the
revenue function gives

$$-Q^2 + 10Q = R \qquad \text{or} \qquad Q^2 - 10Q = -R$$

Completing the square in Q gives

$$Q^2 - 10Q + 25 = 25 - R$$

which can be written

$$(Q - 5)^2 = -1(R - 25)$$

This revenue function is of the form (4), and is therefore a parabola with

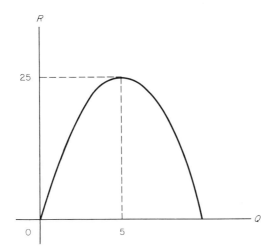

FIGURE 3-33   Parabola as a Total Revenue Curve

the axis parallel to OR and opening downward. The vertex of the parabola is at $Q = 5$ and $R = 25$. The sketch of the revenue function is seen in Figure 3-33.

5. Given the following pair of supply and demand functions, find the equilibrium price and the equilibrium quantity.

$$p = 13 - Q^2 \quad \text{(demand function)}$$

$$p = Q^2 + 2Q + 1 \quad \text{(supply function)}$$

The demand function is a parabola of the form

$$p = -1(Q^2 - 13)$$

which is a parabola with a vertical axis, opening downward. The vertex of this parabola is at $(Q = 0, p = 13)$. The supply function is of the form

$$p = (Q + 1)^2$$

and has a vertical axis with the vertex at $(Q = -1, p = 0)$. The graphic solution is achieved by plotting the supply function and the demand function in the same diagram, and locating the point of intersection between the two curves. Figure 3-34 portrays a graphic solution for example 5. We can also solve for the equilibrium price and the equilibrium quantity by

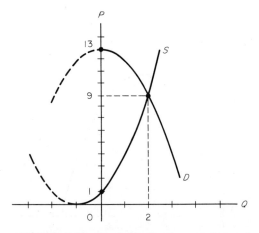

**FIGURE 3-34 Parabolic Supply and Demand
Curves with Equilibrium Quantity and Price**

setting the supply price equal to the demand price:

$$13 - Q^2 = Q^2 + 2Q + 1$$
$$2Q^2 + 2Q - 12 = 0$$
$$Q^2 + Q - 6 = 0$$
$$Q = \frac{-1 \pm \sqrt{1 + 24}}{2} = \frac{-1 + 5}{2} = \frac{4}{2} = 2$$

Substitution into the demand function gives $p = 13 - 2^2 = 9$.

As a second example of finding the equilibrium price and quantity, consider the case in which the demand curve is a parabola and the supply curve is linear. The supply and demand functions, shown in Figure 3-35, are

$$p = 25 - Q^2 \qquad \text{(demand function)}$$
$$p = -2 + 3Q \qquad \text{(supply function)}$$

Solving for the value of Q, set the two equations equal to each other:

$$25 - Q^2 = -2 + 3Q$$
$$Q^2 + 3Q - 27 = 0$$
$$Q = \frac{-3 + \sqrt{9 + 108}}{2} = \frac{-3 + \sqrt{117}}{2} = \frac{-3 + 10.82}{2}$$
$$= \frac{7.82}{2} = 3.91$$

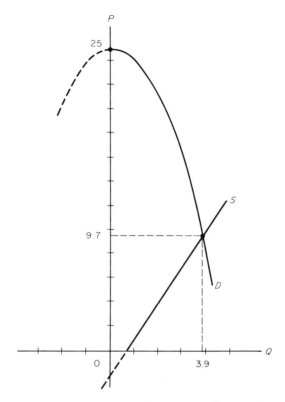

FIGURE 3-35 A Parabolic Demand Curve and a Linear Supply Curve with Equilibrium Quantity and Price

The equilibrium value of quantity is approximately 3.91. Substituting $Q = 3.91$ into either the supply or the demand function will yield the equilibrium price.

$$p = 25 - (3.91)^2 = 9.71 \text{ (approximately)}$$

or

$$p = -2 + 3(3.91) = 9.73 \text{ (approximately)}$$

The Hyperbola

A *hyperbola* is the locus of points the difference of whose distances from 2 fixed points is a constant. The fixed points are the *foci* of the hyperbola.

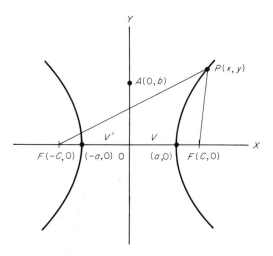

FIGURE 3-36   Derivation of Hyperbolas

Let the distance between the foci be $2c$, and let the constant difference be equal to $2a$. Choose the line passing through the two foci as the x-axis. The midpoint between the foci is the origin O. The foci will have the coordinates $F'(-c, 0)$ and $F(c, 0)$. From the definition of the hyperbola,

$$F'P - FP = 2a$$

From Figure 3-36, it is evident that

$$F'P = \sqrt{(x + c)^2 + y^2}$$

and

$$FP = \sqrt{(x - c)^2 + y^2}$$

The equation of the hyperbola, therefore, is

$$\sqrt{(x + c)^2 + y^2} - \sqrt{(x - c)^2 + y^2} = 2a$$

Transposing the second radical, squaring, and simplifying gives

$$cx - a^2 = a\sqrt{(x - c)^2 + y^2}$$

Again squaring and reducing gives

$$x^2(c^2 - a^2) - a^2y^2 = a^2(c^2 - a^2)$$

From the figure, note that $c > a$. Let $b^2 = c^2 - a^2$. Making this substitution in the equation,

$$b^2x^2 - a^2y^2 = a^2b^2$$

Dividing by a^2b^2, the result is

$$\frac{x^2}{a^2} - \frac{y^2}{b^2} = 1 \tag{1}$$

Equation (1) is the general equation of the hyperbola. To facilitate the evaluation of some points on the hyperbola, write equation (1) for y in terms of x.

$$y = \pm \frac{b}{a} \sqrt{x^2 - a^2} \tag{2}$$

From (2) it is evident that x^2 cannot be less than a^2 if y is to have real values. No real values of y can be defined between $x = -a$ and $x = a$. The hyperbola does not cross the y-axis. Equation (2) also shows that two curves are generated: by taking $x > 0$, the hyperbola is to the right of the y-axis; by taking $x < 0$, the hyperbola is to the left of the y-axis.

When $x = -a$ and $x = a$, the quantity under the radical reduces to zero, and the value of y is zero at these points. The x-intercept of the hyperbola to the left of the y-axis is $x = -a$, and the x-intercept of the hyperbola to the right of the y-axis is $x = a$.

The portion of the line of symmetry of the hyperbola from the point $(-a, 0)$ to the point $(a, 0)$, or the line segment $V'V$ in Figure 3-36, is called the *transverse axis* of the hyperbola. The line segment AB from $(0, b)$ to $(0, -b)$ is the *conjugate axis*. The line segment of length a, $(\frac{1}{2}V'V)$ is the *semi-transverse axis*. The length b $(\frac{1}{2}AB)$ is the *semi-conjugate axis*. The point of intersection between the transverse and the conjugate axes is the *center* of the hyperbola. The hyperbola is symmetrical with respect to the center.

A hyperbola is a curve such that for each value of x there are two values of y equal in magnitude but opposite in sign. When x is taken to be positive, increasing values of x result in progressively larger values of y in both the positive and the negative directions. When x is taken to be negative, the values of y will again become larger positive and negative values for each successively larger negative value of x.

The asymptotes of the hyperbola are defined as the lines

$$y = \pm \frac{b}{a} x$$

As the values of x become larger, the ordinate of the hyperbola

$$y = \pm \frac{b}{a} \sqrt{x^2 - a^2}$$

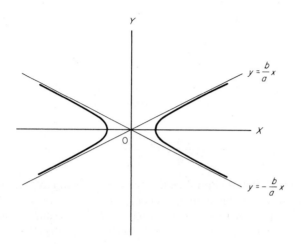

FIGURE 3-37   Hyperbola with Asymptotic Lines

will approach the line

$$y = \pm \frac{b}{a} x$$

The hyperbola will be located to the right of $x = a$ and to the left of $x = -a$. The halves of the hyperbola will be contained within the lines

$$y = \frac{b}{a} x \quad \text{and} \quad y = -\frac{b}{a} x$$

as illustrated in Figure 3-37. Since the asymptote lines have the slopes b/a or $-(b/a)$, the greater the ratio b/a, the more rapidly will the values of the ordinates of the hyperbola increase. The smaller the ratio b/a, the less rapid will be the rate of increase or decrease of the hyperbola.

Consider the hyperbolas

$$\frac{x^2}{4} - \frac{y^2}{9} = 1 \tag{1}$$

$$\frac{x^2}{4} - \frac{y^2}{25} = 1 \tag{2}$$

Equation (1) will generate a hyperbola whose coordinates are defined by

$$y = \pm \tfrac{3}{2}\sqrt{x^2 - 4}$$

This hyperbola has x-intercepts at $x = 2$ and $x = -2$. Assigning a few values to x, find the corresponding values of y:

When $x = 5$ $y = \pm\frac{3}{2}\sqrt{21}$

$\quad\quad x = 6$ $y = \pm\frac{3}{2}\sqrt{32}$

$\quad\quad x = 7$ $y = \pm\frac{3}{2}\sqrt{45}$

$\quad\quad x = 8$ $y = \pm\frac{3}{2}\sqrt{60}$

The asymptotic lines of this hyperbola, sketched in Figure 3-38, are

$$y = \tfrac{3}{2}x \quad\text{and}\quad y = -\tfrac{3}{2}x$$

Equation (2) is a hyperbola of the form

$$y = \pm\tfrac{5}{2}\sqrt{x^2 - 4}$$

with x-intercepts at $x = 2$ and $x = -2$. A few pairs of coordinate values of this hyperbola are:

When $x = 5$ $y = \pm\frac{5}{2}\sqrt{21}$

$\quad\quad x = 6$ $y = \pm\frac{5}{2}\sqrt{32} = \pm10\sqrt{2}$

$\quad\quad x = 7$ $y = \pm\frac{5}{2}\sqrt{45}$

$\quad\quad x = 8$ $y = \pm\frac{5}{2}\sqrt{60} = \pm5\sqrt{15}$

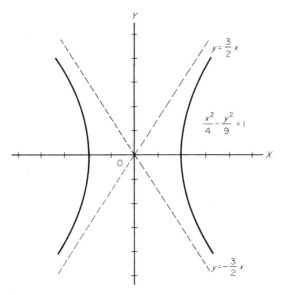

FIGURE 3-38   A Numerical Example of a Hyperbola

This hyperbola has asymptotes with larger numerical slopes than the previous one. The asymptotic lines in this case will have slopes of

$$y = \tfrac{5}{2}x \quad \text{and} \quad y = -\tfrac{5}{2}x$$

Hyperbolas with Foci on the y-Axis. When the foci of the hyperbola are taken on the y-axis, the transverse axis will be on the y-axis. The resulting equation will be

$$\frac{y^2}{a^2} - \frac{x^2}{b^2} = 1 \tag{1}$$

Solving (1) for x in terms of y yields

$$x = \pm \frac{b}{a}\sqrt{y^2 - a^2} \tag{2}$$

From (2) note that in the range of $-a < y < a$ no real values of x exist. The hyperbola does not cross the x-axis. The y-intercepts of the hyperbola are at $y = -a$ and $y = a$. This hyperbola is pictured in Figure 3-39.

The hyperbola with the equation

$$\frac{y^2}{9} - \frac{x^2}{4} = 1$$

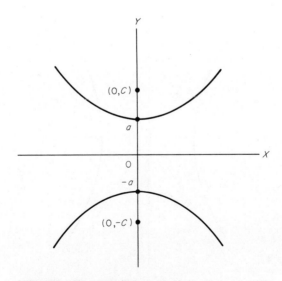

FIGURE 3-39   Hyperbola with Foci on the y-Axis

is an example of hyperbolas with foci on the y-axis. The equivalent equation of the hyperbola is

$$x = \pm \tfrac{2}{3}\sqrt{y^2 - 9}$$

The y-intercepts of the hyperbola are $(0, 3)$ and $(0, -3)$. The length of the transverse axis is 6 (units), and the length of the conjugate axis is 4 (units). Since $c^2 = a^2 + b^2$,

$$c = \pm\sqrt{9 + 4} = \pm\sqrt{13}$$

Therefore, the foci are at the points $(0, 13)$ and $(0, -13)$.

Hyperbolas, Center Not at Origin. By a line of reasoning similar to that applied to the ellipse, it can be argued that the equation of a hyperbola with center at (h, k) is

$$\frac{(x')^2}{a^2} - \frac{(y')^2}{b^2} = 1$$

in relation to the OX' and OY' axes. Since it is known from the discussion of axis translation that

$$x' = x - h \qquad \text{and} \qquad y' = y - k$$

it is apparent that

$$\frac{(x - h)^2}{a^2} - \frac{(y - k)^2}{b^2} = 1 \tag{1}$$

is the equation of the hyperbola in reference to the OX and OY axes. This is a hyperbola with the transverse axis parallel to the x-axis and center at (h, k). Similarly

$$\frac{(y - k)^2}{a^2} - \frac{(x - h)^2}{b^2} = 1 \tag{2}$$

is the equation of the hyperbola with the transverse axis parallel to OY and center at (h, k).

The expansion and simplification of either (1) or (2) will result in the general quadratic equation in x and y of the form

$$Ax^2 + By^2 + Cx + Dy + E = 0$$

where A and B are of opposite signs. For example, a hyperbola with the equation

$$\frac{(y - 1)^2}{9} - \frac{(x + 2)^2}{4} = 1$$

whose center is at $(-2, 1)$ with the transverse axis parallel to OY, may be expanded and simplified into

$$4y^2 - 9x^2 - 36x - 8y - 68 = 0$$

where

$$A = 4 \qquad B = 9 \qquad C = -36 \qquad D = -8 \qquad E = -68$$

Or a general second-degree equation of the hyperbola such as

$$16x^2 - 9y^2 - 128x + 90y - 113 = 0$$

may be transformed into the standard form of the equation of a hyperbola. The steps are illustrated as follows:

1. Arrange together all the terms containing x, and all the terms containing y, and transpose the constant term.

$$16x^2 - 128x - 9y^2 + 90y = 113$$

This can be written as

$$16(x^2 - 8x) - 9(y^2 - 10y) = 113$$

2. Complete the square in x and in y.

$$16(x^2 - 8x + 16) - 9(y^2 - 10y + 25) = 144$$

3. Divide both sides of the equation by 144 and arrange the terms.

$$\frac{(x - 4)^2}{9} - \frac{(y - 5)^2}{16} = 1$$

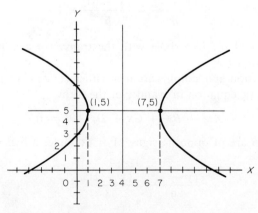

FIGURE 3-40   Hyperbola with Center Not at Origin

4. This is the equation of a hyperbola with the transverse axis parallel to OX. The vertices of the hyperbola are at

$$x = -a + 4 = -3 + 4 = 1 \qquad y = 5$$
$$x = a + 4 = 3 + 4 = 7 \qquad y = 5$$

This hyperbola is shown in Figure 3-40.

Economic Applications of the Hyperbola

Two firms, A and B, are located 50 miles apart. They produce a single homogeneous product. Buyers choose the firm from which to buy solely on the basis of the delivered price of the product, namely the factory price plus the transportation cost. The problem is to find the line separating A's market from B's market. To proceed with the solution, choose the line passing through the location of plant A, point A, and the location of plant B, point B, as the x-axis. Choose the midpoint between A and B on the x-axis as the origin as in Figure 3-41.

Assume that the cost of transportation per unit of the product per mile is \$0.20. This transportation cost holds true for deliveries made from any point to any other point. Also assume initially that each firm charges

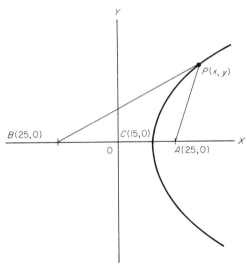

FIGURE 3-41 An Economic Application of the Hyperbola in a Market Division Problem

an identical price of $20. Under these assumptions the customers located to the left of the y-axis will buy exclusively from firm B. Those located to the right of the y-axis will buy only from firm A. Customers located on the y-axis, however, are equidistant from firm A and from firm B. The delivered price to a customer located on the y-axis will be identical whether he buys from A or from B. For example, the buyer located at O pays a delivered price of $25 made up of the factory price of $20, plus the transportation cost of $(\$0.2)(25) = \$5.00$, whether he buys from A or from B.

Now suppose plant B lowers its price at the factory from $20 to $14, while firm A maintains its original factory price of $20. The $6 reduction in price by plant B makes it possible for plant B to sell to customers who are located 30 miles further from it than from firm A at the same delivered price as firm A. For example, the customer located at $C(15, 0)$ is 40 miles from B and 10 miles from A. Firm B charges the customer at C the delivered price of $22 [$14 + ($0.20)(40)], and firm A's delivered price to the customer at C is $22 [$20 + ($0.20)(10)]. With the reduction of $6 in the price of B, the boundary line separating the market of firm B from that of firm A is along the locus of the hyperbola with a constant difference of 30.

The equation of this hyperbola is clearly defined by the relation

$$\overline{BP} - \overline{AP} = 30$$

Since from Figure 3-41,

$$\overline{BP} = \sqrt{(x + 25)^2 + y^2} \qquad \text{and} \qquad \overline{AP} = \sqrt{(x - 25)^2 + y^2}$$

the relationship is

$$\sqrt{(x + 25)^2 + y^2} - \sqrt{(x - 25)^2 + y^2} = 30$$

Transposing the second radical, squaring, and simplifying gives

$$100x - 900 = 60\sqrt{(x - 25)^2 + y^2}$$

Squaring again and simplifying yields

$$6400x^2 - 3600y^2 = 1.44 \text{ million}$$

Dividing both sides of the equation by 1.44 million gives

$$\frac{x^2}{225} - \frac{y^2}{400} = 1$$

The locus of this hyperbolic curve separating the markets of the two firms can be easily plotted from the relation

$$y = \pm {}^{20}\!/_{15}\sqrt{x^2 - 225} = \pm {}^{4}\!/_{3}\sqrt{x^2 - 225}$$

The vertex of this hyperbola is located at (15, 0). The asymptotic lines of the hyperbola are

$$y = \tfrac{4}{3}x \quad \text{and} \quad y = -\tfrac{4}{3}x$$

One type of special significance for economic analysis is the *equilateral or rectangular hyperbola*. If in the standard equation of the hyperbola,

$$\frac{x^2}{a^2} - \frac{y^2}{b^2} = 1$$

it is determined that $a = b$, then the equation will reduce to

$$x^2 - y^2 = a^2 \qquad y^2 = x^2 - a^2$$

The asymptotes of this hyperbola, called the *equilateral* or *rectangular* hyperbola, will have slopes of ± 1, and will have the equation

$$y = \pm x$$

This hyperbola and its asymptotes are illustrated in Figure 3-42.

If the asymptotic line $y = -x$ is designated as the new axis ox' and the asymptotic line $y = x$ the new axis oy', then in relation to the new axes, the equation of the hyperbola becomes

$$x'y' = a^2$$

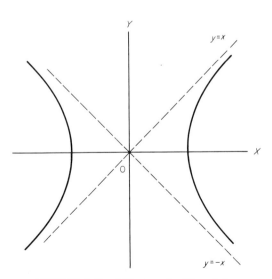

FIGURE 3-42 A Rectangular Hyperbola

Then

$$y' = \frac{a^2}{x'}$$

is the equation of the hyperbola in relation to the new axis.

If, in general, a hyperbola is of the form

$$xy = k \qquad \text{or} \qquad y = \frac{k}{x}$$

the equation expresses a relationship of proportionality between the variables x and y.

Such relationships of proportionality are very important in economic analysis. For example, if the demand curve for a product is such that the amount of expenditure on the good is some constant sum of money, say $10, per period of time, then the equation of the demand function is

$$pQ = 10 \qquad \text{or} \qquad p = \frac{10}{Q}$$

The demand function $p = 10/Q$ will develop the following schedule of corresponding pairs of p and Q, where p is price and Q is quantity demanded:

Point	A	B	C	D	E	F	G	H	I	J
Q	1	2	3	4	5	6	7	8	9	10
p	10	5	3.33	2.5	2	1.66	1.43	1.25	1.11	1

The curve representing the data shown in this schedule is illustrated in Figure 3-43.

In Figure 3-43 each rectangle formed by dropping the perpendiculars from a given point to the axes has an area of 10. From point A the perpendicular drawn to the price axis cuts the price axis at $10, and the perpendicular drawn to the quantity axis cuts the quantity axis at 1. The value of the ordinate of point A is $10, and the value of the abscissa is 1 unit. The area thus formed is $10 × 1 = $10. The coordinates of the point B are (2, 5). The quantity demanded at point B is 2 and the price is $5, and the total expenditure on the good corresponding to point B is $5 × 2 = $10 (the area of the rectangle under B). Likewise, all the rectangles corresponding to all the other points on the demand curve shown in Figure 3-43 have an area of $10.

The P-axis and the Q-axis are the asymptotes of this demand curve. The demand curve shown is a rectangular hyperbola. As any textbook in

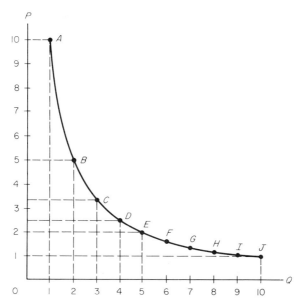

FIGURE 3-43 A Rectangularly Hyperbolic Demand
Curve

economic theory shows, such a demand curve is of unitary elasticity
throughout its range.

The liquidity preference function is generally stated as a function
relating the quantity of cash balances demanded to the rate of interest. It is
generally assumed that the demand for liquidity is inversely related to the
rate of interest. It is argued that the higher is the rate of interest, the
greater is the cost of holding assets in cash form, and hence, the smaller
will tend to be the amount of assets held in liquid form. As the rate of
interest falls, the amount of cash demanded will tend to increase. It is
further postulated in some formulations of the liquidity preference function
that there exists some low (minimum) positive rate of interest at which the
demand for liquidity will become infinitely elastic. An example of such a
liquidity preference function might be

$$M = f(i) = \frac{K}{i - 0.01}$$

where M is the quantity of cash balances demanded, i is the rate of interest
and K is a positive constant. The interest rate 0.01 is the rate at which
the community is unwilling to part with liquidity. The function has as

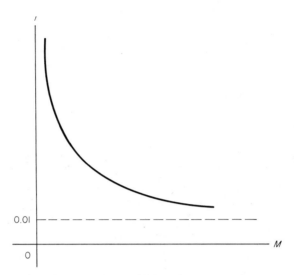

FIGURE 3-44   Liquidity Preference Function

its vertical asymptote the interest axis and as its horizontal asymptote the line $i = 0.01$. This situation is pictured in Figure 3-44.

OTHER ALGEBRAIC FUNCTIONS

Functions of linear and quadratic forms, and their corresponding curves have been described in this chapter. Some important properties of these functions and graphs have been discussed and some of the possibilities of economic applications of the linear and quadratic functions have been noted. Now it is time to consider some other types of algebraic functions and their graphs.

Algebraic functions are functions of the type $f(x, y) = 0$ where $f(x, y)$ is a polynomial function in x and y. Linear and quadratic functions are cases of algebraic functions since they are equations of the type, for example,

$$f(x, y) = y - 10 + x = 0$$

which is a linear function; or

$$f(x, y) = x^2 + y^2 - r^2 = 0$$

which is a quadratic function. Recall that linear equations involve powers of the independent and dependent variables no higher than the first degree, and quadratic equations involve independent and dependent variables of, at most, the second degree.

This section will consider certain other algebraic functions, their graphs and their economic applications.

Equations involving variables of degrees higher than the second will (together with certain other function types) generate the so-called higher plane curves. In economic applications of functions and curves, functions of higher than the third degree are rarely encountered.

A production function in economic theory is a simplified view of a complicated relationship among many inputs and outputs. Ideally, one would express a relationship between quantities of the various outputs and the use of the numerous inputs. A realistic representation of such a complex relationship, however, would become unmanageably complex. For that reason, one uses a highly simplified version of this reality, the production function. In postulating a production function it is assumed that one variable factor of production and one fixed factor of production are used in varying proportions to produce a single output. If y represents the output and x the variable input, then the assumption is that the fixed input enters such a production function as a constant parameter. A hypothetical example of such a simplified production function may involve a cubic equation of the form

$$y = 10x^2 - 2x^3$$

Some pairs of the values of the independent and the dependent variables are

x	0	1	2	3	4	5
y	0	8	24	36	32	0

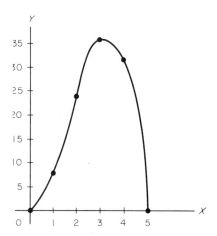

FIGURE 3-45   A Production Curve

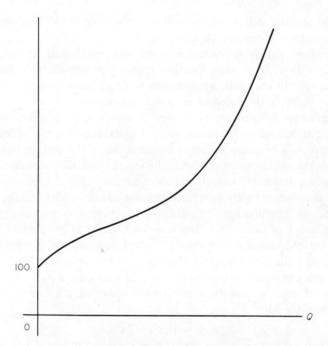

FIGURE 3-46   A Total Cost Curve

This curve, shown in Figure 3-45, has an increasing rate of increase from $x = 0$ to about $x = 1.67$ and a decreasing rate of increase from about $x = 1.67$ to about $x = 3.33$.

A well-behaved normal total cost curve is also generally represented by a cubic equation. For example, the equation of the total cost curve might be

$$C = 100 + 50x - 10x^2 + x^3$$

in which C is the total cost of production and x is the amount of output of the good. In this case the total cost curve is of the form shown in Figure 3-46. However, it is not drawn in proportion to the scale, but is horizontally exaggerated with respect to the Q-axis.

PROBLEMS

1. Find where the following lines intercept the axes:

   (a) $y = 3x + 1$ (c) $y = x$
   (b) $2y = 5x + 4$ (d) $2y - 1 = 0$

2. By observation, what are the slopes of the following lines?

(a) $y = 2 - 2x$ (d) $y = 2$
(b) $y = 3x + 2$ (e) $2 - x - y = 0$
(c) $y = x$ (f) $x + 3 = 0$

3. Given the following two points on a line, find the slope of the line:

(a) $(-3, 1), (2, 3)$ (d) $(-2, 2), (2, -2)$
(b) $(1, 3), (4, 1)$ (e) $(-4, 1), (1, 1)$
(c) $(-1, -1), (2, 2)$ (f) $(2, 1), (2, -1)$

4. Given the equation of a straight line, $y = 2x + 3$, find the equations of two other lines parallel to it and graph the lines.

5. Graph the two lines $y = 4 - 2x$ and $y = \frac{1}{2}x - 2$. What is their relationship? What is the product of their slopes? What conclusions can be drawn?

6. If a point $p(x, y)$ divides a line segment from $p_1(x_1, y_1)$ to $p_2(x_2, y_2)$ into the ratio

$$\frac{p_1 p}{p p_2} = r$$

find and show graphically the ratio if the point (x, y) is given. If the ratio is given and (x, y) is unknown, solve for x and y.

7. Using problem 6, if (x, y) is the midpoint of the line segment, derive the formula for the midpoint.

8. Using problems 6 and 7, find the indicated value:

(a) ratio, $(1, 4), (3, 2), (4, 1)$
(b) ratio, $(-1, 3), (2, 1), (5, -1)$
(c) $(x, y), r = \frac{1}{2}, p_1(1, 2)$ to $p_2(4, -1)$
(d) $(x, y), r = 2, p_1(5, 4)$ to $p_2(-1, -2)$
(e) midpoint $(1, 1), (4, 3)$
(f) midpoint $(2, 1), (6, 1)$

9. Find the equations of the lines, given the following:

(a) $(-5, -1), (-1, -1), (1, 2)$ (c) $m = -2, (4, 3)$
(b) $(2, 3), (1, 0), (0, -3)$ (d) $m = 6, (-1, -2)$

10. Find the market equilibrium if the supply curve is

$$2p - Q - 2 = 0$$

and the demand curve is

$$p + Q = 4$$

11. Find the distances between the following points:

(a) (2, 3), (4, 5)   (c) (6, 5), (6, 12)
(b) (1, 2), (−4, −2)   (d) (2, 7), (−2, 7)

12. On the linear supply curve

$$2p - Q - 40 = 0$$

find the length of the line from

$$Q_1 = 20 \quad \text{to} \quad Q_2 = 40$$

13. The distance d from a point (x_0, y_0) to a line whose equation is

$$ax + by + c = 0$$

is given by the formula

$$d = \frac{|ax_0 + by_0 + c|}{a^2 + b^2}$$

(a) Find the distance from the point (2, 2) to the line

$$x + y - 2 = 0$$

(b) Find the distance between the parallel lines

$$y - 2x - 2 = 0 \quad \text{and} \quad y - 2x + 2 = 0$$

14. Find the equation of a line that is perpendicular to the line

$$y - x - 1 = 0$$

and that passes through the point (−2, 4).

15. Find the equation of a line that is parallel to the line

$$y + 2x - 2 = 0$$

and that passes through the point (1, −4).

16. (a) If two lines

$$ax + by + c = 0 \quad \text{and} \quad Ax + By + D = 0$$

are parallel, prove that

$$\frac{a}{A} = \frac{b}{B}$$

(b) If the two lines are perpendicular, prove that

$$aA + bB = 0$$

17. Find the equations of the following circles with the center at the origin:

    (*a*) circle with radius = 6
    (*b*) circle passing through the point (12, 5)

18. Find the equations of the following circles:

    (*a*) center (−1, −3), radius = 4
    (*b*) center (2, −7), radius = 1

19. Find the center and the radius of each of the following circles:

    (*a*) $x^2 + y^2 - 4x + 2y - 4 = 0$
    (*b*) $x^2 + y^2 + 12x + 20y + 87 = 0$

20. Find the equation, center, and radius of each of the following circles, given three points on the circle:

    (*a*) (1, 1), (4, 2), (7, 1)   (*b*) (12, 5), (13, 0), (−5, 12)

21. Find the maximum and minimum values of x and y on the following circles:

    (*a*) $x^2 + y^2 = 1$
    (*b*) $x^2 + y^2 - 4x + 4y + 4 = 0$
    (*c*) $x^2 + y^2 - 6x = 0$
    (*d*) $x^2 + y^2 - 10x - 8y + 32 = 0$

22. If a circle with center at (5, 5) and radius = 5 represents an isocost curve, determine the segment which represents minimum cost.

23. Given the general equation of the circle

$$x^2 + y^2 + Ax + By + C = 0$$

find the center and radius. When is the circle real, imaginary, or a point?

24. Find the equation, center, and radius of a circle on which the endpoints of a diameter are at (−5, 0) and (1, −6).

25. Find the equation of a circle which has a radius of 2, passes through (−1, 0), and whose abscissa value is −1.

26. Graph the following ellipses and find the major and minor axes, the foci, and the axis-intercepts:

    (*a*) $\dfrac{x^2}{16} + \dfrac{y^2}{9} = 1$ (*b*) $36x^2 + 16y^2 = 576$

27. Find the equations of the ellipses, and graph:

   (a) center $(2, -3)$, vertex $(6, -3)$, minor axis endpoint $(2 - 1)$
   (b) center $(-6, 1)$, vertex $(-6, -2)$, minor axis endpoint $(-4, -1)$
   (c) focus $(3, 0)$, end of minor axis $(0, -4)$
   (d) center $(-2, -1)$, vertex $(11, 1)$, focus $(10, 1)$

28. Find the maximum and minimum values of x and y:

   (a) $36x^2 + 4y^2 = 144$ (c) $9x^2 + 4y^2 - 36x + 8y + 4 = 0$

   (b) $\dfrac{(x-2)^2}{2} + \dfrac{(y-3)^2}{1} = 1$

29. Find the centers, major and minor axes, and foci of the following ellipses:

   (a) $4x^2 + 16y^2 - 16x + 144y + 96 = 0$
   (b) $2x^2 + y^2 + 4x - 2y + 1 = 0$

30. The *eccentricity*, e, of an ellipse is defined as $e = c/a$. What is the relationship of e to a numerical value? What does eccentricity approach as an ellipse approaches a circle; as an ellipse flattens? Find the eccentricities of the following ellipses, and graph:

$$\frac{x^2}{2} + \frac{y^2}{1} = 1 \quad \text{and} \quad \frac{x^2}{8} + \frac{y^2}{4} = 1$$

   What is the relationship?

31. Find the locus of a point such that the sum of its distances from the fixed points $(5, 1)$ and $(-3, 1)$ is 10.

32. Find the equations of the parabolas and graph:

   (a) vertex $(0, 2)$, focus $(0, 0)$
   (b) directrix $y = -1$, focus $(0, 2)$
   (c) directrix $x = 0$, vertex $(-\tfrac{1}{2}, 0)$

33. Find the equations of the parabolas and graph:

   (a) vertex $(1, 3)$, directrix $x = -2$
   (b) focus $(-2, 1)$, directrix $y = -3$
   (c) vertex $(-2, -1)$, focus $(-2, -5)$

34. Find the vertices, foci, and directrices for the following parabolas:

   (a) $x^2 - 4x + 12y + 28 = 0$ (b) $y^2 - 8y + 16x + 32 = 0$

35. If total revenue is $TR = 4Q - Q^2$, find the axis-intercepts, and by symmetry find the point where total revenue is a maximum. Graph the total revenue and average revenue functions.

36. Find the market equilibrium between the demand curve

$$Q^2 + 8p - 144 = 0$$

and the supply curve

$$5Q^2 - 32p = 0$$

37. Derive the equation for a hyperbola of the type shown in Figure 3-36.

38. Find the length of the axes and equations of the asymptotes, and graph the following hyperbolas:

(a) $\dfrac{x^2}{36} - \dfrac{y^2}{25} = 1$ (c) $9y^2 - 4x^2 = -36$

(b) $y^2 - x^2 = 9$

39. Find and graph the following hyperbolas:

(a) vertices $(\pm 5, 0)$, foci $(\pm 13, 0)$
(b) asymptotes $y = \pm 2x$, vertices $(0, \pm 4)$
(c) length of conjugate axis $= 6$, foci at $(2, 2)$ and $(-8, 2)$
(d) foci at $(-3, 2)$ and $(-3, 6)$, length of conjugate axis $= 4$

40. Find the centers, vertices, and lengths of the axes of the following hyperbolas and graph:

(a) $36x^2 - 49y^2 - 144x - 392y - 836 = 0$
(b) $16x^2 - 9y^2 + 64x + 18y - 89 = 0$

41. Two firms producing a homogeneous product and charging a price of $10 are 30 miles apart and the cost of transportation is $0.10 a mile. If one firm reduces price to $8 and the other firm remains constant, find the line separating the markets.

42. Graph the following hyperbolas, finding centers and asymptotes:

(a) $xy = -4$ (b) $xy - x - 2y = 0$

43. Given the liquidity preference function implicitly

$$Mi - 2M - 2i + 2 = 0$$

solve it explicitly, determine the rate of interest at which the demand becomes infinitely elastic, and graph.

44. The *eccentricity* of a hyperbola is defined as $e = c/a$. What is the relationship of eccentricity to a numerical value? What is the eccentricity as the hyperbola diverges slowly; as it diverges rapidly? What is true about similar hyperbolas? Find the eccentricity of the hyperbola

$$\frac{y^2}{36} - \frac{x^2}{64} = 1$$

45. The ellipse and hyperbola both have two directions. Define the locus of both if the directrix is the line

$$x = \pm \frac{a}{e}$$

where $e = c/a$. What is the eccentricity of the parabola and the circle as a limiting case of the other conics? Find the directrices of the following:

(a) $\dfrac{x^2}{64} + \dfrac{y^2}{36} = 1$ (b) $\dfrac{y^2}{16} - \dfrac{x^2}{9} = 1$

46. The general quadratic form is

$$Ax^2 + Bxy + Cy^2 + Dx + Ey + F = 0$$

where A, B, and C cannot all be zero. If $B^2 - 4AC$ is negative, zero, or positive, the equation represents an ellipse, a parabola, or hyperbola (or a degenerate) respectively. Identify the following:

(a) $x^2 + 2xy + y^2 + x - y = 0$
(b) $8x^2 - 12xy + 17y^2 - 20 = 0$
(c) $6xy + 9x - 4y + 30 = 0$
(d) $x^2 - y^2 + 4x + 6y - 5 = 0$

47. The *latus rectum* is the chord perpendicular to the axis of a conic which passes through the focus of the conic. The length of the latus rectum of a parabola is $4a$, and the length is $2b^2/a$ for the ellipse and hyperbola. Find the length of the latus rectum:

(a) $\dfrac{x^2}{36} - \dfrac{y^2}{64} = 1$ (c) $y^2 = x$

(b) $\dfrac{x^2}{36} + \dfrac{y^2}{25} = 1$

48. Two hyperbolas are conjugate hyperbolas if the transverse and conjugate axes of one are respectively the conjugate and transverse axes of the other. What is the procedure to use? Graph and find the conjugate

hyperbola of

$$\frac{x^2}{9} - \frac{y^2}{16} = 1$$

49. A function is called *odd* if

$$f(-x) = -f(x)$$

and *even* if

$$f(-x) = f(x)$$

Find a general polynomial expression for each.

4
TRANSCENDENTAL FUNCTIONS AND THEIR GRAPHS

In Chapter 3 algebraic functions were defined to be those functions which can be expressed as

$$f(x, y) = 0$$

in which $f(x, y)$ are polynomials of x and y. There are some functions which cannot be expressed as

$$f(x, y) = 0$$

These are called *transcendental* functions. Transcendental functions and algebraic functions of powers higher than two trace out *higher plane curves*. The transcendental functions to be considered here are (1) exponential, (2) logarithmic, and (3) trigonometric.

EXPONENTIAL FUNCTIONS

In Chapter 3 an exponential function was shown to be of the form

$$y = a^x$$

The nature of the curve developed for such an exponential curve depends on the base a of the exponential function. The base of an exponential function is usually taken to be a positive number, for then its equivalent expression in terms of logarithms may be easily derived. This discussion, however, will explore the implications of exponential expressions involving both positive and negative bases. Consider the following possibilities:

1. When $a < -1$, the exponential expression approaches zero for very large negative values of the exponent x. As x takes on larger algebraic values (i.e., becomes smaller negative numbers), the value of the function oscillates more and more widely, in both the positive and the negative directions. For odd values of x, y is negative and for even values of x, y is positive. When $x = 0$, $y = 1$. As x takes on greater and greater positive integer values, y becomes progressively larger integers, alternatively negative and positive as x is an odd or an even number. Let $a = -2$.

Then the exponential expression becomes

$$y = -2^x$$

Some of the corresponding values of x and y are

x	-5	-4	-3	-2	-1	0	1	2	3	4	5
y	$-\frac{1}{32}$	$\frac{1}{16}$	$-\frac{1}{8}$	$\frac{1}{4}$	$-\frac{1}{2}$	1	-2	4	-8	16	-32

Graphically, this particular exponential function will have the shape of the oscillating curve shown in Figure 4-1.

2. When $-1 < a < 0$, the function will yield explosively large positive and negative values alternately as x acquires progressively smaller algebraic values (larger negative values). The function is equal to 1 at $x = 0$. As x takes on larger positive values, the exponential expression approaches 0. If $a = -\frac{1}{2}$, the function becomes $y = (-\frac{1}{2})^x$. Some of the

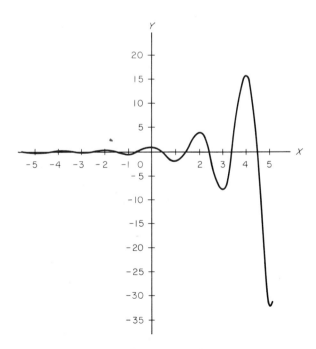

FIGURE 4-1   Exponential Function with the Base $a = -2$

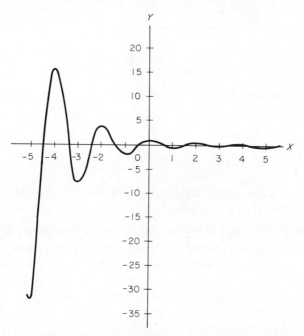

FIGURE 4-2   Exponential Function with the Base $a = -\frac{1}{2}$

corresponding values of x and y are

x	-5	-4	-3	-2	-1	0	1	2	3	4	5
y	-32	16	-8	4	-2	1	$-\frac{1}{2}$	$\frac{1}{4}$	$-\frac{1}{8}$	$\frac{1}{16}$	$-\frac{1}{32}$

These values are plotted in Figure 4-2.

3. When $0 < a < 1$, the function will become a monotonically de-creasing function beginning with extremely large positive values of y for large negative values of x. The function will cross the y axis at $x = 0$, $y = 1$. As x has larger positive values, y will decrease in value and ap-proach zero. If $a = \frac{1}{2}$, the function becomes $y = (\frac{1}{2})^x$. Some of the coordinate values of this function, as sketched in Figure 4-3, are

x	-5	-4	-3	-2	-1	0	1	2	3	4	5
y	32	16	8	4	2	1	$\frac{1}{2}$	$\frac{1}{4}$	$\frac{1}{8}$	$\frac{1}{16}$	$\frac{1}{32}$

4. When $a > 1$, the exponential function becomes a monotonically increasing function. When x is a large negative number, the value of the function is close to zero. As x increases in algebraic value, y increases, crossing the y axis when $x = 0$, $y = 1$, and thereafter increasing very

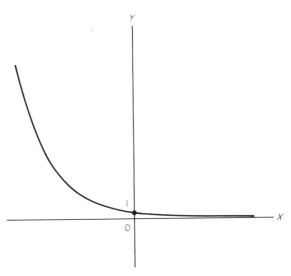

FIGURE 4-3   Exponential Function with the Base $a = \frac{1}{2}$

rapidly. Let $a = 2$. The function is now $y = 2^x$ with the coordinate values

x	-5	-4	-3	-2	-1	0	1	2	3	4	5
y	$\frac{1}{32}$	$\frac{1}{16}$	$\frac{1}{8}$	$\frac{1}{4}$	$\frac{1}{2}$	1	2	4	8	16	32

Figure 4-4 illustrates this function.

5. Three trivial cases of exponential functions should be mentioned in passing. They occur when $a = -1$, $a = 0$, and $a = 1$. In the case where $a = -1$, the exponential function will alternate in value between 1 and -1 as x changes from even to odd numbers. When $a = 0$, the value of the function will be zero for all values of x. When $a = 1$, the value of the function will be equal to 1 no matter what value x may assume.

A very important case of exponential functions is that which has as its base the irrational number $e = 2.71828$. An exponential function of this type is: $y = ae^{cx}$ where a and c are constants. Specific exponential curves can be determined by assuming values for a and c.

1. Let $a = 1$ and $c = 1$. In this case the exponential function becomes $y = e^x$ for which several selected values of x and y are

x	0	1	2	3	4	5
y	1	2.7183	7.3891	20.086	54.598	148.41

Figure 4-5 shows this curve.

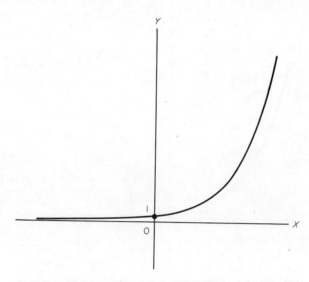

FIGURE 4-4 Exponential Function with the Base $a = 2$

2. Let $a = 1$ and $c = \frac{1}{2}$. The function is now $y = e^{\frac{1}{2}x}$ for which the coordinate values are

x	1	2	3	4	5
y	1.6487	2.7183	4.4817	7.3891	12.182

These coordinates are plotted in Figure 4-5.

3. Let $a = \frac{1}{2}$ and $c = 1$. The exponential expression becomes $y = \frac{1}{2}e^{x}$. The ordinate value of this function for each value of x is now one-half of the ordinate of $y = e^{x}$. The coordinates of $y = \frac{1}{2}e^{x}$ are

x	0	1	2	3	4	5
y	$\frac{1}{2}$	1.3591	3.6945	10.043	27.299	74.205

This curve is plotted in Figure 4-5.

It is apparent that the relationship between the general natural exponential function,

$$y = ae^{cx} \tag{1}$$

and the special case where a and c both equal 1,

$$y = e^{x} \tag{2}$$

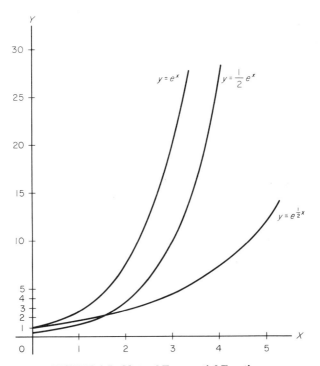

FIGURE 4-5   Natural Exponential Functions

is as follows:

1. If $a < 1$, function (1) will have smaller values than function (2) for all values of x.
2. If $a > 1$, function (1) will have larger values than function (2) for all values of x.
3. If $0 < c < 1$, function (1) will increase less rapidly than function (2) as x increases.
4. If $c > 1$, function (1) will increase more rapidly than function (2) as x increases.

Since an exponential function to whatever base may be converted to a natural exponential function, only natural exponential functions are used for most scientific work.

As an economic example of the use of exponential curves, consider the trend curve in time series analysis. A new firm in a high-growth industry (computers or electronics, perhaps) has a record of sales revenues which fits the exponential growth curve represented by

$$R_t = 5e^{2+0.1t} \qquad (t = 0, 1, 2, \ldots, n)$$

in which R is the total sales revenue and t is time, measured in years. Let the first year of operation be $t = 0$. Thereafter t increases by 1 for each additional year of operation. This sales revenue equation can be separated into 2 parts so that

$$R_t = 5e^2 \cdot e^{0.1t}$$

Then for $t = 0$,

$$R_0 = 5e^2 = 36.95$$

which is the sales revenue for the initial year, $t = 0$. Substituting, write

$$R_t = R_0 e^{0.1t} = 36.95 e^{0.1t}$$

The sales revenue R is a function of time t. Some of the corresponding values of R and t are

t	0	1	2	3	4	5
R	36.95	40.84	45.13	49.88	55.12	60.92

A somewhat modified version of the exponential function is the logistic curve. Biologists have found that animal populations tend to grow, under certain circumstances, according to the logistic law of growth. It has been found that human populations will also, under some conditions, grow along a logistic trend curve. For this reason various economic variables, closely related to population size, can be represented by some

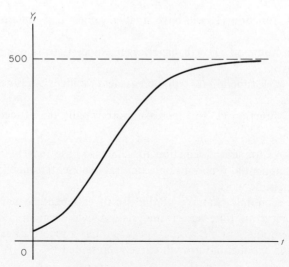

FIGURE 4-6   A Logistic Curve

version of the logistic curve to show their movements through time. The logistic curve has the general equation

$$Y_t = \frac{k}{1 + be^{-at}}$$

where k, b, and a are constants. This function will grow initially at an exponential rate, and then gradually the rate of growth will decrease. As t becomes extremely large, the function Y_t will approach k as a limit.

The curve of

$$Y_t = \frac{500}{1 + 20e^{-0.5t}}$$

is shown in Figure 4-6.

LOGARITHMIC FUNCTIONS

Chapter 2 contained a discussion of the algebraic properties of logarithmic functions. In this section the geometric properties of logarithmic curves will be examined. Take the exponential function $y = 2^x$, whose curve is shown in Figure 4-4. The student will recall that the curve rises very rapidly in ordinate values as the abscissa values are increased with a uniform increment of 1. If the curve is plotted to a semi-logarithmic scale, as in Figure 4-7, it becomes linear. Semi-logarithmic paper is constructed

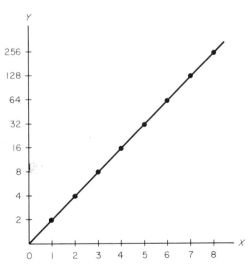

FIGURE 4-7 Exponential Curve with the Base
$a = 2$ Plotted on Semi-Logarithmic Paper

with the ordinate so scaled that it is proportional to the logarithm of y for the chosen base.

In Figure 4-7, x is plotted on the abscissa, and each unit increase in distance represents a unit increase in the value of x. On the ordinate, a unit increase in distance along the y-axis means a unit increase in the logarithm of the number. For example, the number $y = 2$ can be represented by

$$2 = 2^x \quad \text{or} \quad \log_2 2 = 1$$

Therefore, $y = 2$ is plotted 1 unit up on the y-axis. The number $y = 4$ can be represented by

$$4 = 2^x \quad \text{or} \quad \log_2 4 = 2$$

Accordingly, $y = 4$ is plotted 2 units up on the ordinate. By similar reasoning,

$$\text{for } y = \quad 8 \qquad 8 = 2^x \quad \text{or} \quad \log_2 \ \ 8 = 3$$
$$\text{for } y = \quad 16 \qquad 16 = 2^x \quad \text{or} \quad \log_2 \ \ 16 = 4$$
$$\text{for } y = \quad 32 \qquad 32 = 2^x \quad \text{or} \quad \log_2 \ \ 32 = 5$$
$$\text{for } y = \quad 64 \qquad 64 = 2^x \quad \text{or} \quad \log_2 \ \ 64 = 6$$
$$\text{for } y = 128 \qquad 128 = 2^x \quad \text{or} \quad \log_2 128 = 7$$
$$\text{for } y = 256 \qquad 256 = 2^x \quad \text{or} \quad \log_2 256 = 8$$

These values of y are plotted on the ordinate according to their logarithmic values.

Note that on the logarithmic scale, shown on the y-axis, there is no zero value. For $y = 2^x$ to approach zero, x must approach negative infinity.

The plotting of an exponential function on semi-logarithmic scale has the advantage that if the ratio of the change in the values of y is constant, the resulting curve is a straight line. In the example cited, between $x = 3$ and $x = 4$ the value of y doubles from 8 to 16. Again between $x = 4$ and $x = 5$, y doubles from 16 to 32. Therefore, it is apparent that a straight line on a semilogarithmic scale indicates a constant rate of change in the logarithms of numbers.

The relationship defined by

$$\log_2 y = x$$

may also be plotted on an arithmetic scale. Since in this case

$$x = f(y) = \log_2 y$$

x may be plotted on the ordinate and y on the abscissa.

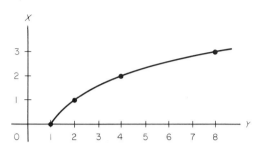

FIGURE 4-8   Logarithmic Graph of $X = \log_2 y$

The curve of this function, shown in Figure 4-8, is a mirror image of the curve in Figure 4-4. The difference is, of course, that the curve in Figure 4-4 is an exponential curve, and the curve in Figure 4-8 is its corresponding logarithmic curve.

As another example of a logarithmic curve, consider the function

$$y = 5^x$$

which can be represented logarithmically as

$$\log_5 y = x$$

Develop the following table of coordinate values of x and y:

x	0	1	2	3	4	5
y	1	5	25	125	625	3125

When plotted on an arithmetic scale, these coordinate values yield an exponential curve as in Figure 4-9.

Plotted on a semilogarithmic scale as in Figure 4-10, however, the function becomes a straight line. The abscissa is in arithmetic scale showing unit increases in x. The ordinate is in logarithmic scale to the base 5. At origin the value of y is 1 with $x = 0$. Thereafter, as x increases by a unit, y increases by a power of 5. Between $x = 0$ and $x = 1$, y increases from 1 to 5, a five-fold increase. When x increases from 1 to 2, y changes in value from 5 to 25, again a five-fold increase.

To plot the logarithmic version of this exponential function, graph the function

$$x = f(y) = \log_5 y$$

The curve in Figure 4-11 is the mirror image of the curve in Figure 4-9.

Now consider an exponential function

$$y = 2^{2x}$$

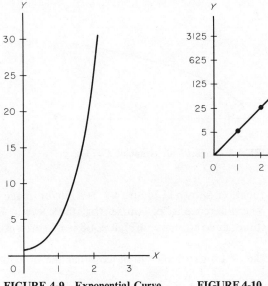

FIGURE 4-9 Exponential Curve to Base $a = 5$ Plotted on Arithmetic Scale

FIGURE 4-10 Exponential Curve to Base $a = 5$ Plotted on Semi-Logarithmic Scale

whose logarithmic equivalent is

$$x = \tfrac{1}{2} \log_2 y$$

In exponential form, this function rises at a constant rate which is twice as large as the rate of increase of the curves shown in Figures 4-4 and 4-7. Plotted on an arithmetic scale, the exponential curve of the equation

$$y = 2^{2x}$$

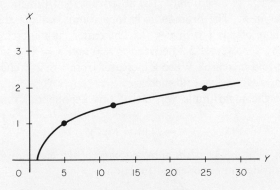

FIGURE 4-11   Logarithmic Graph of $X = \log_5 y$

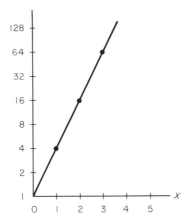

FIGURE 4-12 Exponential Function
$Y = 2^{2x}$ **Plotted on Semilogarithmic**
Scale

will rise at twice the speed of the curve represented by

$$y = 2^x$$

When this function is represented in semilogarithmic scale as in Figure 4-12, the result is a straight line with twice the slope of the semilogarithmic line of Figure 4-7. The logarithmic version of this exponential function, plotted on an arithmetic scale, will generate the curve sketched in Figure 4-13.

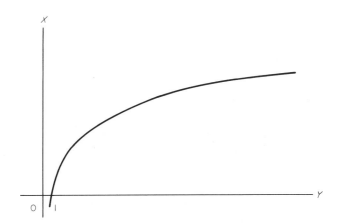

FIGURE 4-13   Logarithmic Graph of $X = \tfrac{1}{2} \log_2 y$

The exponential function representing the growth of sales revenue of the hypothetical firm discussed earlier is

$$R_t = R_0 e^{0.1t}$$

The pattern of growth will be such that

$$R_0 = R_0 e^{(0.1)(0)} = R_0$$

$$R_1 = R_0 e^{(0.1)(1)} = R_0(1.1052)$$

$$R_2 = R_0 e^{(0.1)(2)} = R_0(1.1052)^2$$

.
.
.

$$R_n = R_0 e^{(0.1)(n)} = R_0(1.1052)^n$$

where $R_0 = 5e^2 = 36.95$. It appears, therefore, that from period to period, the sales revenue increases by a common ratio of $e^{0.1} = 1.1052$. When data of this nature are shown on semilogarithmic paper, the resulting graph is again a straight line, indicating that the value of the function R_t grows at a constant ratio. Figure 4-14 shows a sketch of function R_t.

Logarithmic functions, then, can be represented in three ways: (1) an exponential curve can be generated by plotting

$$y = f(x) = a^x$$

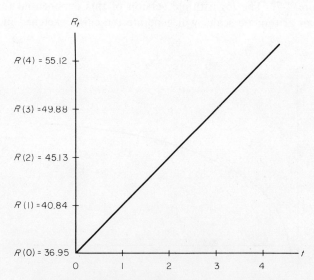

FIGURE 4-14   Semilogarithmic Plotting of $R_t = R_0 e^{.1t}$

on an arithmetic scale, (2) the inverse of the exponential curve can be generated by plotting

$$x = f(y) = \log_a y$$

on an arithmetic scale, and (3) a straight line whose slope represents the constant rate of change can be obtained by plotting

$$y = f(x) = a^x$$

on a semilogarithmic scale.

TRIGONOMETRIC FUNCTIONS

A special set of transcendental functions derived from the study of trigonometry is also very useful in some branches of economic theory.

Trigonometry can be defined as the study of six fundamental ratios of angles, called the trigonometric functions. These functions form the basis of a mathematical theory with application in other areas of mathematics. They can also be used to solve problems involving triangles. Before proceeding with the discussion of the trigonometric functions, it is necessary to become familiar with several definitions and terms.

Definitions

The Radius Vector (r) of a Point P. In a rectangular coordinate system, the distance from the origin O to the point P is defined as the *radius vector* of P. Thus in Figure 4-15 the radius vector is the distance OP. In Chapter

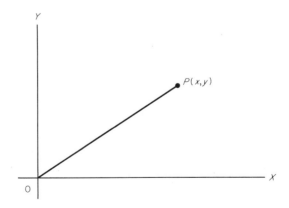

FIGURE 4-15   The Radius Vector of a Point

3, the length r was defined by the Pythagorean theorem to be

$$r = \sqrt{x^2 + y^2}$$

The radius vector r is always considered to be positive. Any point of the plane may be thought to have 3 coordinates, x, y, and r.

Trigonometric Angles. A *trigonometric angle* is the amount of rotation required to move a line from one position to another. A positive angle is generated if the line moves in a counterclockwise direction, and a negative angle results if the line moves clockwise. An angle is contained between two lines, the *initial side* and the *terminal side*. The initial side is the original position of the line, the terminal side is the new position of the line after the required rotation has taken place. Figure 4-16 shows two angles, the first positive and the second negative.

Standard Position of an Angle. An angle is in standard position if its vertex is at origin and its initial side coincides with the positive OX axis. The location of the angle is determined by the terminal side. Thus if the terminal side is in the first quadrant, the angle is said to be in the first quadrant. For example, an angle of 70° is in the first quadrant, of 160° is in the second quadrant, of 200° is in the third quadrant, and of 300° is in the fourth quadrant.

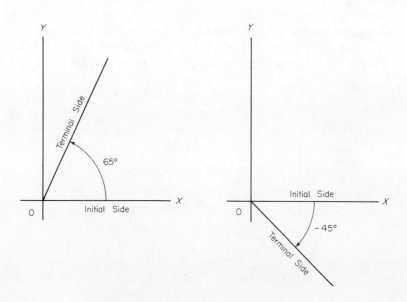

FIGURE 4-16   Positive and Negative Angles

Coterminal Angles. Two angles are said to be *coterminal* if their terminal sides coincide. Thus the angles 10°, 370°, and 730° are coterminal angles.

Related Angles. Trigonometric functions are developed for *acute* angles (angles of less than 90°). This means that trigonometric functions of angles greater than 90°, called *obtuse* angles, must be expressible in terms of functions of acute angles. The concept of the *related angle* is used to define trigonometric functions of angles larger than 90°. The related angle of any angle larger than 90° is the positive acute angle formed between the *x*-axis and the terminal side of the angle. Figure 4-17 shows the related angles of

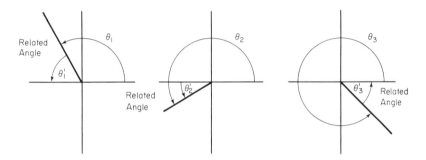

FIGURE 4-17   Related Angles

a few obtuse angles. The trigonometric functions of θ_1 are identical with those of θ_1', the related angle. For the definition of trigonometric functions to be developed shortly, it is important to be able to find the related angle of any angle larger than 90°. From Figure 4-17, it is apparent that

1. if an angle is such that $90° < \theta < 180°$, the related angle is $180° - \theta$,
2. if an angle is such that $180° < \theta < 270°$, the related angle is $\theta - 180°$,
3. if an angle is such that $270° < \theta < 360°$, the related angle is $360° - \theta$.

The foregoing definitions will underlie the following discussion of the meanings and uses of trigonometric functions.

The Meanings and Uses of Trigonometric Functions

Trigonometric functions are best considered in relation to a circle with radius 1, as shown in Figure 4-18. In this figure, the radius of the circle is

$$r = OA = OB = 1$$

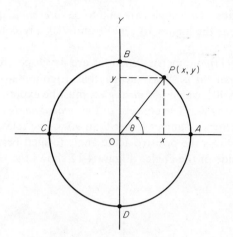

FIGURE 4-18 Trigonometric Functions in
Relation to a Unit Circle

The movable point P follows the circumference of the circle from point A counterclockwise to P to B to C to D and back again to A. When the point P has moved to B, the radius vector OB forms an angle of 90° with OA. When P moves to point C, the angle formed by OC with OA is 180°. At D, the angle formed by OD with OA is 270°. When the point has made the full circle and returns to A, the angle is 360°. The trigonometric functions are functions of the angle θ formed by the radius vector OP with the initial side OA. The trigonometric functions are:

1. sine $\theta = \sin \theta = \dfrac{y}{r}$

2. cosine $\theta = \cos \theta = \dfrac{x}{r}$

3. tangent $\theta = \tan \theta = \dfrac{y}{x}$

4. cotangent $\theta = \cot \theta = \dfrac{x}{y}$

5. secant $\theta = \sec \theta = \dfrac{r}{x}$

6. cosecant $\theta = \csc \theta = \dfrac{r}{y}$

Before discussing these trigonometric functions, it will be useful to define a new method of measuring angles. The unit of measurement of an angle will be changed from degrees to radians.

The magnitude of an angle can be expressed in either *degrees* or *radians*. Although the degree, which is by definition $\frac{1}{360}$ of a circle, is more familiar, the radian is widely used for mathematical applications.

A radian is defined as that angle which subtends a circular arc whose length equals the circle's radius. Look again at the circle pictured in Figure 4-18. The arc AP was formed as point P moved from A to P, forming the angle θ. When P is in such a position that the length of the arc equals the circle's radius, OP, the angle θ will be 1 radian.

Since the circumference of a circle is $2\pi r$, it is evident that 2π radians represent a full circle. The following list shows the relationship between radians and degrees:

$$2\pi \text{ radians} = 360°$$
$$\pi \text{ radians} = 180°$$
$$\frac{\pi}{2} \text{ radians} = 90°$$
$$\frac{\pi}{4} \text{ radians} = 45°$$
$$\frac{\pi}{12} \text{ radians} = 15°$$

In most applications of trigonometric functions, the magnitude of angles is denoted by a variable such as x, without specifically referring to the unit of measure. The functions are written $\sin x$, $\cos x$, etc.

The numerical values of trigonometric functions for angles measured in either degrees or radians can be found by consulting a table of trigonometric functions in any trigonometry textbook.

The six fundamental trigonometric functions lend themselves naturally to discussion in pairs.

1. $\sin \theta = y/r$, $\cos \theta = x/r$. When P coincides with A in Figure 4-18, the angle is of size 0. At that point, $y = 0$. Also when the angle is $0°$, $r = OA = x$. Hence

$$\sin 0° = 0 \qquad \cos 0° = 1$$

When P moves toward B from A, y becomes larger in value while x decreases. Thus, while θ increases from $0°$ to $90°$, $\sin \theta = y/r$ is increasing in value from zero, while $\cos \theta = x/r$ is decreasing from 1. At B, $y = r$ and $x = 0$. At B the angle formed by OB with OA is $90° = \pi/2$ radians. Therefore,

$$\sin 90° = \sin \frac{\pi}{2} = 1 \qquad \cos 90° = \cos \frac{\pi}{2} = 0$$

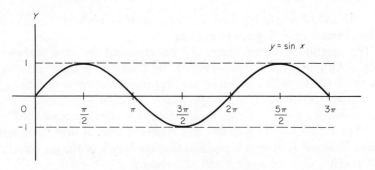

FIGURE 4-19   The Sine Function

As P moves from B to C, x is negative and $\cos\theta$ approaches -1, while y remains positive but decreases in value and $\sin\theta$ approaches zero. At C, $y = 0$ and $-x = r$. Thus,

$$\sin 180° = \sin\pi = 0 \qquad \cos 180° = \cos\pi = -1$$

Between C and D, both x and y are negative. In this range, both $\sin\theta$ and $\cos\theta$ are negative. At D

$$\sin 270° = \sin\frac{3\pi}{2} = -1 \qquad \cos 270° = \cos\frac{3\pi}{2} = 0$$

It is apparent that $\sin\theta$ alternates in value between -1 and 1, as shown in Figure 4-19. $\cos\theta$ also alternates in value between -1 and 1, as shown in Figure 4-20.

2. $\tan\theta = y/x$, $\cot\theta = x/y$. Since $\tan\theta$ and $\cot\theta$ are ratios of the coordinates of the point P, and since either x or y may assume the value zero at some points, these trigonometric functions are undefined at those

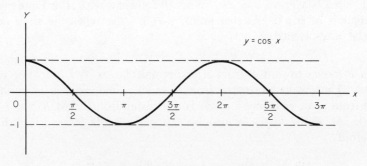

FIGURE 4-20   The Cosine Function

points. When $x = 0$, $\tan \theta$ is undefined, and when $y = 0$, $\cot \theta$ is undefined. Again referring to Figure 4-18, when P is at A, the angle formed is of $0°$. The coordinates of P are $y = 0$ and $x = r = 1$. Thus

$$\tan 0° = \frac{0}{x} = 0 \qquad \cot 0° = \frac{x}{0} \to \infty$$

Between A and B, y is positive and increasing while x is positive but decreasing. In that range, therefore, $\tan \theta$ is increasing toward infinity, and $\cot \theta$ is decreasing toward zero. At B, $y = r = 1$ and $x = 0$, and

$$\tan 90° = \tan \frac{\pi}{2} = \frac{1}{0} \to \infty \qquad \cot 90° = \cot \frac{\pi}{2} = \frac{0}{1} = 0$$

Between B and C, $y > 0$ and $x < 0$, and since x and y are of opposite signs, both $\tan \theta$ and $\cot \theta$ are negative. In this range the tangent is rising from extremely large negative values toward 0. The cotangent is decreasing from 0 to extremely large negative values. At C, $y = 0$ and $x = r = 1$, and

$$\tan 180° = \tan \pi = 0 \qquad \cot 180° = \cot \pi \to -\infty$$

Between C and D both x and y are negative. Thus $\tan \theta$ and $\cot \theta$ in this range are both positive. Tan x and cot x are shown graphically in Figures 4-21 and 4-22.

3. $\sec \theta = r/x$, $\csc \theta = r/y$. Reference to Figure 4-18 will show the patterns of variation of $\sec \theta$ and $\csc \theta$. Since $\sec \theta = r/x$, this function is

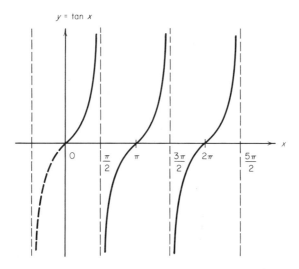

Figure 4-21   The Tangent Function

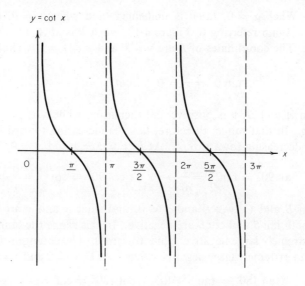

Figure 4-22   The Cotangent Function

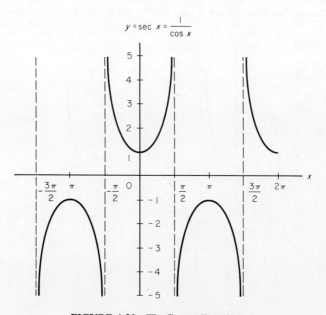

FIGURE 4-23   The Secant Function

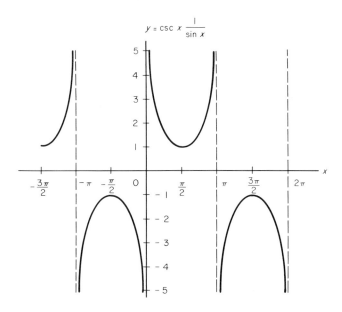

FIGURE 4-24   The Cosecant Function

undefined for $x = 0$ and similarly csc $\theta = r/y$ is undefined for $y = 0$. The student is urged to describe for himself the behavior of these trigonometric functions between $x = 0$ and $x = \pi/2$; between $x = \pi/2$ and $x = \pi$; and so on until the point P makes a full circle. The graphic representations of sec θ and csc θ are shown in Figures 4-23 and 4-24.

Trigonometric Identities

Trigonometric identities establish relationships among the trigonometric functions, and make operations with these functions possible. The following identities can be shown:

1. $\cot x = \dfrac{1}{\tan x}$ 2. $\tan x = \dfrac{\sin x}{\cos x}$

3. $\cot x = \dfrac{\cos x}{\sin x}$ 4. $\csc x = \dfrac{1}{\sin x}$

5. $\sec x = \dfrac{1}{\cos x}$ 6. $\sin^2 x + \cos^2 x = 1$

7. $\sin (x + y) = \sin x \cos y + \cos x \sin y$

8. $\sin(x - y) = \sin x \cos y - \cos x \sin y$

9. $\cos(x + y) = \cos x \cos y - \sin x \sin y$

10. $\cos(x - y) = \cos x \cos y + \sin x \sin y$

11. $\sin x + \sin y = 2 \sin \frac{1}{2}(x + y) \cos \frac{1}{2}(x - y)$

12. $\sin x - \sin y = 2 \cos \frac{1}{2}(x + y) \sin \frac{1}{2}(x - y)$

13. $\cos x + \cos y = 2 \cos \frac{1}{2}(x + y) \cos \frac{1}{2}(x - y)$

14. $\cos x - \cos y = -2 \sin \frac{1}{2}(x + y) \sin \frac{1}{2}(x - y)$

ECONOMIC APPLICATIONS OF TRIGONOMETRIC FUNCTIONS

Periodic Functions

Coterminal angles have been defined as having the same trigonometric functions. Thus any trigonometric function of any angle θ is exactly equal to that same function of the angle $\theta + n360°$ where n is any integer. For example

$$\sin 40° = \sin(40° + 360°) = \sin(40° + 720°) \cdots$$

The trigonometric function $\sin \theta$ assumes all possible values as θ ranges from $0°$ to $360°$. Thereafter the values of $\sin \theta$ repeat themselves as θ moves from $360°$ to $720°$, etc. Since

$$\sin \theta = \sin(\theta + 360°)$$

it can be said that the sine is a *periodic* function of period $360°$.

Similarly, the cosine function of angle θ is a periodic function of period $360°$, since

$$\cos \theta = \cos(\theta + 360°)$$

This property of periodicity of the sine and the cosine functions makes them readily adaptable for use in describing wave-like motions of various types in many branches of science. Business cycles are an example of the type of problem which may be represented by sine and cosine functions.

The measurement of a business cycle involves the determination of its *amplitude* and *duration*. The amplitude of a business cycle is the amount of change in economic activity either from the peak to the next succeeding trough or from the trough to the next succeeding peak. The first method measures the amount of contraction in economic activity during the cycle, while the second method measures the expansion. The duration of the cycle is the length of time required for the full cycle to take its course. One might measure the duration of the cycle by measuring the length of time from one peak to the next succeeding peak, or from an initial trough to the next trough.

In using time series data to measure cyclical fluctuations of data, there are problems of removing the influence of trend and certain seasonal variations so that the data will reflect only the influence of the business cycle fluctuations. A full discussion of the treatment of time series data for either trend analysis or cycle analysis is not properly a part of this text. But a trigonometric function may be used to show the application of these functions in the study of business cycles.

Assume that the trend influence has already been removed. The turning points of the cycle have been dated. The peaks and troughs have been identified. The average level of economic activity during the cycle has been determined. An examination of the data shows that the following function generates a curve of good fit for the data:

$$y = 200 + 50 \sin \frac{\pi}{6} t$$

where y is the level of economic activity and t is time measured in years. The values of the dependent and independent variables are shown in Table 4-1. The curve is shown in Figure 4-25.

The average level of economic activity is 200. The amplitude of the cycle is 100 measured from peak to trough as the difference $250 - 150 = 100$. The amplitude may also be thought of as the maximum amount of

TABLE 4-1

t	$f(t)$	y
0	$200 + 50(0.0000)$	$= 200.0$
1	$200 + 50(0.5000)$	$= 225.0$
2	$200 + 50(0.8660)$	$= 243.3$
3	$200 + 50(1.0000)$	$= 250.0$
4	$200 + 50(0.8660)$	$= 243.3$
5	$200 + 50(0.5000)$	$= 225.0$
6	$200 + 50(0.0000)$	$= 200.0$
7	$200 + 50(-0.5000)$	$= 175.0$
8	$200 + 50(-0.8660)$	$= 156.7$
9	$200 + 50(-1.0000)$	$= 150.0$
10	$200 + 50(-0.8660)$	$= 156.7$
11	$200 + 50(-0.5000)$	$= 175.0$
12	$200 + 50(-0.0000)$	$= 200.0$

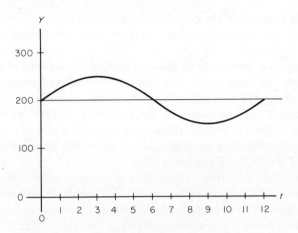

**FIGURE 4-25   The Levels of Economic Activity During
a Business Cycle**

variation of the data from the average. In that event the amplitude is 50, the coefficient of the sine function.

The duration of the cycle is 12 years. This could be determined from the equation of the cycle. Since the sine function is a periodic function of period $2\pi = 360°$, the duration of the cycle measured in terms of t is

$$\frac{\pi}{6} t = 2\pi$$

Solving for t gives $t = 12$.

A more violently fluctuating cycle may be represented by increasing the coefficient of the sine function from 50 to, say, 75. Then the amplitude will be increased to 75 above and 75 below the cycle average of 200. A cycle with a longer duration may be shown by increasing the denominator of π from 6 to, say, 12. Then the duration will be

$$\frac{\pi}{12} t = 2\pi \qquad t = 24$$

This represents a 24-year cycle.

Averages

Consider a consumption function drawn from macroeconomic theory. Let the consumption function be

$$C = 100 + 0.8y$$

where C is the amount of consumption and y is the amount of disposable income. The average propensity to consume is defined as the ratio of consumption to income

$$APC = \frac{C}{y} = \frac{100}{y} + 0.8$$

In Figure 4-26 consumption, C, is measured on the ordinate and income, y, on the abscissa.

At point A on the consumption function where $y = 100$ and $C = 180$, drop a perpendicular to the OY income axis. This perpendicular cuts the income axis at 100. Join point A with origin, O. The result is a right triangle with the corners at O, A, and $y = 100$. If $C_1 =$ the value of C at point A and $y_1 =$ the value of y at point A, the average propensity to consume at point A is

$$\frac{C_1}{y_1} = \tan \theta_1 = \frac{180}{100} = 1.8$$

This is the tangent of the angle at origin. The measurement of the average propensity to consume at point B is

$$\frac{C_2}{y_2} = \tan \theta_2 = \frac{340}{300} = 1.13$$

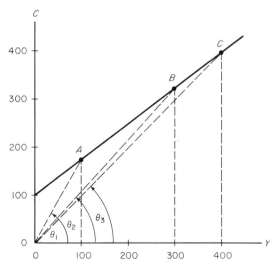

FIGURE 4-26   Average Propensity to Consume as the
Tangent of the Angle θ

At point D the consumption is 420 and income is 400. The average propensity to consume is

$$\frac{C_3}{y_3} = \tan \theta_3 = \frac{420}{400} = 1.05$$

As the point at which the average propensity to consume is to be measured is taken farther along the consumption function, the angle formed at the origin decreases and $\tan \theta$ decreases, approaching 0.8. The average propensity to consume decreases at higher values of y.

The total cost curve is usually represented as a cubic curve. Total cost is shown on the ordinate and the quantity of output is shown on the abscissa. The average cost is the ratio of the total cost divided by the quantity of output.

The average cost at point A on the total cost function in Figure 4-27 is the ratio

$$\frac{AB}{OA} = \tan \theta_1$$

and the average cost at D is

$$\frac{DE}{OE} = \tan \theta_2$$

As θ decreases $\tan \theta$ decreases. When θ increases, $\tan \theta$ increases.

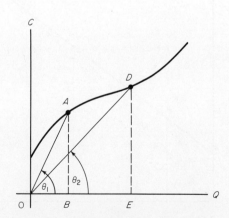

FIGURE 4-27   Average Cost as the Tangent of the Angle θ

POLAR EQUATIONS

All the discussions of the location of points in a plane, thus far, have been based on rectangular (or Cartesian) coordinates. This system of coordinates is both useful and familiar. Points in a plane, however, may also be identified by another set of coordinates, called *polar* coordinates.

Developing polar coordinates requires a fixed point and a fixed line. Call the fixed point O and the fixed line OM. From the point P draw a line to O. The distance OP is the *radius vector*, r, of the point P. The point O is the *pole*. The line OM is the *polar axis*. The angle formed by the radius vector OP with the polar axis OM, MOP or θ, and the radius vector OP together identify the point, as seen in Figure 4-28. Thus the coordinates of the point are r, θ.

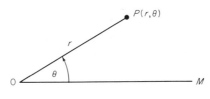

FIGURE 4-28   Polar Coordinates of a Point

If the fixed point O is considered to coincide with the origin O of the rectangular coordinate system and if the polar axis OM is taken to coincide with the positive OX axis, polar coordinates can be readily converted into Cartesian coordinates, and vice versa.

The triangle OPM in Figure 4-29 illustrates the following relationships which are used in coordinate conversion:

$$x = r \cos \theta$$

$$y = r \sin \theta$$

$$x^2 + y^2 = r^2$$

$$r = \sqrt{x^2 + y^2}$$

$$\cos \theta = \frac{x}{r} = \frac{x}{\sqrt{x^2 + y^2}}$$

$$\sin \theta = \frac{y}{r} = \frac{y}{\sqrt{x^2 + y^2}}$$

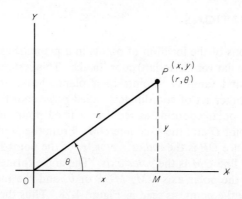

FIGURE 4-29   Relation Between Polar and Cartesian Coordinates

From these relationships it is readily apparent that numbers represented by *x* or *y* in Cartesian coordinates have their counterparts in polar coordinates. Conversely, polar coordinates may be converted into rectangular coordinates.

Polar coordinates have been introduced here to generalize the geometric representations of points and equations. A knowledge of polar coordinates and their relationship to rectangular coordinates will prove useful in discussing the geometry of complex numbers and rotation of axes.

COMPLEX NUMBERS

In Chapter 2 the algebra of complex numbers was discussed in connection with solutions of equations. Now it is time to consider the geometric representation of complex numbers.

Complex numbers are of the form $a \pm bi$. To represent such a number as a point in the plane, construct a rectangular coordinate system as in Figure 4-30 with the $X'X$ axis and $Y'Y$ axis intersecting at right angles at the point O, the origin. Designate the $X'X$ axis as the axis along which real numbers are to be represented. Let $Y'Y$ be the axis along which pure imaginary numbers are to be represented. The point on $Y'Y$ 1 unit above O will correspond to the imaginary unit i. Any distance b above O on the $Y'Y$ axis will represent the pure imaginary number bi. Thus $2i$ will be 2 units above O on $Y'Y$.

In such a system of rectangular coordinates any complex number $a + bi$ is designated by a point a units along the x-axis and b units on the

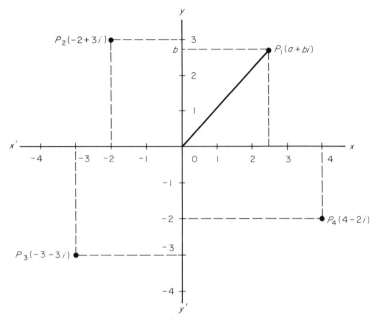

FIGURE 4-30   Rectangular Coordinates of Complex Numbers

y-axis. The $X'X$ axis is called the *axis of real numbers* or the *axis of reals.* The $Y'Y$ axis is called the *axis of pure imaginary numbers*, or the *axis of imaginaries.*

A complex number such as $a + bi$ represented in Figure 4-30 by P_1 may also be represented by a vector formed by joining the point P_1 with origin. Thus the vector OP_1, which has length and direction, represents the complex number $a + bi$.

Polar Coordinates of a Complex Number

Any complex number of the form $a + bi$ may be graphically represented on a complex plane by giving it polar coordinates. Let OP be the complex number $a + bi$ in Figure 4-31. The length r of OP is found by

$$r = \sqrt{a^2 + b^2}$$

This length r is called the *absolute value* or the *modulus* of the complex number $a + bi$. The positive angle XOP is called the *argument* or *amplitude*

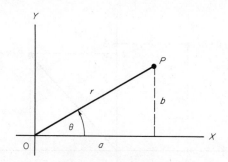

FIGURE 4-31 Polar Coordinates of a
Complex Number

of the complex number. The modulus of a complex number is always positive or zero. The argument of a complex number is usually designated as the angle θ. The polar coordinates of a complex number represented by OP are given by the relations

$$a = r \cos \theta \quad \text{and} \quad b = r \sin \theta \tag{1}$$

Thus

$$a + bi = r(\cos \theta + i \sin \theta) \tag{2}$$

When the rectangular form of a complex number is given, it is easily convertible into its equivalent polar form by

$$r = \sqrt{a^2 + b^2}$$

and the equations of (1) above.

The following examples show the conversion of complex numbers from rectangular to polar form and from polar to rectangular form.

1. Show graphically the complex number $2 + 2i$ and write the number in polar form. Solution: From Figure 4-32,

$$r = \sqrt{a^2 + b^2} = \sqrt{2^2 + 2^2} = 2\sqrt{2} \quad \tan \theta = 1$$

If $\tan \theta = 1$, then $\theta = 45°$, and from equation (2) above, the polar form of $2 + 2i$ is

$$2\sqrt{2} \, (\cos 45° + i \sin 45°)$$

2. Show graphically the complex number

$$6(\cos 240° + i \sin 240°)$$

and write it in rectangular form. Solution: From Figure 4-33 and the

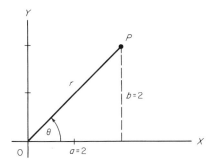

FIGURE 4-32   The Graphic Representation
of the Complex Number 2 − 2i

earlier discussion of related angles,

$$a = 6 \cos 240° = 6(0.5000) = -3$$
$$b = 6 \sin 240° = 6(0.86603) = -5.19$$

Therefore, the rectangular form of the complex number is

$$-3 - 5.19i$$

Addition of Complex Numbers

Two complex numbers, $2 + 3i$ and $4 + 2i$, are to be added. Using vector representation they can be written, as in Figure 4-34, $OP_1 = 2 + 3i$ and

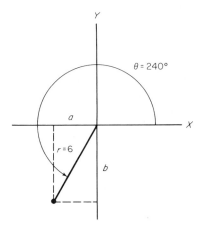

FIGURE 4-33   Rectangular Coordinates
of the Complex Number −3 − 5.19i

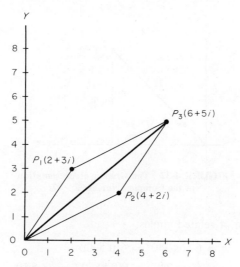

FIGURE 4-34 Addition of Two Complex Numbers

$OP_2 = 4 + 2i$. Since, in Figure 4-34, vector OP_1 represents the complex number $2 + 3i$ and vector OP_2 represents the complex number $4 + 2i$, the addition of these two complex numbers is the addition of the two vectors $OP_1 + OP_2$. To perform such an addition geometrically, complete the parallelogram $OP_1P_3P_2$. The complex number represented by the vector OP_3 is the sum of the other two complex numbers. The complex number represented by OP_3 is $6 + 5i$. From the earlier discussion on the algebraic addition of complex numbers,

$$(2 + 3i) + (4 + 2i) = 6 + 5i$$

The geometric representation of addition agrees with the algebraic operation of addition of complex numbers.

Perfectly analogous geometric rules are used to show the subtraction of one complex number from another. Suppose the following subtraction is to be performed:

$$(2 + 4i) - (3 + 2i) = 2 + 4i - 3 - 2i = (2 + 4i) + (-3 - 2i)$$

The problem now is to add two vectors

$$OP_1 = 2 + 4i \quad \text{and} \quad OP_2 = -3 - 2i$$

These vectors are shown graphically in Figure 4-35. Again complete the

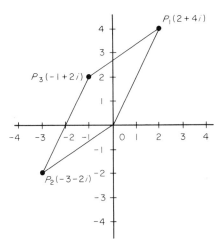

**FIGURE 4-35   Subtraction of One Complex
Number from Another Complex Number**

parallelogram. The vector OP_3 is the complex number representing the
difference $OP_1 - OP_2$.

Multiplication of Complex Numbers

The following two complex numbers are to be multiplied:

$$r_1(\cos \theta_1 + i \sin \theta_1) \quad \text{and} \quad r_2(\cos \theta_2 + i \sin \theta_2)$$

Multiplying gives the result

$$[r_1(\cos \theta_1 + i \sin \theta_1)][r_2(\cos \theta_2 + i \sin \theta_2)]$$

$$= r_1 r_2(\cos \theta_1 \cos \theta_2 + i \cos \theta_1 \sin \theta_2 + i \sin \theta_1 \cos \theta_2$$

$$+ i^2 \sin \theta_1 \sin \theta_2)$$

$$= r_1 r_2[(\cos \theta_1 \cos \theta_2 - \sin \theta_1 \sin \theta_2) + i(\sin \theta_1 \cos \theta_2$$

$$+ \cos \theta_1 \sin \theta_2)]$$

Since from trigonometric identities it is known that

$$\cos \theta_1 \cos \theta_2 - \sin \theta_1 \sin \theta_2 = \cos (\theta_1 + \theta_2)$$

$$\sin \theta_1 \cos \theta_2 + \cos \theta_1 \sin \theta_2 = \sin (\theta_1 + \theta_2)$$

the equation becomes

$$[r_1(\cos \theta_1 + i \sin \theta_1)][r_2(\cos \theta_2 + i \sin \theta_2)]$$

$$= r_1 r_2[\cos (\theta_1 + \theta_2) + i \sin (\theta_1 + \theta_2)]$$

The preceding results lead to an important theorem, the **theorem of multiplication:** *The absolute value of the product of two or more complex numbers is the product of their absolute values, and the argument of the product of two or more complex numbers is the sum of their arguments.*

To illustrate: find the product of

$$[4(\cos 60° + i \sin 60°)][5(\cos 80° + i \sin 80°)]$$

Solution:

$$[4(\cos 60° + i \sin 60°)][5(\cos 80° + i \sin 80°)]$$

$$= [(4)(5)][\cos (60° + 80°) + i \sin (60° + 80°)]$$

$$= 20[-0.766 + i\, 0.643]$$

$$= -15.32 + 12.86i$$

Division of Complex Numbers

By a similar process, the quotient of two complex numbers may be expressed in the form

$$\frac{r_1(\cos \theta_1 + i \sin \theta_1)}{r_2(\cos \theta_2 + i \sin \theta_2)} = \frac{r_1}{r_2} [\cos (\theta_1 - \theta_2) + i \sin (\theta_1 - \theta_2)]$$

which leads to the **theorem of division:** *The absolute value of the quotient of two complex numbers is the quotient of their absolute values. The argument of the quotient of two complex numbers is the argument of the dividend minus the argument of the divisor.*

To illustrate: find the quotient of

$$\frac{6(\cos 60° + i \sin 60°)}{3(\cos 30° + i \sin 30°)}$$

Solution:

$$\frac{6(\cos 60° + i \sin 60°)}{3(\cos 30° + i \sin 30°)} = \frac{6}{3} [\cos (60° - 30°) + i \sin (60° - 30°)]$$

$$= 2(\cos 30° + i \sin 30°)$$

$$= 2(0.866 + 0.5i)$$

$$= 1.732 + i$$

Complex numbers may be represented in rectangular coordinate form or in trigonometric form. In either form, algebraic manipulations of complex numbers may be carried out with consistent results.

PROBLEMS

1. Graph and compare these functions:
   (a) $y = 3^x$ (e) $y = -3^x$
   (b) $x = 3^y$ (f) $x = y^3$
   (c) $y = x^3$ (g) $x = -3^y$
   (d) $y = 3x$ (h) $xy = 3$

2. Graph these functions. What conclusions can be drawn?
   (a) $y = 3^x$ (e) $y = (\frac{1}{3})^x$
   (b) $y = -3^x$ (f) $y = (-\frac{1}{3})^x$
   (c) $y = (-1)^x$ (g) $y = (1)^x$
       x is an integer
   (d) $y = 3^{-x}$ (h) $y = (-3)^{-x}$

3. Prove the following laws of exponents using logarithms:

   (a) $a^x a^y = a^{x+y}$ (e) $\left(\dfrac{a}{b}\right)^x = \dfrac{a^x}{b^x}$

   (b) $(a^x)^y = a^{xy}$ (f) $a^0 = 1$

   (c) $a^{-x} = \dfrac{1}{a^x}$ (g) $a^{x-y} = \dfrac{a^x}{a^y}$

   (d) $(ab)^x = a^x b^x$

4. Graph and compare the following functions:
   (a) $y = e^x$ (e) $y = e^{-x}$
   (b) $y = 2e^x$ (f) $y = e^1$
   (c) $y = e^{2x}$ (g) $y = \frac{1}{2}e^{1/2x}$
   (d) $y = e^{x^2}$ (h) $y = -e^x$
                                   (i) $y = \ln x$

5. Prove the laws of the exponential function:

   (a) $e^{x+y} = e^x e^y$ (d) $e^{-x} = \dfrac{1}{e^x}$

   (b) $e^{x-y} = \dfrac{e^x}{e^y}$ (e) $e^0 = 1$

   (c) $e^{rx} = (e^x)^r$

6. If each of the following exponential functions represents growth of sales revenue, find R_t and the revenue for $t = 0, 1, 2, 3, 4$, and graph using semilogarithmic scales.

   (a) $R_t = 3e^{-1+2t}$ $(t = 0, 1, \ldots, n)$
   (b) $R_t = 4e^{1+t/2}$ $(t = 0, 1, \ldots, n)$
   (c) $R_t = 2e^{3-t/4}$ $(t = 0, 1, \ldots, n)$

   [A table of exponential functions is necessary.]

7. Sketch the graph of the logistic curve

$$Y_t = \frac{2000}{1 + 49e^{-st}}$$

   What does Y_t approach as a limit?

8. Graph the functions
$$y = 3^x \qquad y = 2^x \qquad y = 1^x$$

   on a semilogarithmic scale.

9. Graph and compare the functions
$$y = e^x \quad \text{and} \quad y = \ln x$$

   What is the line they are reflected into?

10. Graph $x = \log_3 y$ and $x = \log_{10} y$.

11. Graph the functions
$$y = 3^x \quad \text{and} \quad y = 3^{3x}$$

   on both arithmetic and semilogarithmic scales. Compare the slopes.

12. Since ln and e are inverse functions, this means that $\ln(e^x) = x$ for all x and $e^{\ln x} = x$ for $x > 0$. Simplify the following:

   (a) $\ln(e^{1/x})$

   (b) $\ln\left(\dfrac{1}{e^x}\right)$

   (c) $\ln(e^{-x^2})$
   (d) $e^{\ln 3x^2}$
   (e) $e^{-\ln x^3}$
   (f) $e^{2\ln 6x}$

   (g) $e^{7x^2 + 3\ln 3x}$

   (h) $\ln(e^{-x+x^2-x^3})$

   (i) $e^{-\ln(1/x)}$
   (j) $\ln(3x^4 e^{-x^2})$
   (k) $e^{2\ln x} - \frac{1}{2}\ln y$
   (l) $e^{\ln 1 + 2\ln x}$

13. Verify the following:

   (a) $a = e^{\ln a}$ for $a > 0$ (c) $\ln a^u = u \ln a$ for $a > 0$
   (b) $a^u = e^{u \ln a}$ for $a > 0$

14. Prove the following for x, a, and $b > 0$:

(a) $\ln x = (\ln a)(\log_a x)$

(c) $\log_b a = \dfrac{1}{\log_a b}$

(b) $\log_b x = \dfrac{\log_a x}{\log_a b}$

(d) $\log_b x = (\log_b a)(\log_a x)$

15. Find the radius vectors for these points:

(a) $(2, 4)$

(b) $(-1, 6)$

(c) $(-5, -12)$

(d) $(3, -4)$

16. Locate the following angles by indicating magnitude with a curved arrow with respect to a rectangular system of coordinates:

(a) $60°$

(b) $270°$

(c) $-90°$

(d) $320°$

(e) $360°$

(f) $180°$

17. Find two coterminal angles and the related angle:

(a) $120°$

(b) $240°$

(c) $330°$

(d) $480°$

(e) $-330°$

(f) $180°$

18. Find the angles in radian measure:

(a) $120°$

(b) $330°$

(c) $210°$

(d) $-60°$

19. Find the angles in degrees:

(a) $\dfrac{3\pi}{2}$

(b) $\dfrac{5\pi}{4}$

(c) $\dfrac{7\pi}{15}$

(d) $\dfrac{7\pi}{3}$

20. What are the signs of the six trigonometric functions in each quadrant?

21. Find the trigonometric functions for the angle θ in standard position for the points (a) $(-12, -5)$, and (b) $(3, -4)$.

22. Given that the angle θ is in the fourth quadrant and that

$$\sin \theta = \frac{-15}{17}$$

find the other trigonometric functions.

23. Determine the lengths of the sides of a triangle whose angles are 30°, 60°, and 90°, and make a table of the trigonometric functions for each angle.

24. Find the values of the trigonometric functions for 45°.

25. Verify the following trigonometric identities:

   (a) $\sin^2 x + \cos^2 x = 1$; $\tan^2 x + 1 = \sec^2 x$; $\cot^2 x + 1 = \csc^2 x$

   (b) $\csc x = \dfrac{\sec x}{\tan x}$

   (c) $\cos^2 x - \sin^2 x = 2\cos^2 x - 1$

   (d) $\csc^2 x - \cos^2 x \csc^2 x = 1$

   (e) $\sec^2 x \csc^2 x = \sec^2 x + \csc^2 x$

   (f) $\sin x \tan x = \sec x - \cos x$

26. Solve the following trigonometric equations for x in the range $0° \leq x < 360°$:

   (a) $\cos^2 x = \cos x$ (c) $\tan^2 x = 1$

   (b) $\cot x + \csc x = 0$ (d) $\sec^2 x - 1 = \tan^2 x$

27. An *inverse* trigonometric function is a function such as $\sin^{-1} x$ (or arcsin x), which means the angle whose sine is x. The superscript -1 indicates the inversion; it is not an exponent. Graph the six inverse functions $\sin^{-1} x$, $\cos^{-1} x$, $\tan^{-1} x$, $\cot^{-1} x$, $\sec^{-1} x$, $\csc^{-1} x$.

28. Find all values of the angle θ in the range $0° \leq \theta \leq 360°$ (see problem 27):

   (a) $\theta = \arcsin\left(-\tfrac{1}{2}\right)$ (d) $\theta = \text{arcsec}\,(-1)$

   (b) $\theta = \arccos\left(-\tfrac{1}{2}\sqrt{3}\right)$ (e) $\theta = \text{arccsc}\,(2)$

   (c) $\theta = \arctan\left(-\sqrt{3}\right)$ (f) $\theta = \text{arccot}\,(1)$

29. A function $f(x)$ whose value is not changed by increasing or decreasing its position by a constant p, the period, such that

$$f(x + p) \equiv f(x)$$

is a *periodic* function of x. Find the period for the $\tan \theta$ and $\cot \theta$.

30. Graph the business cycle given by the function

$$y = 10 + 10 \cos \frac{\pi}{4} t$$

and find all values of y and the length of the cycle.

31. If the consumption function is given by the equation

$$c = 50 + 0.5y$$

find the average propensity to consume at $y = 20$, $y = 60$, and $y = 100$, and express the angle in inverse trigonometric form.

32. Find the Cartesian coordinates of these points:

(a) $(4, \pi)$

(d) $(7, -\pi)$

(b) $\left(2, \dfrac{\pi}{6}\right)$

(e) $\left(4, \dfrac{8\pi}{3}\right)$

(c) $\left(\sqrt{2}, \dfrac{5\pi}{4}\right)$

(f) $\left(2, \dfrac{-\pi}{4}\right)$

33. Find the polar coordinates of these points with $0° \le \theta < 2\pi$.

(a) $(0, 6)$

(c) $(-6, -6)$

(b) $(4\sqrt{3}, 4)$

(d) $(\sqrt{3}, -1)$

34. Find the polar form of the complex numbers:

(a) $-3i$

(c) -5

(b) $\frac{1}{2}\sqrt{3} + \dfrac{i}{2}$

(d) $-4 - 4i$

35. Perform the indicated operation:

(a) $\dfrac{2\left(\cos \dfrac{2\pi}{3} + i \sin \dfrac{2\pi}{3}\right)}{\left(\cos \dfrac{\pi}{3} + i \sin \dfrac{\pi}{3}\right)}$

(c) $\dfrac{3\left(\cos \dfrac{2\pi}{5} + i \sin \dfrac{2\pi}{3}\right)}{7\left(\cos \dfrac{\pi}{6} + i \sin \dfrac{\pi}{6}\right)}$

(b) $\dfrac{6\left(\cos \dfrac{5\pi}{4} + i \sin \dfrac{5\pi}{4}\right)}{5\left(\cos \dfrac{\pi}{4} + i \sin \dfrac{\pi}{4}\right)}$

(d) $\left[9\left(\cos \dfrac{5\pi}{4} + i \sin \dfrac{5\pi}{4}\right)\right]\left[9\left(\cos \dfrac{\pi}{4} + i \sin \dfrac{\pi}{4}\right)\right]$

(e) $\left[\sqrt{2}\left(\cos \dfrac{\pi}{6} + i \sin \dfrac{\pi}{6}\right)\right]\left[\sqrt{8}\left(\cos \dfrac{2\pi}{3} + i \sin \dfrac{2\pi}{3}\right)\right]$

36. Prove De Moivre's Theorem

$$[r(\cos \theta + i \sin \theta)]^n = r^n(\cos n\theta + i \sin n\theta)$$

by mathematical induction.

37. If the definition of e^{ix} is

$$e^{ix} = \cos x + i \sin x$$

verify the following:

(a) $|e^{ix}| = 1$

(b) $|e^{x+iy}| = e^x$

(c) $\sin x = \dfrac{1}{2i}(e^{ix} - e^{-ix})$

(d) $\cos x = \frac{1}{2}(e^{ix} + e^{-ix})$

(e) $e^{x+i(y+2\pi)} = e^{x+iy}$

(f) $e^{\overline{(x+iy)}} = \overline{(e^{x+iy})}$

(g) $e^{(\pi/2)i} = i$

38. A *parametric* equation expresses the two variables x and y in terms of a third variable. Eliminate parameters x and y from the following equations and identify the curves.
    (a) $x = \cos \theta$ $y = 2 \sin \theta$
    (b) $x = 4 \sec \theta$ $y = 2 \tan \theta$
    (c) $x = 3 \cos \theta - 2$ $y = 2 \sin \theta + 1$

39. Solve the equations for x in the range $0° \leq x < 360°$:

    (a) $\sin^2 x - \frac{3}{2} \sin x + \frac{1}{2} = 0$ (b) $2 \cos^2 x + 3 \cos x - 2 = 0$

5
LIMITS, CONTINUITY, AND DERIVATIVES

In an equation of the form $y = f(x)$, the value of the function changes as different values are assigned to x. An ordered sequence of numbers developed by a function will behave in one of four ways:

1. Tend to infinity, as for example
   $1, 2, 3, 4, 5, 6, 7, \ldots, \infty$

2. Tend to negative infinity,
   $2, 1, 0, -1, -2, -3, \ldots, -\infty$

3. Tend to a numerical limit,
   $\frac{1}{2}, \frac{2}{3}, \frac{3}{4}, \frac{4}{5}, \frac{5}{6}, \ldots, 1$

4. Fluctuate in value without tending to any limit,
   $1, \frac{3}{2}, 3, \frac{5}{4}, 5, \frac{7}{6}, \ldots$
   or
   $-2, 4, -8, 16, -32, \ldots$

THE CONCEPT OF LIMITS

The limit of a mathematical function involves the question, "What value will one variable, say y, assume, when another variable, say x, approaches a specific value?" The concept of the limit of a mathematical function must rest upon the functional relationship between x and y. The concept of the limit can be illustrated by exploring the relationship $y = f(x)$. If, as x approaches the value N, y approaches the value L, the relationship may be stated

$$\lim_{x \to N} y = L.$$

This says that as x approximates ever more closely the value of N, y will become closer and closer to the value of L.

More generally, the limiting values assumed by $f(x)$ as x approaches any value whatever can be postulated. For example, in any given relationship $y = f(x)$ some limiting value of y may be stated when (1) x approaches some numerical value, (2) x approaches 0, or (3) x approaches positive or negative infinity. To fix these three cases firmly in mind, examine the limits of the following case:

$$\lim_{x \to 3} y = \lim_{x \to 3} (2 + x^2)$$

This limit may be approached from both the values of x less than 3 and the values of x greater than 3. Using the first approach, substitute values of x less than 3, such as 2, 2.5, 2.9. As these substitutions are made, y changes in value from 6 to 8.25 to 10.41. At $x = 3$, y assumes the value 11. Alternatively as x approaches the value of 3 from the right side, let x be 4, 3.5, 3.1, and evaluate the values of y. Now y changes in value from 18 to 14.25 and to 11.61. Again when x actually assumes the value of 3, y becomes 11. From this analysis of the behavior of the function as x nears the limiting value of 3 from both sides it is clear that

$$\lim_{x \to 3} y = \lim_{x \to 3} (2 + x^2) = 11$$

This function is shown in Figure 5-1.

The limiting value of a function as the independent variable approaches the value zero can be determined similarly.

$$\lim_{x \to 0} y = \lim_{x \to 0} \left(4 + \frac{x}{2}\right)$$

Allowing x to approach zero from the left, substitute values of x such as

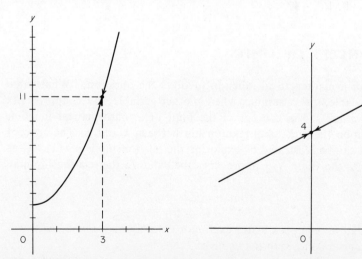

FIGURE 5-1 The Limit of the   FIGURE 5-2 The Limit of the Function

Function $\lim_{x \to 3} y = \lim_{x \to 3} (2 + x^2)$ $\lim_{x \to 0} y = \lim_{x \to 0} \left(4 + \frac{x}{2}\right)$

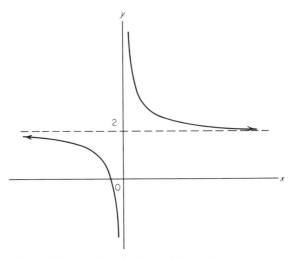

**FIGURE 5-3 Rectangular Hyperbolas as Illustrations of
the Concept of the Limit of a Function**

−1, −0.1 and −0.01. Then y approaches closer and closer to 4. Alternatively x may be allowed to approach zero from the right by assigning it values such as 1, 0.1, and 0.01, in which case the value of y again approaches 4. Figure 5-2 illustrates this example.

The limiting value of y may be estimated as the independent variable x approaches either negative or positive infinity (see Figure 5-3). Consider the function

$$\lim_{x \to \infty} y = \lim_{x \to \infty} \left(2 + \frac{1}{x}\right)$$

In this function, $y = 2$ as $x \to \infty$. The value of x may also be allowed to approach negative infinity to estimate the limiting value of y.

$$\lim_{x \to -\infty} y = \lim_{x \to \infty} \left(2 + \frac{1}{x}\right)$$

The value of y will once again approach 2 as x approaches negative infinity.

Certain special limits occur frequently:

1. $\lim_{x \to 0} \dfrac{c}{x} = \infty$

2. $\lim_{x \to \infty} cx = \infty$

3. $\lim_{x \to \infty} \dfrac{x}{c} = \infty$

4. $\lim_{x \to \infty} \dfrac{c}{x} = 0$

Certain properties of the relationships among limits of functions may also be stated. For any two single-valued functions $f(x)$ and $g(x)$, assume that the following limits exist: $f(x) \to M$, $g(x) \to N$, as $x \to \infty$. The limits M and N are finite values. Then the following relationships may be established:

5. $f(x) + g(x) \to M + N$ as $x \to \infty$

6. $f(x) - g(x) \to M - N$ as $x \to \infty$

7. $f(x) \cdot g(x) \to MN$ as $x \to \infty$

8. $\dfrac{f(x)}{g(x)} \to \dfrac{M}{N}$ as $x \to \infty$ and $N \neq 0$

From these eight known relationships, the limits of various functions can be deduced.

Example 1: Find the limit of the function

$$y = 8 - \frac{2}{x} \quad \text{as} \quad x \to \infty$$

Solution:

$$\lim_{x \to \infty} y = \lim_{x \to \infty} \left(8 - \frac{2}{x} \right) = 8$$

Example 2: Find the limit of the function

$$y = \frac{4x + 2}{6x - 3} \quad \text{as} \quad x \to \infty$$

Solution: (a) Divide both the numerator and the denominator by x, and write

$$y = \frac{\dfrac{4x}{x} + \dfrac{2}{x}}{\dfrac{6x}{x} - \dfrac{3}{x}} = \frac{4 + \dfrac{2}{x}}{6 - \dfrac{3}{x}}$$

(b) The expressions $2/x \to 0$ and $3/x \to 0$ as $x \to \infty$. Thus

$$\lim_{x \to \infty} y = \lim_{x \to \infty} \frac{(4x/x) + (2/x)}{(6x/x) - (3/x)} = \lim_{x \to \infty} \frac{4 + (2/x)}{6 - (3/x)} = \frac{4}{6} = \frac{2}{3}$$

Example 3: Prove

$$\lim_{x \to \infty} \frac{2x^2 - 4x + 5}{5x + 2x^2 - 10} = 1$$

Solution: (a) Divide both the numerator and the denominator by x^2:

$$\lim_{x \to \infty} \frac{\dfrac{2x^2}{x^2} - \dfrac{4x}{x^2} + \dfrac{5}{x^2}}{\dfrac{5x}{x^2} + \dfrac{2x^2}{x^2} - \dfrac{10}{x^2}} = \lim_{x \to \infty} \frac{2 - \dfrac{4}{x} + \dfrac{5}{x^2}}{\dfrac{5}{x} + 2 - \dfrac{10}{x^2}}$$

(b) Find the limiting value of each term containing x:

$$\lim_{x \to \infty} \frac{4}{x} = 0 \qquad \lim_{x \to \infty} \frac{5}{x^2} = 0$$

$$\lim_{x \to \infty} \frac{5}{x} = 0 \qquad \lim_{x \to \infty} \frac{10}{x^2} = 0$$

(c) Substituting these limiting values for the expressions containing x, find the value of the function as $x \to \infty$:

$$\lim_{x \to \infty} \frac{2x^2 - 4x + 5}{5x + 2x^2 - 10} = \lim_{x \to \infty} \frac{2 - \dfrac{4}{x} + \dfrac{5}{x^2}}{\dfrac{5}{x} + 2 - \dfrac{10}{x^2}} = \frac{2}{2} = 1$$

Example 4: Prove

$$\lim_{x \to \infty} \frac{4x + 10}{3x + 4} = \frac{4}{3}$$

Solution: (a) Divide both the numerator and the denominator by x:

$$\lim_{x \to \infty} \frac{\dfrac{4x}{x} + \dfrac{10}{x}}{\dfrac{3x}{x} + \dfrac{4}{x}} = \lim_{x \to \infty} \frac{4 + \dfrac{10}{x}}{3 + \dfrac{4}{x}}$$

(b) Find the limiting value of each term containing x:

$$\lim_{x \to \infty} \frac{10}{x} = 0 \qquad \lim_{x \to \infty} \frac{4}{x} = 0$$

(c) Substituting these limiting values for the expressions containing x, find the value of the function as $x \to \infty$:

$$\lim_{x \to \infty} \frac{4x + 10}{3x + 4} = \frac{4}{3}$$

Example 5: Prove

$$\lim_{x \to 0} \frac{4x^2 + 3x + 2}{x^3 + 2x - 6} = \frac{2}{-6} = -\frac{1}{3}$$

Solution: (a) Find the limiting values of all terms containing x:

$$\lim_{x \to 0} 4x^2 = 0 \qquad \lim_{x \to 0} x^3 = 0$$

$$\lim_{x \to 0} 3x = 0 \qquad \lim_{x \to 0} 2x = 0$$

(b) Substitute these limiting values of the terms containing x into the function to obtain the limiting value of the function:

$$\lim_{x \to 0} \frac{4x^2 + 3x + 2}{x^3 + 2x - 6} = \frac{2}{-6} = -\frac{1}{3}$$

Example 6: To illustrate the principle that the sum of the limits of two functions as x approaches infinity is the sum of the individual limits, consider the limits of the following functions:

(a) $\lim_{x \to \infty} \dfrac{6x^2 + 2x + 10}{3x^2 + 10x + 5} = 2$

(b) $\lim_{x \to \infty} \dfrac{3x^2 - x + 5}{x^2 - 1} = 3$

(c) $\lim_{x \to \infty} \left[\dfrac{6x^2 + 2x + 10}{3x^2 - 10x + 5} + \dfrac{3x^2 - x + 5}{x^2 - 1} \right]$

$$= \lim_{x \to \infty} \frac{15x^4 - 31x^3 + 44x^2 - 57x + 15}{3x^4 - 10x^3 + 2x^2 + 10x - 5} = \frac{15}{3} = 5$$

It is seen that the function c is the sum of the functions a and b. The limit of the function c is the sum of the limits of the functions a and b as $x \to \infty$.

Example 7: This example is designed to show the product of the limits of two functions.

(a) $\lim_{x \to \infty} \dfrac{3x^2 + 5}{2x + x^2} = 3$

(b) $\lim_{x \to \infty} \dfrac{2x + 10}{x - 5} = 2$

(c) $\lim_{x \to \infty} \left[\dfrac{3x^2 + 5}{2x + x^2} \cdot \dfrac{2x + 10}{x - 5} \right] = \lim_{x \to \infty} \dfrac{6x^3 + 30x^2 + 10x + 50}{x^3 - 3x^2 - 10x} = 6$

The function c is the product of the functions a and b. The limit of the function c as x approaches ∞ is the product of the limits of the functions a and b.

Example 8: Consider the following functions:

(a) $\lim\limits_{x \to \infty} \dfrac{4x - 1}{x + 2} = 4$

(b) $\lim\limits_{x \to \infty} \dfrac{2x^2 - 5}{x^2 + x} = 2$

(c) $\lim\limits_{x \to \infty} \dfrac{\dfrac{4x - 1}{x + 2}}{\dfrac{2x^2 - 5}{x^2 + x}} = \lim\limits_{x \to \infty} \left[\dfrac{4x - 1}{x + 2} \cdot \dfrac{x^2 - x}{2x^2 - 5} \right]$

$$= \lim\limits_{x \to \infty} \dfrac{4x^3 - 5x^2 + x}{2x^3 + 4x^2 - 5x - 10} = 2$$

It is apparent that the limit of the quotient of two functions is the quotient of the respective limits.

Under certain circumstances, the rules which have just been illustrated may *not* be used to determine the limits of functions. For example, the limits of the following equation as $x \to \infty$ may not be separately calculated and found to be equal:

$$\frac{x^2 + x - 5}{x + 2} - \frac{x^2 + 5}{x - 2} = \frac{-3x^2 - 12x}{(x + 2)(x - 2)}$$

On the left side

$$\lim\limits_{x \to \infty} \frac{x^2 + x - 5}{x + 2} = \infty \quad \text{and} \quad \lim\limits_{x \to \infty} \frac{x^2 + 5}{x - 2} = \infty$$

while on the right side

$$\lim\limits_{x \to \infty} \frac{-3x^2 - 12x}{(x + 2)(x - 2)} = \lim\limits_{x \to \infty} \frac{-3(x^2/x^2) - 12(x/x^2)}{(x^2/x^2) - (4/x^2)} = -3$$

In this case, the individual limits of each function do not exist, but when the difference is calculated, the limit of the entire function exists. This example does not illustrate rule 5 for the limit of the difference of two functions since the property requires that the limit of each function exist.

The function $(x + 1)/(x - 1)$ may not be evaluated as the product of the limits of the functions $(1/x - 1) \cdot (x + 1)$ as $x \to \infty$, since the limit as $x \to \infty$ does not exist for $f(x) = x + 1$.

The concept of the limit is a very important foundation of the mathematics of calculus. Differential calculus is concerned with the rate of change in the dependent variable with respect to the change in the independent variable as the amount of change of the independent variable approaches zero as a limit.

CONTINUITY

The notion that a mathematical function is *continuous* requires that for each value of x within a specified range, there is at least one corresponding value of y which is finite. Within the range of continuity, the function must not have any gaps or jumps. The following conditions must be fulfilled by any mathematical function $f(x)$ that is continuous at $x = a$:

1. The function $f(x)$ is defined at $x = a$; i.e., $f(a)$ must exist.
2. There must exist finite values of $f(x)$ in the neighborhood of $x = a$.
3. The function $f(x)$ must be such that $\lim\limits_{x \to a} f(x) = f(a)$.

Given a function $y = f(x)$, define the point $x = a$. Next establish a range $a - \epsilon < a + \epsilon$ where ϵ is some small positive number. The range involved is the range of values of x from $x = a - \epsilon$ to $x = a + \epsilon$, $a - \epsilon \leq x \leq a + \epsilon$. For the function $y = f(x)$ to be continuous,

$$y = f(a - \epsilon) \quad \text{when } x = a - \epsilon$$

$$y = f(a + \epsilon) \quad \text{when } x = a + \epsilon$$

$$\lim\limits_{x \to a} f(x) = f(a)$$

This would require that in the range of the values of x between $x = a - \epsilon$ and $x = a + \epsilon$, the function $f(x)$ must exist for every value of x, and be of a definite and finite value. Further, between $x = a - \epsilon$ and $x = a + \epsilon$, the function must not have any gaps or jumps, and must not approach infinity. These conditions are illustrated in Figure 5-4.

The function $y = x^2$ may be used to illustrate a continuous function which fulfills all the conditions of continuity. In Figure 5-5, if $x = 3$, $f(x) = f(3) = 9$; when $x = 3 - 1 = 2$, $f(x) = f(2) = 4$; when $x = 3 + 1 = 4$, $f(x) = f(4) = 16$. It is also evident that

$$\lim\limits_{x \to 3} x^2 = 9$$

Thus the function $y = x^2$ is continuous between $x = 2$ and $x = 4$. In fact this function is continuous everywhere, not merely within the range of this illustration.

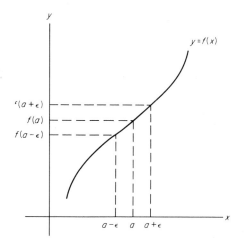

FIGURE 5-4   Conditions for Continuity of a
Function

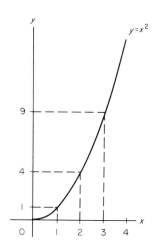

FIGURE 5-5   Continuity of
a Specific Function

An example of a *discontinuous* function is:

$$y = \frac{x + 2}{x + 1}$$

From Chapter 3, this function can be recognized as a hyperbola with two perpendicular asymptotes. Graphically, the function traces out the hyperbola shown in Figure 5-6. The hyperbola depicted has a range of continuity, but as x approaches -1 from the right side, the upper curve approaches infinity; and as x approaches -1 from the left side, the lower curve approaches negative infinity. At $x = -1$, the function is discontinuous.

A function may be continuous but not smooth, in the sense that it has a sharp turning point at some value. The function

$$y = f(x) = 2 + \sqrt[3]{(x - 1)^2}$$

is everywhere continuous, but has an abrupt change of slope at $x = 1$, as shown in Figure 5-7.

A discontinuous function with jumps is a *step* function. Such functions are often found in economic literature. Although a demand function is usually represented graphically as a smooth and continuous function, in fact price usually varies only by discrete amounts, and in most cases quantity demanded of a good also varies by discrete units. For example, in the demand function for an automobile, the price variations may be stated in terms of either dollars or cents, but not in terms of fractions of

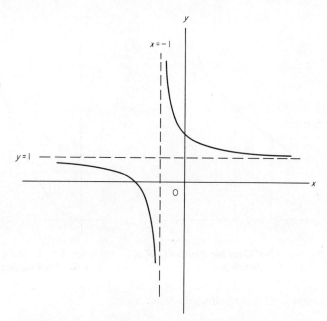

**FIGURE 5-6   Rectangular Hyperbolas to Illustrate Disconti-
nuity of a Function**

cents; the quantity demanded of the automobile is in terms of whole automobiles but never in terms of either one-half or one-quarter of an automobile. Such a demand function is really most accurately represented by a step function. But since the step function is incapable of application to any significant or meaningful analysis, economists adopt the slight fiction that the functions they are dealing with are continuous.

An example of a discontinuous step function may be generated by

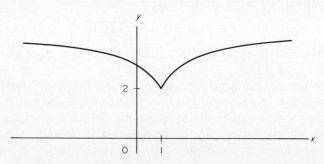

**FIGURE 5-7   A Function Which is Continuous But Not Smooth
at a Given Point**

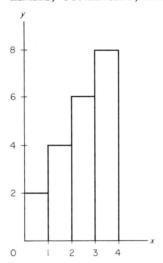

FIGURE 5-8   A Step Function

the following schedule, and graphically represented by Figure 5-8.

$0 \leq x \leq 1$	$1 \leq x \leq 2$	$2 \leq x \leq 3$	$3 \leq x \leq 4$
$y = 2$	$y = 4$	$y = 6$	$y = 8$

THE DERIVATIVE

The derivative of a function is a measure of the rate at which the function's value changes in response to small variations of the independent variable, in the neighborhood of a specific point. Geometrically, the derivative of a line or a curve measures the slope of the line or the curve at a point.

Given a function $y = f(x)$, if x takes on an increment of Δx, then y will take on an increment of Δy. The amount of the increment to y, i.e., Δy, will depend on the nature of the specific functional relationship which exists between y and x, and upon the value of Δx. The problem is to determine the ratio of $\Delta y / \Delta x$ as Δx becomes very small. This is in essence the process of taking the rate of change of the function, or the measurement of the slope of the curve it generates.

Consider the function

$$y = x^2 \qquad (1)$$

Assume some arbitrarily chosen value of x with its corresponding value of y. Then as x takes on an increment Δx, y will take on an increment of Δy. Thus

$$y + \Delta y = (x + \Delta x)^2$$

which is

$$y + \Delta y = x^2 + 2x\,\Delta x + (\Delta x)^2$$

Subtract (1) $\dfrac{y \qquad\qquad = x^2}{\Delta y = \qquad\quad 2x\,\Delta x + (\Delta x)^2}$ (2)

To find the ratio of the increase in y to the increase in x, divide Δx into both sides of the equation

$$\frac{\Delta y}{\Delta x} = 2x + \Delta x$$

If the initial value of x were 3, the ratio of $\Delta y/\Delta x$ would be equal to 6, or using limit notation,

$$\lim_{\Delta x \to 0} \frac{\Delta y}{\Delta x} = \lim_{\Delta x \to 0} (2x + \Delta x) = 2x =$$

Now consider in detail the pattern of change of the ratio $\Delta y/\Delta x$ as Δx becomes very small. An examination of Table 5-1 shows that by taking successively smaller increments of x and calculating the ratios of the resulting increments in y to the increments of x, one can see the ratios approach the limiting value of 6.

The notation for the derivative of a function $y = f(x)$ is

$$\frac{dy}{dx} = y' = f'(x)$$

The derivative of the function $y = f(x)$ can be designated by dy/dx, y', or $f'(x)$. Each symbol represents the limiting value of the ratio $\Delta y/\Delta x$ as

TABLE 5-1

Original Value of x	New Value of x	Δx	Original Value of y	New Value of y	Δy	$\dfrac{\Delta y}{\Delta x}$
3	4.00	1.00	9	16.00	7.0000	7.00
3	3.80	0.80	9	14.44	5.4400	6.80
3	3.60	0.60	9	12.96	3.9600	6.60
3	3.40	0.40	9	11.56	2.5600	6.40
3	3.20	0.20	9	10.24	1.2400	6.20
3	3.10	0.10	9	9.61	0.6100	6.10
3	3.01	0.01	9	9.06	0.0601	6.01

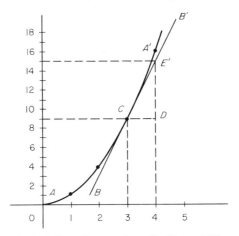

FIGURE 5-9 Construction of a Tangent Line
to a Point on a Curve

Δx approaches zero as a limit.

$$\lim_{\Delta x \to 0} \frac{\Delta y}{\Delta x} = \frac{dy}{dx}$$

$$\lim_{\Delta x \to 0} \frac{\Delta y}{\Delta x} = y'$$

$$\lim_{\Delta x \to 0} \frac{\Delta y}{\Delta x} = f'(x)$$

Figure 5-9 shows the curve generated by the function $y = x^2$, with a line BB' constructed tangent to the curve at the point where $x = 3$ and $y = 9$. The slope of the tangent line BB' is equal to 6, for $\Delta y = DE = 6$ and $\Delta x = CD = 1$, and the ratio

$$\frac{\Delta y}{\Delta x} = \frac{DE}{CD} = \frac{6}{1} = 6$$

This value therefore measures the rate of change of y at point C.

This has been a general introduction to the concept of the derivative and its geometric interpretation. The next step is to develop some of the methods of differentiating functions of various kinds.

RULES OF DIFFERENTIATION

The Derivative of a Constant

If the given function is $y = k$, then no matter what the value of x, y retains the constant value of k, and a Δx is incapable of creating any Δy. Since

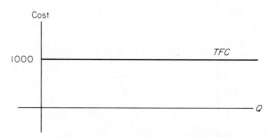

FIGURE 5-10   Total Fixed Cost Curve

$\Delta y = 0$, the ratio $\Delta y/\Delta x = 0$, whatever the value of Δx. As an example, consider the amount of total fixed cost of production of a firm. Let the total fixed cost be represented by the function $TFC = 1000$, which means that the amount of total fixed cost is 1000 units for quantities of output ranging from zero to whatever the upper limit of the capacity may be. Increase the quantity of output from $Q = 10$ to $Q = 20$ so that $\Delta Q = 10$. Total fixed cost is 1000 at $Q = 10$ and at $Q = 20$, so $\Delta TFC = 0$. Then the rate of change of TFC with respect to Q is

$$\frac{\Delta TFC}{\Delta Q} = 0$$

The first rule of differentiation is

$$\lim_{\Delta x \to 0} \frac{\Delta y}{\Delta x} = \frac{dy}{dx} = 0$$

when $y = k$. The geometric interpretation of such a function is illustrated in Figure 5-10. Since the equation of total fixed cost is $TFC = 1000$ for all values of Q, the curve representing TFC is a horizontal straight line. There is no ΔTFC, so $\Delta TFC = 0$.

The Derivative of a First-Degree Term

Suppose that a total revenue function is of the form $R = 5Q$, where R is total revenue and Q is the quantity sold. The function says that total revenue R will increase by 5 units for every unit increase in Q, the quantity. The rate of change in R for a unit change in quantity is then 5. Take some arbitrarily chosen value of Q and let Q take on an increment ΔQ.

$$R \qquad\qquad\qquad = 5Q \qquad\qquad (1)$$

Subtract (1)

$$R + \Delta R = 5(Q + \Delta Q) = 5Q + 5\,\Delta Q \qquad (2)$$
$$\underline{R \qquad\qquad\qquad = 5Q \qquad\qquad\qquad}$$
$$\Delta R \qquad\qquad = \qquad 5\,\Delta Q \qquad (3)$$

Substituting the incremented value $Q + \Delta Q$ into the original function (1) yields an incremented value $R + \Delta R$ in (2). Subtract (1) from (2) to obtain the change in R, (3). Expressing the ratio of ΔR to ΔQ,

$$\frac{\Delta R}{\Delta Q} = \frac{5\Delta Q}{\Delta Q} = 5 \qquad (4)$$

The derivative of the function $R = 5Q$ is the limiting value of the ratio $\Delta R/\Delta Q$ as ΔQ approaches 0. Thus in derivative form, (4) is written

$$\lim_{\Delta Q \to 0} \frac{\Delta R}{\Delta Q} = \frac{dR}{dQ} = 5$$

The procedure which has just been outlined is summarized for any function $y = ax$ by the relationship

$$\frac{dy}{dx} = a$$

In the function $R = 5Q$, the corresponding relationships to the general formulation are $y = R$, $a = 5$, and $x = Q$. The use of the general formula of derivation would then give

$$\frac{dR}{dQ} = 5$$

This is the procedure for finding the derivative of any first-degree function. Procedures for other types of functions will be shown in the discussion which follows.

The total revenue function $R = 5Q$ is plotted in Figure 5-11. The

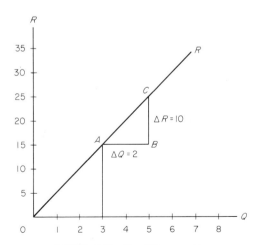

FIGURE 5-11   Total Revenue Curve

measurement of the slope of the function is achieved by taking

$$\frac{R}{Q} = \frac{10}{2} = 5$$

In this case, because the total revenue function is a straight line, the value of the slope is constant no matter where or over what range the slope is measured.

The Differentiation of a Power Function

The rate of change of the function

$$y = 3x^3 \tag{1}$$

can be measured by letting the function take on an increment Δy while increasing x by Δx. The new value of the function is

$$y + \Delta y = 3(x + \Delta x)^3$$
$$= 3[x^3 + 3x^2 \, \Delta x + 3x(\Delta x)^2 + (\Delta x)^3]$$
$$= 3x^3 + 9x^2 \, \Delta x + 9x(\Delta x)^2 + 3(\Delta x)^3$$

or

$$y + \Delta y = 3x^3 + 9x^2 \, \Delta x + 9x \, (\Delta x)^2 + 3 \, (\Delta x)^3 \tag{2}$$

Subtract (1)

$$y \quad\quad\quad = 3x^3$$
$$\overline{\Delta y = \quad\quad 9x^2 \, \Delta x + 9x \, (\Delta x)^2 + 3 \, (\Delta x)^3} \tag{3}$$

Divide (3) by Δx

$$\frac{\Delta y}{\Delta x} = \frac{9x^2 \, \Delta x}{\Delta x} + \frac{9x(\Delta x)^2}{\Delta x} + \frac{3(\Delta x)^3}{\Delta x}$$

$$= 9x^2 + 9x \, \Delta x + 3(\Delta x)^2$$

The limit of the ratio $\Delta y / \Delta x$ as Δx approaches 0 is

$$\lim_{\Delta x \to 0} \frac{\Delta y}{\Delta x} = \frac{dy}{dx} = 9x^2$$

The rate of change of $y = 3x^3$ is no longer constant. The rates of change of the function at some selected values of x are

Value of x	dy/dx
1	9
2	36
3	81
4	144

The slope of the tangent line to the function $y = 3x^3$ at $x = 1$ is 9, at $x = 2$ is 36, at $x = 3$ is 81, and so on. The function is changing at different rates at different points on the function.

In general, then, the derivative of any function $y = ax^n$ can be shown to be

$$\frac{dy}{dx} = nax^{n-1}$$

Some further examples of the differentiation of power functions using this rule are given below.

1. $y = \sqrt{x} = x^{\frac{1}{2}}$

$$\frac{dy}{dx} = \tfrac{1}{2}x^{-\frac{1}{2}} = \frac{1}{2\sqrt{x}}$$

2. $y = 7x^6$

$$\frac{dy}{dx} = 42x^5$$

3. $y = \dfrac{5}{x^3} = 5x^{-3}$

$$\frac{dy}{dx} = -15x^{-4} = -\frac{15}{x^4}$$

4. $y = \dfrac{3}{\sqrt[4]{x}} = 3x^{-\frac{1}{4}}$

$$\frac{dy}{dx} = -\tfrac{3}{4}x^{-\frac{5}{4}} = -\frac{3}{4\sqrt[4]{x^5}}$$

The Differentiation of Sums and Differences

Consider the function

$$y = u + v - w \tag{1}$$

in which y, u, v, and w are all functions of x. As u changes by Δu, v by Δv, and w by Δw, the function becomes

$$y + \Delta y = u + \Delta u + v + \Delta v - w - \Delta w \tag{2}$$

Now subtract (1) from (2):

$$
\begin{aligned}
y + \Delta y &= u + \Delta u + v + \Delta v - w - \Delta w \\
-y &= -u - v + w \\
\hline
\Delta y &= \Delta u + \Delta v - \Delta w
\end{aligned}
\tag{3}
$$

Divide (3) by Δx:

$$\frac{\Delta y}{\Delta x} = \frac{\Delta u}{\Delta x} + \frac{\Delta v}{\Delta x} - \frac{\Delta w}{\Delta x} \tag{4}$$

Take the limit of (4) as Δx approaches 0:

$$\lim_{\Delta x \to 0} \frac{\Delta y}{\Delta x} = \frac{dy}{dx} = \frac{du}{dx} + \frac{dv}{dx} - \frac{dw}{dx} \tag{5}$$

Equation (5) is the derivative of equation (1).

To summarize the derivative of a sum or a difference of functions in words, *the derivative of an algebraic sum of n functions is that same algebraic sum of the derivatives of the functions.*

Take as an example the derivative of the total revenue function

$$R = 10Q - Q^2 \tag{1}$$

As Q takes on an increment of ΔQ, the function becomes

$$R + \Delta R = 10(Q + \Delta Q) - (Q + \Delta Q)^2$$
$$= 10Q + 10\,\Delta Q - Q^2 - 2Q\,\Delta Q - (\Delta Q)^2 \tag{2}$$

Now subtract (1) from (2):

$$R + \Delta R = 10Q + 10\,\Delta Q - Q^2 - 2Q\,\Delta Q - (\Delta Q)^2 \tag{2}$$
$$\underline{R \quad\quad\quad = 10Q \quad\quad\quad\quad - Q^2 \quad\quad\quad\quad\quad\quad\quad\quad} \tag{1}$$
$$\Delta R = \quad\quad 10\,\Delta Q \quad\quad - 2Q\,\Delta Q - (\Delta Q)^2 \tag{3}$$

Divide (3) by ΔQ:

$$\frac{\Delta R}{\Delta Q} = \frac{10\,\Delta Q}{\Delta Q} - \frac{2Q\,\Delta Q}{\Delta Q} - \frac{(\Delta Q)^2}{\Delta Q}$$
$$= 10 - 2Q - \Delta Q \tag{4}$$

Take the limit of (4) as ΔQ approaches 0:

$$\lim_{\Delta Q \to 0} \frac{\Delta R}{\Delta Q} = \frac{dR}{dQ} = 10 - 2Q \tag{5}$$

Equation (5) is the derivative of equation (1).

Some values of dR/dQ at selected values of Q are

Q	dR/dQ	Q	dR/dQ
1	8	6	-2
2	6	7	-4
3	4	8	-6
4	2	9	-8
5	0	10	-10

A few more examples of differentiation of sums and differences of functions are given below:

1. $y = 18 - 6x$

$$\frac{dy}{dx} = -6$$

2. $y = x^6 + 5x^5 - 3x^4 + 4x^2 - x + 100$

$$\frac{dy}{dx} = 6x^5 + 25x^4 - 12x^3 + 8x - 1$$

3. $y = ax^3 + bx^2 + cx + d$

$$\frac{dy}{dx} = 3ax^2 + 2bx + c$$

4. $y = x^{1/3} + 6x^{3/4}$

$$\frac{dy}{dx} = \tfrac{1}{3}x^{1/3} + {}^{18}\!\!/_4 x^{-1/4}$$

Differentiation of the Product of Two Functions

Let the function be

$$y = uv \tag{1}$$

where y, u, and v, are functions of x. When u and v change by the amounts Δu and Δv respectively, y will change by the amount Δy, and the altered value of the function will become

$$y + \Delta y = (u + \Delta u)(v + \Delta v)$$

Multiplying out gives

$$y + \Delta y = uv + v\,\Delta u + u\,\Delta v + \Delta u\,\Delta v \tag{2}$$

Subtract (1) from (2) in order to find the amount of change from (1) to (2):

$$
\begin{aligned}
y + \Delta y &= uv + v\,\Delta u + u\,\Delta v + \Delta u\,\Delta v \\
-y &= -uv \\
\hline
\Delta y &= v\,\Delta u + u\,\Delta v + \Delta u\,\Delta v
\end{aligned}
\tag{3}
$$

To measure the rate of change, divide Δx into (3), which yields

$$\frac{\Delta y}{\Delta x} = v\frac{\Delta u}{\Delta x} + u\frac{\Delta v}{\Delta x} + \frac{\Delta u\,\Delta v}{\Delta x} \tag{4}$$

To set (4) in the form of a derivative, take the limit of the function as Δx approaches 0:

$$\lim_{\Delta x \to 0} \frac{\Delta y}{\Delta x} = \frac{dy}{dx} = v\frac{du}{dx} + u\frac{dv}{dx} + du\frac{dv}{dx}$$

Since, as Δx approaches zero, Δu approaches zero and the last term

$$du\frac{dv}{dx} = 0$$

the derivative becomes

$$\frac{dy}{dx} = v\frac{du}{dx} + u\frac{dv}{dx} \tag{5}$$

Equation (5) is the derivative of equation (1).

In words, *the derivative of the product of two functions is the sum of the derivative of the first function times the second function and the derivative of the second function times the first function.*

As illustrations:

1. $y = (4x^2 + x)(6x^2 + 5)$

$$\frac{dy}{dx} = (8x + 1)(6x^2 + 5) + (12x)(4x^2 + x)$$

$$= 48x^3 + 40x + 6x^2 + 5 + 48x^3 + 12x^2$$

$$= 96x^3 + 18x^2 + 40x + 5$$

2. $y = (x^4 + 2x^3)(x^2 + 2x)$

$$\frac{dy}{dx} = (4x^3 + 6x^2)(x^2 + 2x) + (2x + 2)(x^4 + 2x^3)$$

$$= 4x^5 + 8x^4 + 6x^4 + 12x^3 + 2x^5 + 4x^4 + 2x^4 + 4x^3$$

$$= 6x^5 + 20x^4 + 16x^3$$

3. $y = \left(\frac{1}{x} + \sqrt{x}\right)\left(\frac{1}{x^2} - x^{1/2}\right)$

Rearranging the function yields

$$y = (x^{-1} + x^{1/2})(x^{-2} - x^{1/2})$$

Differentiating gives

$$\frac{dy}{dx} = (-x^{-2} + \tfrac{1}{2}x^{-\frac{1}{2}})(x^{-2} - x^{\frac{1}{2}}) + (-2x^{-3} - \tfrac{1}{2}x^{-\frac{1}{2}})(x^{-1} + x^{\frac{1}{2}})$$

$$= -x^{-4} + x^{-1\frac{1}{2}} + \tfrac{1}{2}x^{-2\frac{1}{2}} - \tfrac{1}{2}x^{0} - 2x^{-4} - 2x^{-2\frac{1}{2}} - \tfrac{1}{2}x^{-1\frac{1}{2}} - \tfrac{1}{2}x^{0}$$

$$= -3x^{-4} + \tfrac{1}{2}x^{-1\frac{1}{2}} + \tfrac{1}{2}x^{-2\frac{1}{2}} - 1 - 2x^{-2\frac{1}{2}}$$

$$= -3x^{-4} + \tfrac{1}{2}x^{-1\frac{1}{2}} - 1\tfrac{1}{2}x^{-2\frac{1}{2}} - 1$$

$$= \frac{-3}{x^{4}} + \frac{1}{2x\sqrt{x}} - \frac{3}{2x^{2}\sqrt{x}} - 1$$

Differentiation of a Quotient

Suppose a function involves the quotient of two functions:

$$y = \frac{u}{v} \tag{1}$$

As usual, u and v are allowed to change by Δu and Δv respectively, and these changes bring about a new value of the function expressed by

$$y + \Delta y = \frac{u + \Delta u}{v + \Delta v} \tag{2}$$

To find the amount of change in y from (1) to (2), subtract (1) from (2):

$$y + \Delta y - y = \frac{u + \Delta u}{v + \Delta v} - \frac{u}{v}$$

$$\Delta y = \frac{v(u + \Delta u) - u(v + \Delta v)}{v(v + \Delta v)}$$

Multiplying out gives

$$\Delta y = \frac{vu + v\,\Delta u - uv - u\,\Delta v}{v^{2} + v\,\Delta v}$$

$$\Delta y = \frac{v\,\Delta u - u\,\Delta v}{v^{2} + v\,\Delta v} \tag{3}$$

Now divide both sides of the equation by Δx to get the ratio of the change in y to the change in x:

$$\frac{\Delta y}{\Delta x} = \frac{v\dfrac{\Delta u}{\Delta x} - u\dfrac{\Delta v}{\Delta x}}{v^{2} + v\,\Delta v}$$

Taking the limit of the function $\Delta y/\Delta x$ as Δx approaches zero yields the derivative

$$\lim_{\Delta x \to 0} \frac{\Delta y}{\Delta x} = \frac{dy}{dx} = \frac{v \dfrac{du}{dx} - u \dfrac{dv}{dx}}{v^2}$$

The second term of the denominator is zero because Δv approaches zero as Δx approaches zero.

In words, the derivative of a quotient of two functions is the denominator times the derivative of the numerator minus the numerator times the derivative of the denominator, all divided by the square of the denominator. For instance, take the derivative of the function

$$y = \frac{3x^2}{(4x - 5)}$$

Using the rule for finding the derivative of the quotient of two functions gives

$$\frac{dy}{dx} = \frac{6x(4x - 5) - 4(3x^2)}{(4x - 5)^2}$$

$$= \frac{24x^2 - 30x - 12x^2}{(4x - 5)^2}$$

$$= \frac{12x^2 - 30x}{(4x - 5)^2}$$

Some additional examples of the derivatives of function quotients are given below:

1. $y = \dfrac{x^2 - 2}{2x + 3}$

$$\frac{dy}{dx} = \frac{2x(2x + 3) - 2(x^2 - 2)}{(2x + 3)^2}$$

$$= \frac{4x^2 + 6x - 2x^2 + 4}{(2x + 3)^2}$$

$$= \frac{2x^2 + 6x + 4}{(2x + 3)^2}$$

2. $y = \dfrac{5}{x^2}$

The derivative of this function can be found either by converting it into a power function or by treating it as the quotient of a constant and a variable. When using the first method, convert the function into

$$y = 5x^{-2}$$

Then the derivative is

$$\frac{dy}{dx} = -10x^{-3} = -\frac{10}{x^3}$$

By the second method

$$\frac{dy}{dx} = \frac{-(2x)5}{x^4} = \frac{-10x}{x^4} = -\frac{10}{x^3}$$

3. The demand curve

$$p = \frac{10}{q}$$

can be differentiated to measure the slope of the demand curve.

$$\frac{dp}{dq} = -\frac{10}{q^2}$$

When $q = 2$, the slope of the demand curve will be

$$\frac{dp}{dq} = -\frac{10}{2^2} = -\frac{10}{4} = -2.5$$

Differentiation of a Composite Function

Sometimes y is expressed as a function of v when v is a function of x, so that y is a function of x through v. For example, if

$$y = \frac{3v}{1 - v^2} \qquad \text{and} \qquad v = x^2 + 2$$

then y is a function of a function. One approach to the problem of finding dy/dx would be to substitute for v its value in terms of x, which would eliminate v. Then y could be expressed directly as a function of x for differentiation, but this is often a very awkward method of finding dy/dx. Fortunately, dy/dx can be calculated without eliminating v first.

Let $y = f(u)$ and $u = \theta(x)$. Now find the derivative of y with respect to u, and then calculate the derivative of u with respect to x. The product of these 2 derivatives is the rate of change of y relative to x.

$$\frac{dy}{du} = f'(u) \qquad \text{and} \qquad \frac{du}{dx} = \theta'(x)$$

The product of the derivatives is

$$\frac{dy}{du} \cdot \frac{du}{dx} = \frac{dy}{dx}$$

The use of this process can be illustrated by a simple example. Suppose that enrollment of students in colleges c is a function of high school graduates h such that $c = 0.3h$. Further assume that the number of high school graduates is a function of elementary school graduates shown by the relationship $h = 0.9e$. Then

$$\frac{dc}{dh} = 0.3 \quad \text{and} \quad \frac{dh}{de} = 0.9$$

and

$$\frac{dc}{de} = \frac{dc}{dh} \cdot \frac{dh}{de} = 0.3 \cdot 0.9 = 0.27$$

As another example, consider the familiar notion of marginal revenue product of a factor of production such as labor. The marginal revenue product of labor measures the rate of change of total revenue of a firm with respect to changes in the amount of labor employed. But the relationship is not direct. Usually the total revenue of the firm is first related to the quantity sold, and the quantity available for sale is treated as a function of the amount of labor hired, subject to certain technological assumptions. Thus two separate functional relationships are usually postulated:

$$R = f(Q) \quad Q = g(L)$$

Marginal revenue is the derivative of the first function

$$MR = \frac{dR}{dQ}$$

and the marginal physical productivity is the derivative of the second function

$$MPP = \frac{dQ}{dL}$$

Marginal revenue product is the product of

$$MR \cdot MPP = \frac{dR}{dQ} \cdot \frac{dQ}{dL} = \frac{dR}{dL}$$

Calculating the marginal revenue product of labor measures the rate of change of total revenue with respect to the amount of labor employed. It is essentially the derivative of a composite function.

Consider another example. Let the function be

$$y = (5x^4 + 3x^3 - 4x^2 + 10)^5$$

One way to proceed would be to expand the function and then take the derivative of the result, but this would be tedious. So it is convenient to define a new function

$$u = 5x^4 + 3x^3 - 4x^2 + 10$$

then to express y as a function of u:

$$y = u^5$$

Taking the derivatives of both functions gives

$$\frac{dy}{du} = 5u^4 \qquad \frac{du}{dx} = 20x^3 + 9x^2 - 8x$$

Multiplying the two derivatives gives

$$\frac{dy}{dx} = \frac{dy}{du} \cdot \frac{du}{dx} = 5u^4(20x^3 + 9x^2 - 8x)$$

Substituting for u gives

$$\frac{dy}{dx} = 5(5x^4 + 3x^3 - 4x^2 + 10)^4(20x^3 + 9x^2 - 8x)$$

A few more examples of the differentiation of a composite function are:

1. $y = u^4 \qquad u = 1 + \sqrt{x}$

Solution:

$$\frac{dy}{du} = 4u^3$$

$$\frac{du}{dx} = \tfrac{1}{2}x^{-\frac{1}{2}}$$

$$\frac{dy}{dx} = \frac{dy}{du} \cdot \frac{du}{dx} = \frac{4u^3}{2\sqrt{x}} = \frac{2u^3}{\sqrt{x}} = \frac{2(1 + \sqrt{x})^3}{\sqrt{x}}$$

2. $y = \sqrt{3u - u^3} \qquad u = x^2 - x$

Solution:

$$\frac{dy}{du} = \frac{1}{2}\sqrt{3}\,u^{-\frac{1}{2}} - 3u^2 = \frac{\sqrt{3}}{2\sqrt{u}} - 3u^2$$

$$\frac{du}{dx} = 2x - 1$$

$$\frac{dy}{dx} = \frac{dy}{du}\cdot\frac{du}{dx} = \left(\frac{\sqrt{3}}{2\sqrt{u}} - 3u^2\right)(2x - 1)$$

$$= \left[\frac{\sqrt{3}}{2\sqrt{x^2 - x}} - 3(x^2 - x)^2\right][2x - 1]$$

3. $y = \dfrac{a - u}{a + u}$ $u = \dfrac{b + x}{b - x}$

Solution:

$$\frac{dy}{du} = \frac{(-1)(a + u) - (a - u)}{(a + u)^2} = \frac{-2a}{(a + u)^2}$$

$$\frac{du}{dx} = \frac{(b - x) + (b + x)}{(b - x)^2} = \frac{2b}{(b - x)^2}$$

$$\frac{dy}{dx} = \frac{dy}{du}\cdot\frac{du}{dx} = \left[\frac{-2a}{(a + u)^2}\right]\left[\frac{2b}{(b - x)^2}\right]$$

$$= \left[\frac{-2a}{\left(a + \dfrac{b + x}{b - x}\right)^2}\right]\left[\frac{2b}{(b - x)^2}\right]$$

Differentiation of an Inverse Function

In a function such as

$$y = f(x) = 2x + 10 \tag{1}$$

it is possible to get the inverse function, by solving for x as a function of y. Thus

$$x = g(y) = \frac{1}{2}y - 5 \tag{2}$$

The function (2) is an inverse function of (1).

The derivatives of (1) and (2) are

$$\frac{dy}{dx} = 2 \tag{3}$$

$$\frac{dx}{dy} = \frac{1}{2} \tag{4}$$

Note that the derivative of the inverse function (4) is exactly the reciprocal of the derivative of the direct function (3). The reason for this relationship can be seen from the steps outlined below:

Multiply dy/dx by dx/dy:

$$\frac{dy}{dx} \cdot \frac{dx}{dy} = 1$$

Solving for dy/dx yields

$$\frac{dy}{dx} = \frac{1}{dx/dy}$$

Thus dy/dx is equal to the reciprocal of dx/dy.

Occasionally x is expressed as a function of y and the inverse function is either difficult or impossible to derive. Then in order to find dy/dx, one must use the rule of differentiation of inverse functions. For example, consider the function

$$x = y + y^3 + 2y^4$$

To find dy/dx, first find dx/dy:

$$\frac{dx}{dy} = 1 + 3y^2 + 8y^3$$

Since

$$\frac{dy}{dx} = \frac{1}{dx/dy}$$

then

$$\frac{dy}{dx} = \frac{1}{1 + 3y^2 + 8y^3}$$

Differentiation of Implicit Functions

When y is expressed as an implicit function of x, i.e., $f(x, y) = 0$, it may be inconvenient to show y as an explicit function of x, or x as an explicit function of y. In such a situation, it is necessary to invoke yet another rule: Differentiate each term of the equation as given, regarding y as a function of x, and solve for dy/dx. In general the resulting derivative will contain both x and y. Consider the function

$$3x^4 + x^3y - xy^4 = 10$$

Then

$$\frac{d}{dx}(3x^4) + \frac{d}{dx}(x^3y) - \frac{d}{dx}(xy^4) = \frac{d}{dx}(10)$$

$$12x^3 + 3x^2y + x^3\frac{dy}{dx} - y^4 - 4xy^3\frac{dy}{dx} = 0$$

$$(x^3 - 4xy^3)\frac{dy}{dx} = y^4 - 12x^3 - 3x^2y$$

$$\frac{dy}{dx} = \frac{y^4 - 12x^3 - 3x^2y}{x^3 - 4xy^3}$$

Successive Differentiation

The derivative of a function of x is often itself a function of x. This new function may also be differentiable. Then the derivative of the new function which is a derivative of an original function of x is called the second derivative of the original function. The derivative of the second derivative is called the third derivative, and so on to the nth derivative. If the original function were $y = 2x^5$, then

$$\frac{dy}{dx} = 10x^4$$

$$\frac{d}{dx}\left(\frac{dy}{dx}\right) = 40x^3$$

$$\frac{d}{dx}\left[\frac{d}{dx}\left(\frac{dy}{dx}\right)\right] = 120x^2$$

The symbols for the successive derivatives are

$$\frac{d}{dx}\left(\frac{dy}{dx}\right) = \frac{d^2y}{dx^2}$$

$$\frac{d}{dx}\left[\frac{d}{dx}\left(\frac{dy}{dx}\right)\right] = \frac{d}{dx}\left(\frac{d^2y}{dx^2}\right) = \frac{d^3y}{dx^3}$$

and so on for higher derivatives. For any $y = f(x)$, the successive derivatives can also be represented by

$$\frac{dy}{dx} = y' = f'(x)$$

$$\frac{d^2y}{dx^2} = y'' = f''(x)$$

$$\frac{d^3y}{dx^3} = y''' = f'''(x)$$

and so on to the nth derivative of the original function.

As illustrations, consider the successive derivatives of the following functions:

1. $y = 3x^4 - 2x^3 + 6x$

$$\frac{dy}{dx} = 12x^3 - 6x^2 + 6$$

$$\frac{d^2y}{dx^2} = 36x^2 - 12x$$

$$\frac{d^3y}{dx^3} = 72x - 12$$

$$\frac{d^4y}{dx^4} = 72$$

$$\frac{d^5y}{dx^5} = 0$$

2. $y = x^3 - \dfrac{3}{x}$

$$\frac{dy}{dx} = 3x^2 + 3x^{-2} = 3x^2 + \frac{3}{x^2}$$

$$\frac{d^2y}{dx^2} = 6x - 6x^{-3} = 6x - \frac{6}{x^3}$$

3. $y = 4x^2 - 2\sqrt{x} + \dfrac{1}{x^2}$

Rearranged, the function becomes

$$y = 4x^2 - 2x^{\frac{1}{2}} + x^{-2}$$

$$\frac{dy}{dx} = 8x - x^{-\frac{1}{2}} - 2x^{-3} = 8x - \frac{1}{\sqrt{x}} - \frac{2}{x^3}$$

$$\frac{d^2y}{dx^2} = 8 + \frac{1}{2}x^{-\frac{3}{2}} + 6x^{-4} = 8 + \frac{1}{2x\sqrt{x}} + \frac{6}{x^4}$$

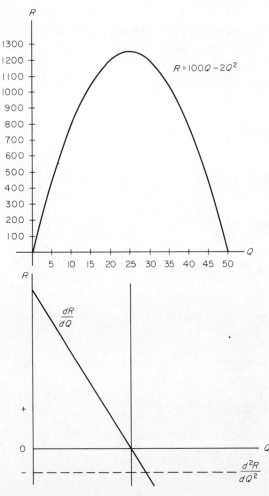

FIGURE 5-12   Total Revenue Curve and a Marginal Revenue Curve

The interpretation of the second derivative is that the second derivative measures the rate of change of the first derivative. If the total revenue function were

$$R = 100Q - 2Q^2$$

where R is the total revenue and Q is the quantity sold, then the first derivative is marginal revenue:

$$\frac{dR}{dQ} = 100 - 4Q$$

The marginal revenue function is decreasing at the rate of four units for every unit increase in quantity. The second derivative therefore is the slope of the first derivative function represented geometrically:

$$\frac{d^2R}{dQ^2} = -4$$

Figure 5-12 shows the three functions.

DIFFERENTIALS

The derivative dy/dx has been treated thus far as a symbol of a mathematical operation. The expressions dy and dx have not been treated as having any independent meanings. There are circumstances under which it is useful to think of dy and dx as quantities possessing unique and specific meanings. It is particularly useful to be able to think in terms of separate meanings for dy and for dx, in connection with integral calculus.

Definition of a Differential

If $f'(x)$ is the derivative of $f(x)$, at a particular value of x, and if Δx is an increment of x, then the differential of $f(x)$ is

$$df(x) = f'(x)\,dx = \frac{dy}{dx}\Delta x$$

If $f'(x)$ is equal to 1, then the equation above becomes

$$dx = \Delta x$$

The differential of a function $f(x)$ is designated by

$$dy = df(x) = f'(x)\,dx = \frac{dy}{dx}\,dx$$

In words, this says that the differential of a function is equal to the derivative of the function times the differential of the independent variable.

Geometric Interpretation of a Differential

The interpretation of a differential is illustrated geometrically in Figure 5-13. The curve $f(x)$ has a derivative at point C equal to

$$\frac{dy}{dx} = \tan \theta = \frac{DF}{CD}$$

Let $dx = CD$. Then the differential of y at point C is

$$df(x) = \frac{DF}{CD} CD = DF$$

This means that as x increases by an amount $dx = CD$, y is expected to increase by an amount $dy = DF$. But note that when x increases by CD, $f(x)$ actually increases by only DE. In general, the differential of a function dy is not equal to the increment of the function Δy. In this case, $dy > \Delta y$, or $DF > DE$. But it can be seen that as dx becomes smaller, so that D approaches C, the difference between DF and DE will become smaller.

As another example of a geometrical interpretation of a differential,

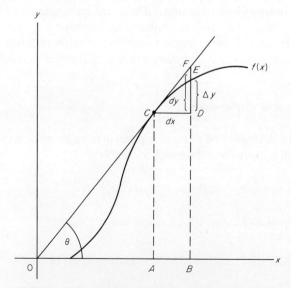

**FIGURE 5-13   Relation Between an Increment and a
Differential of a Function**

examine the curve in Figure 5-14. In this case, $f(x)$ has a derivative at point C equal to

$$\frac{dy}{dx} = \tan \theta = \frac{DE}{CD}$$

The differential at point C on $f(x)$ is

$$df(x) = f'(x)\,dx = \frac{DE}{CD}\,CD = DE$$

In this case, the differential of the function DE is less than the increment of the function DF.

Notice the difference in the shapes of the two curves. The curve in Figure 5-13 is concave downward at C. The rate of change of $f(x)$ is decreasing. The derivative of the function at C is greater than the derivative of the function at E. A linear extrapolation on the basis of the value of the derivative at C, corresponding to $x = A$, will overestimate the value of the function at E when $x = B$. This is the reason that in this case dy is greater than Δy.

In the case of the curve in Figure 5-14, the situation is reversed. Now the curve is convex below at C. This means that the rate of change of $f(x)$ is increasing. The value of dy/dx at C is less than at F. Therefore, the estimation of the value of y at $x = B$ on the basis of the value of the

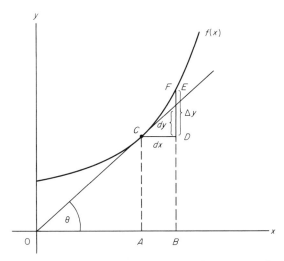

FIGURE 5-14 Relation Between an Increment and a Differential of a Function

derivative at $x = A$ will result in underestimating the new value of y. This results in the fact that, in this case, Δy is greater than dy.

Some Numerical Examples of Differentials

1. $y = 2x^2 + x - 10$

$$dy = d(2x^2 + x - 10) = 4x\,dx + dx$$

Let $x = 2$, and $dx = 1$. Then the value of the differential of y at $x_1 = 2$, with the differential of x equal to 1, can be found:

$$dy = 4(2)(1) + 1 = 9$$

Now compare dy with Δy. When $x_1 = 2$,

$$y_1 = 2x_1^2 + x_1 - 10 = 2(2^2) + 2 - 10 = 0$$

When $x_2 = x_1 + dx = 2 + 1 = 3$,

$$y_2 = 2x_2^2 + x_2 - 10 = 2(3^2) + 3 - 10 = 11$$
$$\Delta y = y_2 - y_1 = 11 - 0 = 11$$
$$dy = 9$$

2. $y = x^3 - 4x^2$

$$dy = d(x^3 - 4x^2) = 3x^2\,dx - 8x\,dx$$

Let $x_1 = 3$, and $dx = 2$.

$$dy = 3(3^2)(2) - 8(3)(2) = 54 - 48 = 6$$

To compare dy with Δy: When $x_1 = 3$,

$$y_1 = 3^3 - 4(3^2) = 27 - 36 = -9$$

When $x_2 = x_1 + dx = 3 + 2 = 5$,

$$y_2 = 5^3 - 4(5^2) = 125 - 100 = 25$$
$$\Delta y = y_2 - y_1 = 25 - (-9) = 34$$

In this case the difference between Δy and dy is considerable because the differential of the independent variable (dx) was intentionally made large, and because of the nature of the function.

PROBLEMS

1. Find the limits of the following sequences:
   (a) $1, \frac{1}{2}, \frac{1}{3}, \frac{1}{4}, \frac{1}{5}, \ldots$
   (c) $2, \frac{5}{2}, \frac{8}{3}, \frac{11}{4}, \frac{14}{5}, \ldots$
   (b) $0.9, 0.99, 0.999, 0.9999, \ldots$
   (d) $2, \frac{5}{2}, \frac{10}{3}, \frac{17}{4}, \frac{26}{5}, \ldots$

2. From the examples in this chapter, list theorems on limits for constants, sums, differences, products, quotients, and roots of functions.

3. State the concept of the limit in terms of

$$\lim_{x \to a} f(x) = A$$

4. A pure mathematical definition for the limit is that

$$\lim_{x \to a} f(x) = A$$

   if for any chosen positive number ϵ, however small, there exists a positive number δ, usually dependent on ϵ, such that whenever

$$0 < |x - a| < \delta$$

   then graphically $|f(x) - A| < \epsilon$. Illustrate the meaning of this definition. What does this imply about how $x \to a$?

5. Give a pure mathematical definition for the following limits (see problem 4):

   (a) $\lim_{x \to a} f(x) = \infty$
   (c) $\lim_{x \to \infty} f(x) = A$

   (b) $\lim_{x \to a} f(x) = -\infty$
   (d) $\lim_{x \to \infty} f(x) = \infty$

6. Evaluate the following limits using the pure mathematical definitions as given in problems 4 and 5, and check with some numerical values for ϵ and δ:

   (a) $\lim_{x \to 4} (5x - 2) = 18$
   (c) $\lim_{x \to 0} \frac{1}{x} = \infty$

   (b) $\lim_{x \to 3} x^2 = 9$ choose $\delta < 1$ first

7. Evaluate the following limits:

(a) $\lim\limits_{x \to -1} (x^3 + 3x^2 + 3x + 1)$

(i) $\lim\limits_{h \to 0} \dfrac{(x + h)^3 - x^3}{h}$

(b) $\lim\limits_{x \to 5} \sqrt{169 - x^2}$

(j) $\lim\limits_{x \to \infty} \dfrac{x^3 + x^2 + x + 1}{x + 1}$

(c) $\lim\limits_{x \to 1} \dfrac{x^3 + 4x^2 + x - 6}{x - 1}$

(k) $\lim\limits_{x \to \infty} \dfrac{x^2 + 2}{x^4 + 2x^2 + 1}$

(d) $\lim\limits_{x \to 2} \dfrac{x^2 - 3x + 2}{(x - 2)^2}$

(l) $\lim\limits_{x \to 0} \dfrac{x^2}{x^2 + 1}$

(e) $\lim\limits_{x \to 3} \dfrac{x - 3}{x^2 + x - 12}$

(m) $\lim\limits_{x \to -\infty} \dfrac{5^x - 5^{-x}}{5^x + 5^{-x}}$

(f) $\lim\limits_{x \to 0} \dfrac{7x^2 + 5x + 2}{3x + 1}$

(n) $\lim\limits_{x \to \infty} \dfrac{3x^5 + 2x + 1}{5x^5 + 4x^4 + 3x}$

(g) $\lim\limits_{x \to 0} \dfrac{2^x - 2^{-x}}{3^x + 3^{-x}}$

(o) $\lim\limits_{x \to 0} \dfrac{\sqrt{9 + x} - 3}{x}$

(h) $\lim\limits_{x \to x_1} \dfrac{x^3 - x_1^3}{x - x_1}$

8. Illustrate that the limit of a function exists if and only if the limit from the positive direction is equal to the limit from the negative direction, using the function

$$f(x) = \frac{|x|}{x} \quad \text{as } x \to 0, \text{ i.e. } (x \to 0^+ \text{ and } x \to 0^-)$$

9. What is the limit of the polynomial if

$$\lim\limits_{x \to \infty} \frac{a_0 x^m + a_1 x^{m-1} + \cdots + a_m}{b_0 x^n + b_1 x^{n-1} + \cdots + b_n}$$

when

(a) $m = n$ (b) $m > n$ (c) $m < n$

for m and n positive integers?

10. A function $f(x)$ is continuous at $x = x_0$ if (1) $f(x_0)$ is defined, (2) $\lim\limits_{x \to x_0} f(x)$ exists, and (3) $\lim\limits_{x \to x_0} f(x) = f(x_0)$. Check these functions for continuity.

(a) $f(x) = x^3 + x^2 + x + 1$

(c) $f(x) = \dfrac{x^2 - 9}{x - 3}$

(b) $f(x) = \dfrac{1}{x - 1}$

(d) $f(x) = \sqrt{9 - x^2}$

11. Do theorems on limits of sums, products, quotients, etc., apply to continuous functions? What is true for polynomials and rational functions? What is the property of a graph of a continuous function?

12. A pure mathematical definition of a continuous function $f(x)$ is that $f(x)$ is continuous at $x = x_0$ if for any positive number ϵ, however small, there exists a positive number δ such that whenever $|x - x_0| < \delta$ then $|f(x) - f(x_0)| < \epsilon$. Compare this definition with the one for a limit. Use this definition to prove the following functions are continuous:

(a) $f(x) = x$ at point $x = x_0$

(b) $f(x) = x^2$ at point $x = 3$ by choosing $\delta < 1$ first

13. A function $f(x)$ is uniformly continuous in an interval if for any positive number ϵ, however small, there exists a positive number δ such that whenever $|x_1 - x_2| < \delta$ for any two points x_1 and x_2 in the interval, then $|f(x_1) - f(x_2)| < \epsilon$. Compare uniform continuity and continuity. Prove that the functions are uniformly continuous:

(a) $f(x) = x^2 + 1$ for $2 < x < 6$

(b) $f(x) = x^3$ for $0 < x < 2$

14. Find $\Delta y / \Delta x$ for the following:

(a) $y = x^3$

(e) $y = \dfrac{x}{x + 1}$

(b) $y = x^2 + x + 1$

(f) $y = \dfrac{x - 1}{x + 1}$

(c) $y = \sqrt{x}$

(g) $y = x + \dfrac{1}{x}$

(d) $y = \dfrac{1}{x}$

(h) $y = 2x^2 + 3x$

15. Find $\lim\limits_{\Delta x \to 0} \Delta y / \Delta x$ for the functions given in problem 14.

16. Find dy/dx:

(a) $y = 10\frac{2}{3}$

(p) $y = \dfrac{4x^2}{(x-5)^2}$

(b) $y = 19x$

(q) $y = \dfrac{2x-3}{x^2+2}$

(c) $y = 12x^3$

(r) $y = (5x^4 + 4x^3 + 3x^2 + 2x + 1)^6$

(d) $y = 2000$

(s) $y = x^2(x^3 - 1)^3$

(e) $y = 6x^2 + 5x + 1$

(t) $y = \dfrac{\sqrt{x-1}}{x+1}$

(f) $y = x^{1/3}$

(u) $y = \left(\dfrac{x}{x-1}\right)^6$

(g) $y = ax^n + bx^{n-1} + \dfrac{c}{x^n}$

(v) $y = \sqrt{x} + \sqrt{x}$

(h) $y = x^3 + x^{-5}$

(w) $x = y^3 + y$

(i) $y = 4x^{-1/2} + 3x^{-1/3}$

(x) $y = \dfrac{x}{\sqrt{x}}$

(j) $y = \sqrt{x^2} + x + 1$

(y) $y = \dfrac{x}{\sqrt{x+1}}$

(k) $y = (x^3 + 3x^2 + 3x + 1)^2$

(z) $x = \sqrt{y^2 + y}$

(l) $y = 45x^3$

(i) $xy = 1 + x + \dfrac{1}{x} + x^2$

(m) $y = (x-1)^2(x^2 + x)^3$

(ii) $y = \dfrac{1}{2-x}$

(n) $y = (2x^2)^{1/3}(5x^2 + 1)^4$

(iii) $y = \left(\dfrac{x^2}{x+1}\right)^{-1}$

(o) $y = \dfrac{x}{x-5}$

17. Find the dy/dx of these implicit functions:

(a) $x^2 + y^2 + xy = 1$

(d) $b^2x^2 + a^2y^2 = a^2b^2$

(b) $x^2y + y^2x = x$

(e) $16x^2 - 25y^2 = 400$

(c) $x + y + xy = 7$

(f) $x^3y + y^3x = xy$

18. Find dy/dx for the following:

(a) $y = \dfrac{v}{v - 1}$, $v = (x + 1)^2$

(b) $y = v^2\sqrt{v^2 + v + 1}$, $v = (x^2 + x + 1)$

(c) $y = v^2$, $v = v^2 + 3v + 1$, $v = 2x + 3$

(d) $y = v^3 + 1$ $v = x^2 + x$

19. Find dy/dx when x and y are in parametric form.

(a) $x = t$, $y = 3t^2$

(b) $x = 2t^2 + t + 1$, $y = 6t + 10$

(c) $x = t^3$, $y = -\dfrac{1}{t}$

(d) $x = (t^2 + 1)^3$, $y = \sqrt{t^2 + 1}$

20. The derivative of $f(x)$ at $x = x_0$ is defined as

$$f'(x_0) = \lim_{\Delta x \to 0} f(x_0 + \Delta x) - f'(x_0) = \lim_{\Delta x \to 0} \frac{f(x + \Delta x) - f(x_0)}{\Delta x}$$

if the limit exists. If $\Delta x = x - x_0$, give another definition of the derivative.

21. Give a pure mathematical definition of the derivative of a function $f(x)$ at $x = x_0$ using the "ϵ, δ" notation (see problems 4 and 12).

22. Find the derivative of $f(x) = |x|$ at $x = 0$ by taking the limit from both the positive side and the negative side. What does this imply?

23. If $\Delta f(x) = f(x + \Delta x) - f(x)$, then prove

(a) $\Delta[\Delta f(x)] = \Delta^2 f(x) = f(x + 2\,\Delta x) - 2f(x + \Delta x) + f(x)$

(b) $\Delta[\Delta^2 f(x)]$

$$= \Delta^3 f(x) = f(x + 3\,\Delta x) - 3f(x + 2\,\Delta x) + 3f(x + \Delta x) - f(x)$$

(c) $\lim\limits_{\Delta x \to 0} \dfrac{\Delta^n f(x)}{(\Delta x)^n} = f^{(n)}(x)$

24. Use the definition of the derivative to prove that if $f'(x) = 0$ in an interval, then $f(x)$ is a constant in the interval.

25. If $f(x)$ has a derivative at $x = x_0$, then prove that $f(x)$ is continuous at $x = x_0$.

26. Find dy/dx:

(a) $x = y^3$

(b) $x = 6y^2 + 4y + 1$

(c) $x = \sqrt{y^3 + 1}$

(d) $2xy = y^5 + y^3 + y$

(e) $8y^2x = 1 + 16y^4$

(f) $x = U^2 + 1$

$U = y^2 + y$

27. Find the order of the derivative specified and evaluate at the point specified.

(a) $f(x) = 3x^2 + 2x^2 + x$ $f'(2)$

(b) $f(x) = \sqrt{x^2 - 1}$ $f'(4)$

(c) $f(x) = 6x^5 + 3x^2 + 1$ $f'''(-2)$

(d) $f(x) = 10x^3 + 2x + 7$ $f'''(3)$

(e) $f(x) = \dfrac{x - 1}{x^2 + 1}$ $f'(1)$

(f) $f(x) = x^{1/3}$ $f''(0)$

(g) $f(x) = x^4 + x^2 + 1$ $f^{(5)}(1)$

(h) $f(x) = \dfrac{x^2}{2 - x}$ $f''(2)$

(i) $f(x) = \dfrac{1}{x^2}$ $f'''(-1)$

(j) $f(x) = \dfrac{1}{x} + x^2$ $f''(-2)$

28. Use (a) the binomial theorem and (b) mathematical induction to prove

$$\frac{d}{dx} x^n = nx^{n-1}$$

29. If U is a differentiable function of x and $y = U^{p/q}$ for p and q integers, $q > 0$, and $p/q < 1$, then prove

$$\frac{dy}{dx} = \frac{p}{q} U^{(p/q)-1} \frac{dU}{dx}$$

30. Find the dy/dx and evaluate:

(a) $xy + x + y = 1$ at $(2, 2)$ (b) $x^2 + y^2 + xy = 4$ at $(1, 3)$

31. Find d^2y/dx^2 implicitly for the following:

(a) $x^2 - y^2 = 16$ (b) $x^2 + y^2 = 25$

32. If the

$$\lim_{x \to a} \frac{f(x)}{g(x)}$$

is of the form $0/0$ or ∞/∞, and $f(x)$ and $g(x)$ are differentiable, then

$$\lim_{x \to a} \frac{f(x)}{g(x)} = \lim_{x \to a} \frac{f'(x)}{g'(x)} \qquad \text{if } g'(x) \neq 0$$

This is L'Hospital's rule, and can be repeated if $f'(x)$ and $g'(x)$ satisfy the indeterminant form. Apply L'Hospital's rule:

(a) $\lim\limits_{x \to \infty} \dfrac{4x^2 + 2x + 5}{7x^2 + 6x + 2}$

(b) $\lim\limits_{x \to 4} \dfrac{x^4 - 256}{x - 4}$

(c) $\lim\limits_{x \to -1} \dfrac{x^3 - x^2 - x + 1}{2x^3 + 3x^2 + 3x + 2}$

(d) $\lim\limits_{x \to 0} \dfrac{x^2 + x + 4}{x^2 + 3x + 1}$

(e) $\lim\limits_{x \to 1} \dfrac{x^3 + 3x^2 + 3x + 1}{x^4 + 5x^3 + 9x^2 + 7x + 2}$

33. Illustrate graphically the meaning of (a) Rolle's theorem: If $f(x)$ is continuous for $a \leq x \leq b$ and $f'(x)$ exists for $a < x < b$, and $f(a) = f(b) = 0$, then $f'(x) = 0$ for at least one value of x between a and b; and (b) Mean Value theorem: If $f(x)$ is continuous for $a \leq x \leq b$ and $f'(x)$ exists for $a < x < b$, then there is at least one value of x, say x_0, between a and b such that

$$\frac{f(b) - f(a)}{b - a} = f'(x_0)$$

34. If u, v, and w are differentiable functions of x, find $(d/dx)\,(uvw)$.

35. Use mathematical induction to verify

$$\frac{d^n}{dx^n}\,[xf(x)] = x\,\frac{d^n}{dx^n} f(x) + n\,\frac{d^{n-1}}{dx^{n-1}} f(x)$$

36. Verify the following:

(a) $\dfrac{1}{3}\dfrac{d^2y}{dx^2} + \dfrac{1}{x}\dfrac{dy}{dx} = 0 \qquad$ for $x^2 y = 6$

(b) $\dfrac{d^3y}{dx^3} + \left(\dfrac{3}{y}\right)\left(\dfrac{dy}{dx}\right)\left(\dfrac{d^2y}{dx^2}\right) = 0 \qquad$ for $x^2 - y^2 = 1$

(c) $\dfrac{d^3y}{dx^3} + x\dfrac{d^2y}{dx^2} - \dfrac{dy}{dx} = -6 \qquad$ for $y = 2x^2 + 6x$

37. If

$$\epsilon = \frac{\Delta y}{\Delta x} - \frac{dy}{dx}$$

show that as $\Delta x \to 0$ then $\epsilon \to 0$ for:

(a) $y = x^3$ (c) Solve for Δy, for $\epsilon = \frac{\Delta y}{\Delta x} - \frac{dy}{dx}$

(b) $y = 3x^2 + x$

38. Find the differential, dy, for the following:

(a) $y = x^7$ (d) $x^4 + x^2 y^2 + y^4 = 7$

(b) $y = 5x^6 + 4x^2 + 2$ (e) $y = \frac{x^2 + 1}{3 - 2x}$

(c) $y = 2x^2 + x$

39. Using differentials, find dy/dx:

(a) $9xy - 3x - 6y - 5 = 0$
(b) $x^2 + 3xy + 4y^2 - 2x + 5y + 9 = 0$

40. Prove $\lim_{\Delta x \to 0} \frac{\Delta y - dy}{\Delta x} = 0$.

41. Compute Δy, dy, and $\Delta y - dy$ for the following:

(a) $y = x^2 + 5x$, $x = 4$ $dx = 1$

(b) $y = x^3 + x + 1$ $x = 2$ $dx = 0.1$

(c) $y = \frac{1}{x} + x^2$ $x = 3$ $dx = 0.01$

(d) $y = 4x^2$ $x = 100$ $dx = 10$

6

ECONOMIC APPLICATIONS
OF DERIVATIVES

The usual distinction between classical economics and neoclassical economics is the use by neoclassical economists of a method called *marginal analysis*, concerned with the measurement of the rate of change in some economic variable relative to changes in another variable. Thus marginal cost is the change in cost associated with some specific change in quantity produced. Marginal revenue is the change in revenue associated with a change in quantity. Used in this sense, marginal cost is the first derivative of the total cost function, and marginal revenue is the first derivative of total revenue.

With the rise of neoclassical economics, the mathematical techniques of calculus became an important and integral part of economic analysis. The purpose of this chapter is to discuss some of the applications of the concept of derivatives in economic theory.

THE THEORY OF DEMAND

The neoclassical theory of demand assumes that in the consumption of most goods, the phenomenon of diminishing marginal utility applies. If $U = f(Q)$, where U is an index of utility and Q is the quantity consumed of some good, then $f'(Q)$ is postulated to be a decreasing function, resulting in a negative $f''(Q)$.

As an illustration, assume a utility function of the form

$$U = 10Q - Q^2$$

Marginal utility is the rate of change of total utility with respect to the quantity of the good consumed, or symbolically

$$MU = \frac{dU}{dQ} = 10 - 2Q$$

Marginal utility is a decreasing function. As quantity Q increases without limit, MU decreases without limit. When plotted out, the marginal utility curve is a negatively sloping curve. The slope of marginal utility is

$$\frac{d(MU)}{dQ} = \frac{d^2U}{dQ^2} = -2$$

Given these particular assumptions about the nature of the utility function, some interesting observations about the likely behavior of a consumer can be made. Consider the case of a consumer who is making a decision about the quantities of some two goods which he might buy, in the light of the prices of the two goods and the income which he has available to spend on them. The consumer can maximize his total utility by adjusting his consumption of the goods to the level where the ratio of the marginal utility of the first good to its price exactly equals the ratio of the marginal utility of the second good to its price. Maximum utility is achieved when

$$\frac{MU_A}{P_A} = \frac{MU_B}{P_B}$$

To illustrate consumption equilibrium in the case of two goods consider the following example:

1. The total utility function for the consumption of good A is given by

$$U_A = 36Q_A - 2Q_A^2$$

The marginal utility of good A is the first derivative of U_A with respect to Q_A:

$$\frac{d(U_A)}{dQ_A} = 36 - 4Q_A$$

2. The total utility function for the consumption of good B is given by the equation

$$U_B = 20Q_B - Q_B^2$$

The marginal utility is

$$\frac{d(U_B)}{dQ_B} = 20 - 2Q_B$$

3. Let the price of good A be \$4, and the price of good B be \$2; so that

$$P_A = 4 \quad \text{and} \quad P_B = 2$$

Assume further that the consumer has a total of \$20 to be spent on goods A and B in a given period of time. Then the consumer's budget equation would be

$$4Q_A + 2Q_B = 20$$

4. Equilibrium of consumption will be found at those values of Q_A and Q_B where

$$\frac{d(U_A)}{dQ_A} \bigg/ P_A = \frac{d(U_B)}{dQ_B} \bigg/ P_B$$

subject to the constraint

$$P_A Q_A + P_B Q_B = 20$$

5. These conditions are fulfilled by the following equations. (Note that the first equation sets up the condition for equilibrium, and the second equation introduces the budget constraint.)

$$\frac{36 - 4Q_A}{4} = \frac{20 - 2Q_B}{2} \tag{1}$$

$$4Q_A + 2Q_B = 20 \tag{2}$$

The values of Q_A and Q_B satisfying both (1) and (2) will maximize the consumer's total utility subject to the budget constraint. Simplifying (1) yields

$$9 - Q_A = 10 - Q_B \tag{3}$$

Solving (2) for Q_A,

$$Q_A = 5 - 0.5Q_B \tag{4}$$

Substituting (4) into (3), and solving for Q_B gives

$$9 - (5 - 0.5Q_B) = 10 - Q_B$$
$$4 + 0.5Q_B = 10 - Q_B$$
$$1.5Q_B = 6$$
$$Q_B = 4$$

Substituting $Q_B = 4$ into the original budget constraint equation, solve for the equilibrium value of Q_A:

$$4Q_A + (2)(4) = 20$$
$$4Q_A = 12$$
$$Q_A = 3$$

6. Substituting the values $Q_A = 3$ and $Q_B = 4$ into the budget constraint equation shows that the total expenditure on good A and good B just equals the budget:

$$4(3) + 2(4) = 12 + 8 = 20$$

7. When $Q_A = 3$ and $Q_B = 4$ are substituted into (1), the result is

$$\frac{36 - 4(3)}{4} = \frac{20 - 2(4)}{2}$$
$$24/4 = 12/2$$
$$6 = 6$$

Thus the consumer equates the ratio of the marginal utility of good A to its price, to the ratio of the marginal utility of good B to its price. This combination of the two goods is the utility-maximizing combination subject to the consumer's budget constraint.

The consumer's achievement of this utility-maximizing equilibrium consumption of the two goods depends on his ability to conceptualize his marginal utility, which is in fact the first derivative of his total utility function.

ELASTICITY

One of the useful and suggestive tools of economic analysis is the concept of *elasticity*. There are several widely used measures of elasticity. Three in particular will be considered here: price elasticity of demand, cross elasticity of demand, and income elasticity of demand.

Price Elasticity

Price elasticity measures the ratio of a percentage change in quantity demanded to a given percentage change in price of the good under consideration. The formula for price elasticity is

$$\frac{\Delta Q/Q}{\Delta P/P} = \frac{\Delta Q}{\Delta P}\frac{P}{Q}$$

In terms of limits, the formula for price elasticity of demand becomes

$$e = \frac{dQ}{dP}\frac{P}{Q}$$

The first formulation of elasticity involving ΔQ and ΔP is used for the calculation of elasticity over a finite range of the demand curve in which finite changes in quantity and price are assumed to occur. The price elasticity, calculated this way, is known as a measure of *arc* elasticity. In the second formulation, the change in price is allowed to approach zero as a limit, and the resulting calculation of elasticity pertains to a given point on the demand curve. Such a measure of price elasticity is called a *point* elasticity of demand.

Consider first the problems involved in the use of the arc elasticity of demand. Suppose one is interested in calculating some elasticity measure on a demand function

$$Q = 50 - 2P$$

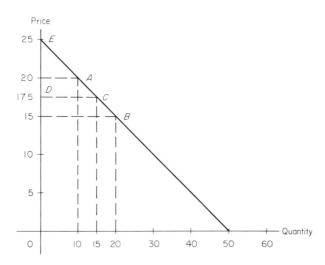

FIGURE 6-1   A Demand Curve with Measurement of Elasticity at Point C

whose demand curve is shown in Figure 6-1. On the demand curve shown in the figure, measure the price elasticity of demand between points A and B. At point A, price is 20 and quantity is 10; at point B, price is 15 and quantity is 20. The increase in quantity is $20 - 10 = 10$ units, and the increment in price (a decrease) is $15 - 20 = -5$ units. Between points A and B the change in quantity and the change in price are known unambiguously. The arc elasticity of demand calculation, however, requires a single price figure P and a single quantity figure Q as well, and it is not clear whether the price and quantity figures for point A or point B should be used. The conventional technique is to use the sum of the two prices for P and the sum of the two quantities for Q. Then the desired measure of price elasticity between points A and B becomes

$$e = \frac{10/30}{-5/35} = \frac{10}{30} \cdot \frac{35}{-5} = -2.33$$

It is necessary to clarify two points relative to the measure of elasticity just calculated. First, the elasticity of demand for most goods will be negative, because of the negative slope of the conventional demand curves. The usual practice is to use the absolute value of the measure of elasticity, with its negativity understood. Second, the measure of elasticity of 2.33 calculated here pertains neither to point A nor to point B on the demand curve. Rather it is an average of the elasticity between points A and B. Therefore, the elasticity measure of 2.33 actually pertains to point C on the demand curve, midway between A and B. At point C the price is 17.5 and the quantity is 15. Price theory textbooks state that the point-elasticity of demand can be shown to be OD/DE. Since $OD = 17.5$ and $DE = 25 - 17.5 = 7.5$, elasticity can be shown to be

$$e = \frac{OD}{DE} = \frac{17.5}{7.5} = 2.33$$

Finally, the price elasticity of demand can be calculated by using the derivative of the demand function. From the demand function,

$$Q = 50 - 2P$$

it is clear that

$$\frac{dQ}{dP} = -2$$

At point C, $P = 17.5$ and $Q = 15$. The price elasticity of demand is therefore

$$e = \frac{(-2)(17.5)}{15} = \frac{(-35)}{15} = -2.33$$

The elasticity of demand as calculated by the geometric method of OD/DE, by the arc formula using finite changes in P and Q, and by the derivative method are the same.

Now consider a demand function of the form

$$Q = \frac{10}{P}$$

The first derivative of such a function is

$$\frac{dQ}{dP} = - \frac{10}{P^2}$$

Elasticity is the derivative times the ratio P/Q, or

$$e = - \frac{10}{P^2} \frac{P}{Q} = - \frac{10}{PQ}$$

Since the original demand function is of the form

$$PQ = 10$$

elasticity is

$$e = - \frac{10}{PQ} = -1$$

The elasticity of demand on such a demand curve equals unity throughout

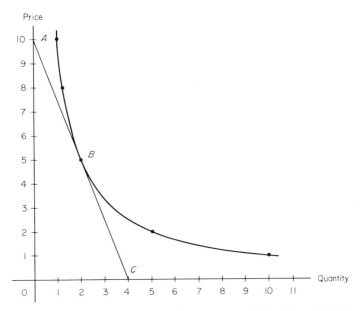

**FIGURE 6-2   A Demand Curve with Measurement of Elasticity at Point B
with the Aid of the Tangent Line AC**

the entire range of the demand curve. The demand curve of the form

$$Q = \frac{10}{P}$$

is plotted in Figure 6-2. On the demand curve, measure the elasticity at
point B, corresponding to $P = 5$ and $Q = 2$. At point B, the slope of the
demand curve is

$$\frac{dP}{dQ} = -\frac{P^2}{10}$$

By the inverse function rule

$$\frac{dQ}{dP} = -\frac{10}{P^2}$$

and so elasticity is

$$\frac{dQ}{dP} \cdot \frac{P}{Q} \quad \text{or} \quad -\frac{10}{P^2} \cdot \frac{P}{Q}$$

Since $P = 5$ and $Q = 2$,

$$e = -\frac{10}{5^2} \cdot \frac{5}{2} = -\frac{50}{50} = -1$$

Geometrically, the line tangent to the demand curve at point B is AC, which measures the slope of the demand curve at point B. Elasticity is then the price at point A minus the price at point B divided by the price at point B, or

$$e = \frac{10 - 5}{5} = 1$$

Cross Elasticity of Demand

In Chapter 3 there is a discussion of a demand function of the form

$$Q_x = P_x + P_1 + 2P_2 - 0.5P_3 + 0.05\,Y$$

The quantity demanded of X was not only a function of the price of X, but also a function of the prices of three other commodities with prices P_1, P_2, and P_3, and of the income of the consumer, Y.

Cross elasticity of demand refers to the ratio of the percentage change in the quantity demanded of X to a given percentage change in the price of one of the other three goods. Thus, if one is to calculate the cross elasticity of demand between good X and the good whose price is designated as P_2, then the formula for cross elasticity is

$$e_c = \frac{\Delta Q_x / Q_x}{\Delta P_2 / P_2} = \frac{\Delta Q_x}{\Delta P_2} \cdot \frac{P_2}{Q_x}$$

Assume that $P_x = 15$, $P_1 = 6$, $P_3 = 20$, and $Y = 100$. The cross elasticity of demand is to be measured at $P_2 = 2$. When $P_2 = 2$, $Q_x = 20$. With the use of these constants for P_x, P_1, P_3, and Y, the demand function becomes a function of one variable, P_2. Then the derivative of the quantity demanded of X with respect to P_2 is

$$\frac{dQ_x}{dP_2} = 2$$

Cross elasticity of demand is given as

$$e_c = \frac{dQ_x}{dP_2} \frac{P_2}{Q_x} = \frac{2(2)}{20} = \frac{4}{20} = 0.2$$

This means that an increase in the price of the second commodity by 1 percent will result in an increase in the quantity demanded of X by 0.2 of 1 percent. When P_2 increases, the quantity demanded of the second commodity is expected to decrease, if it is a normal good. If as the quantity demanded of the second good decreases, there is an increase in the quantity demanded of the good X, then, other things being equal, it can be said that the two goods are substitutes for each other.

The cross elasticity of demand between commodity X and the third commodity, whose price has been designated as P_3, may also be calculated. Assume that the values of P_x, P_1, and Y are unchanged, and that $P_2 = 2$. When $P_3 = 10$, $Q_x = 25$. Cross elasticity is

$$e_c = \frac{dQ_x}{dP_3} \cdot \frac{P_3}{Q_x} = \frac{(-0.5)(10)}{25} = \frac{-5}{25} = -\frac{1}{5} = -0.2$$

The relationship between commodity X and commodity number 3 is such that a 1-percent increase in the price of the third commodity will result in a decrease in the quantity demanded of X by 0.2 of 1 percent. This may mean a complementary relationship between these two goods.

Income Elasticity

Income elasticity of demand measures the percentage change in the quantity demanded of a good as a ratio to a given percentage change in income.

$$e_y = \frac{\Delta Q/Q}{\Delta Y/Y} = \frac{\Delta Q}{\Delta Y} \frac{Y}{Q}$$

This equation can be applied to the same demand function, using the values $P_x = 15$, $P_1 = 6$, $P_2 = 2$, $P_3 = 20$, and $Y = 100$. Then $Q_x = 20$, and the income elasticity of demand can be calculated as follows:

$$e_y = \frac{0.05(100)}{20} = \frac{5}{20} = 0.25$$

This means that a 1 percent increase in income will result in a 0.25 percent increase in the quantity demanded of commodity X.

ELASTICITY OF THE TOTAL REVENUE FUNCTION

Just as price elasticity of demand measures the responsiveness of changes in the quantity demanded to a given proportional change in the price of the product, the price elasticity of total revenue measures the proportion of change in the total sales revenue in response to a given proportional change in the price of the product. Since there are well-known relationships between the price elasticity of demand and total revenue, it would be expected that the elasticity of total revenue is related to the price elasticity of demand.

Conceptually, what is to be measured by the elasticity of sales is the proportion of the percentage change in total revenue to a given percentage change in price. Symbolically, this may be stated as

$$S = \frac{\frac{\Delta(PQ)}{PQ}}{\frac{\Delta P}{P}} = \frac{\Delta(PQ)}{PQ} \cdot \frac{P}{\Delta P} = \frac{\Delta(PQ)}{\Delta P} \cdot \frac{P}{PQ}$$

This statement using $\Delta(PQ)$ and ΔP measures the elasticity of total revenue over a finite range. Obviously it is possible to let ΔP approach zero as a limit and use the derivative notation, which leads to

$$S = \frac{d(PQ)}{dP} \cdot \frac{P}{PQ} \tag{1}$$

Performing the indicated differentiation of (1) yields

$$S = \left[Q + P\frac{dQ}{dP} \right]\frac{1}{Q}$$

$$S = 1 + \frac{P}{Q}\frac{dQ}{dP} \tag{2}$$

Since the price elasticity of demand is defined as

$$e = - \frac{P}{Q}\frac{dQ}{dP}$$

then $S = 1 - e$. As it turns out, the price elasticity of total revenue is simply 1 minus the price elasticity of demand.

In economic theory, the critical value of the price elasticity of demand is the number 1. If the absolute value of the price elasticity of demand is less than 1, the demand function at that point (or over that range) is said to be inelastic; if greater than 1, elastic; if equal to 1, the price elasticity is said to be unitary.

In the case of the price elasticity of total revenue, the critical value occurs at $S = 0$. When the price elasticity of demand e is greater than 1, the price elasticity of total revenue is negative. When the price elasticity of demand is less than 1, the price elasticity of total revenue is positive. When the price elasticity of demand is equal to 1, the price elasticity of total revenue is zero.

These relationships are most clearly seen geometrically.

The upper diagram of Figure 6-3 shows a demand curve and its accompanying marginal revenue curve with the axes reversed. The price

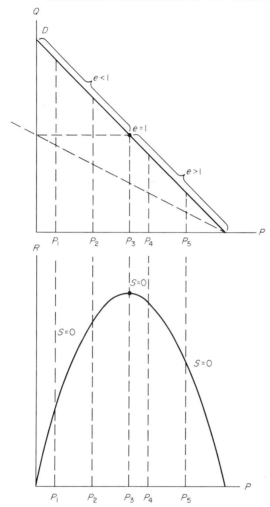

FIGURE 6-3   The Relationship Between the Elasticity of Sales Revenue and the Elasticity of Demand

axis is horizontal and the quantity axis is vertical. The further to the right one moves along the horizontal price axis, the greater is the price, and the further up one moves along the vertical quantity axis the greater is the quantity demanded. The elasticity of demand is less than 1 on that portion of the demand curve in which quantity is large and price is low. The price elasticity of demand is equal to 1 at the mid-point of this linear demand curve. Finally, $e > 1$ in that part of the demand curve associating high prices with low quantities demanded.

As price is increased from P_1 to P_2 in the range of inelastic demand, total revenue rises as shown in the lower diagram of Figure 6-3. In this range the price elasticity of total revenue is positive. At P_3, the demand curve has price elasticity of 1, and marginal revenue of zero. Correspondingly, the total revenue function is at its maximum, and the price elasticity of total revenue is $S = 0$. As price increases from P_4 to P_5 in the range of elastic demand, total revenue falls. Between P_4 and P_5, the price elasticity of total revenue is negative.

The relationship between the elasticity of demand and the price elasticity of total revenue becomes apparent from this discussion.

MARGINAL REVENUE

Marginal revenue is defined as the rate of change of total revenue with respect to quantity; in other words, marginal revenue is the first derivative of the total revenue function relative to quantity:

$$MR = \frac{d(PQ)}{dQ} = P + Q\frac{dP}{dQ}$$

Factoring P out of the right-hand member of the equation yields

$$MR = P\left[1 + \left(\frac{Q}{P}\cdot\frac{dP}{dQ}\right)\right]$$

The term in parentheses is exactly the inverse of the elasticity. And since elasticity of demand is always negative,

$$MR = P\left(1 - \frac{1}{e}\right)$$

Some helpful relationships emerge from this formulation of marginal revenue. It appears that when $e = 1$, marginal revenue will be equal to zero. As e approaches infinity, marginal revenue and price will be equal. In the case of a firm operating under conditions of perfect competition, the elasticity of demand is infinite, and average revenue is equal to marginal revenue. Such a situation is confirmed in the equation above. As elasticity of demand approaches zero as a limit, marginal revenue will approach negative infinity as a limit. Some additional relationships of interest result from rearranging the last expression for marginal revenue and solving it for e. From

$$MR = P\left(1 - \frac{1}{e}\right)$$

comes

$$MR = P - \frac{P}{e}$$

Multiplying both sides of the equation by e gives

$$MR(e) = P(e) - P$$

Simplifying and solving for e yields

$$e = \frac{P}{P - MR}$$

This formulation of elasticity is helpful in understanding the relationships among total revenue, marginal revenue, and elasticity (see Figure 6-4). Since marginal revenue is the first derivative of the total revenue

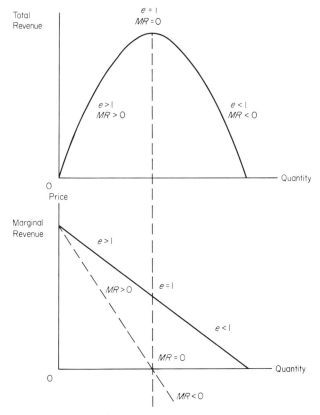

FIGURE 6-4   The Relationships Among Total Revenue, Elasticity of Demand, and Marginal Revenue

function, when marginal revenue is positive, total revenue is increasing. When marginal revenue is positive, the denominator $P - MR$ will be less than the numerator P in the expression for elasticity. Elasticity will, therefore, be greater than 1.

When marginal revenue is equal to zero, total revenue is at a stationary value (say at a maximum). Marginal revenue being at zero, the denominator $P - MR$ in the expression for elasticity will equal P. The denominator and the numerator will be the same, and the ratio will equal 1.

When marginal revenue is negative, total revenue is decreasing. In this case, $P - (-MR) = P + MR$. Thus the denominator of the expression for elasticity becomes greater than the numerator, and the value of the elasticity becomes less than 1.

There is yet another well-known relationship in economics, the relationship between average values and marginal values. To show this relationship, it is necessary to review the formulation for marginal revenue:

$$MR = AR + Q \frac{d(AR)}{dQ}$$

AR (average revenue) has been substituted for P (price) in the earlier formulation. When average revenue is decreasing, $d(AR)/dQ$ will be negative. Marginal revenue will, in that event, be less than average revenue by the amount of the product, Q times the negative rate of change of average revenue. This means that when average revenue is falling, marginal revenue will be less than average revenue.

If for some reason (the Giffin case), the average revenue is increasing, then $d(AR)/dQ$ will be positive. Marginal revenue will be greater than average revenue by the amount of the product, Q times the positive rate of change of average revenue. This means that when average revenue is rising, marginal revenue will be greater than average revenue.

When average revenue is constant, its slope will be zero, and $d(AR)/dQ$ will be zero. In this case, marginal revenue will be exactly equal to average revenue.

MARGINAL COST

The definition of *marginal cost* is perfectly analogous to that of marginal revenue. Marginal cost is the rate of change of total cost as quantity of output varies. Marginal cost is the first derivative of the total cost function. Geometrically, marginal cost is the measure of the slope of the total cost curve.

Suppose a total cost function to be

$$C = 100 + 50x - 10x^2 + x^3$$

where C is total cost, and x is the quantity of output. Marginal cost is the derivative of total cost with respect to quantity x:

$$\frac{dC}{dx} = 50 - 20x + 3x^2$$

Notice that the total cost function is a cubic equation, which means

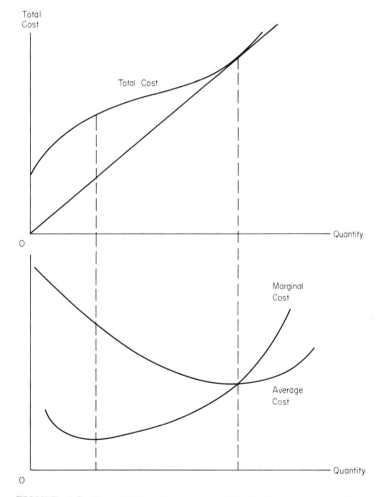

FIGURE 6-5 The Relationships Among Total Cost, Average Cost, and Marginal Cost

that the total cost curve, when plotted, will have two turns. Initially, total cost will increase at a decreasing rate; and at larger quantities of output, total cost will increase at an increasing rate. Marginal cost function is a quadratic equation, indicating that it will have one turn in its curvature. These relationships become clear after taking the second derivative of the total cost function, or the first derivative of the marginal cost function.

$$\frac{d^2C}{dx^2} = -20 + 6x$$

If the second derivative is set equal to zero, and this equation is solved for x, the result is that quantity at which marginal cost is at its minimum. That value of x is found to be $x = 3.33$.

When x is less than 3.33, the second derivative is negative, meaning that the rate of increase of total cost is decreasing. When x is greater than 3.33, the second derivative is positive, indicating an increasing rate of increase of the total cost function. At values of x less than 3.33, the total cost function will be concave downward; at values of x greater than 3.33, the total cost curve will be convex downward.

These relationships are illustrated in Figure 6-5 with the total cost function shown in the upper diagram, and the corresponding average and marginal curves in the lower one.

There is a clear correspondence between the significant points of the total curve and the average and marginal cost curves. Note that when the average cost curve is at its minimum, marginal cost is equal to average cost. When average cost is falling, marginal cost is below average cost. When average cost is rising, marginal cost is above average cost.

ELASTICITY OF TOTAL COST

Yet another application of the derivatives discussed in the previous chapter is the concept of the *elasticity of total cost*.† The elasticity of total cost measures the ratio of the percentage change in total cost to a given percentage change in quantity produced. If a firm produces an output Q at a total cost of $C = f(Q)$, the elasticity of total cost is

$$E_k = \frac{\Delta C/C}{\Delta Q/Q} = \frac{\Delta C}{C} \cdot \frac{Q}{\Delta Q} = \frac{\Delta C}{\Delta Q} \cdot \frac{Q}{C} = \frac{\Delta C/\Delta Q}{C/Q}$$

---

† For another discussion of this topic, see R. G. D. Allen, *Mathematical Analysis for Economists* (London: Macmillan, 1956, p. 260. Also available in paperback, St. Martins, 1967).

Stated in derivative form, this equation becomes

$$E_k = \frac{dC}{dQ} \cdot \frac{Q}{C} = \frac{dC/dQ}{C/Q} \tag{1}$$

The last member of equation (1) clearly shows that the elasticity of total cost is the ratio of the marginal cost dC/dQ to the average cost C/Q.

When the elasticity of total cost is less than 1, a given percentage increase in output Q may be achieved with a less than proportional increase in total cost. Stated another way this is the case in which marginal cost is less than average cost, and average cost is falling.

When the elasticity of total cost is equal to 1, the percentage increase in total cost is exactly equal to the percentage increase in output Q. In this case, marginal cost is equal to average cost and average cost is at its minimum.

When the elasticity of total cost is greater than 1, a given percentage change in output may be achieved with greater than proportional increase in total cost. This is the situation in which marginal cost is greater than average cost, and average cost is rising.

It will be helpful to apply this concept to a specific numerical example. Assume the total cost function

$$C = 20Q - 8Q^2 + Q^3$$

The elasticity of total cost of this function is

$$E_k = \frac{dC/dQ}{C/Q} = \frac{20 - 16Q + 3Q^2}{20 - 8Q + Q^2}$$

First find the value of Q at which this elasticity is equal to unity, which requires

$$\frac{20 - 16Q + 3Q^2}{20 - 8Q + Q^2} = 1$$

this is to say

$$20 - 16Q + 3Q^2 = 20 - 8Q + Q^2$$

or $2Q^2 - 8Q = 0$. Factoring Q gives

$$Q(2Q - 8) = 0$$

This condition is satisfied when $Q = 4$. At $Q = 4$, average cost will be a minimum and marginal cost will equal average cost, as may be demonstrated. When $Q < 4$, it is apparent that marginal cost (the numerator of E_k) will be less than average cost (the denominator), and $E_k < 1$. For all values of $Q > 4$, marginal cost will be greater than average cost, and $E_k > 1$.

LONG-RUN AND SHORT-RUN COSTS

Economists distinguish between long-run costs and short-run costs. In the short run, it is assumed that certain factors of production are fixed in supply, particularly plant and equipment. These fixed factors of production cause certain costs to be fixed; such costs are independent of the quantity of output. In addition, there are variable costs of production, arising from the use of variable production factors such as direct labor. When the plant size is changed, as in an expansion, a greater supply of fixed production factors is committed, and a larger total fixed cost results. The new plant size will also lead to a different set of variable costs.

Assuming that the fixed factors of production can be varied in very small amounts, there can be an infinite number of plant sizes, and an infinite number of corresponding short-run cost functions. These short-run costs of production are of the form

$$K_i = K_i(Q) = f_i(Q) + M_i \qquad i = 1, 2, 3, \ldots, n$$

K_i is the short-run total cost of plant size i; $f_i(Q)$ is the short-run total variable cost of plant size i, and it is a function of output; M_i is the short-run total fixed cost for plant size i, and M_i is fixed at a constant amount once the plant size i is determined. The long-run total cost function may be thought of as the lowest possible total cost (using whatever plant size) at which any given amount of output may be produced. For each short-run total cost, there are corresponding short-run average and short-run marginal cost functions, of the forms

$$\phi_i = \frac{K_i}{Q} = \frac{f_i(Q)}{Q} + \frac{M_i}{Q} \qquad \text{(average cost)}$$

where ϕ_i is the average cost of production using plant size i, and

$$\frac{dK_i}{dQ} = f'_i(Q) \qquad \text{(marginal cost)}$$

Applying the techniques of mathematical analysis already developed permits an examination of the way in which the long-run and short-run cost curves may be constructed. For convenience of exposition, only three short-run cost functions corresponding to a given long-run cost function will be illustrated.

Assume that a firm finds that the lowest long-run average cost of production is achieved at an output of 5 units. Assume further that the minimum average cost of production is achieved with plant size number 2. The total fixed cost of plant size number 2 is 150 and the total cost of production is 225. This indicates that the total variable cost of producing 5 units with plant size 2 is 75. Since the quantity is 5 units, the average variable cost is 15, the average fixed cost is 30, and the average total cost is 45 per unit. The normal total cost curve has first a range of concavity below and then a range of convexity below, meaning that the total cost of production increases initially at a decreasing rate, and then at an increasing rate. Assuming these normal behavior patterns for the short-run total cost function of plant size 2, it may then be assumed that the relevant short-run total cost function is of the form

$$K_2 = A_2 Q^3 - B_2 Q^2 + C_2 Q + M_2 \qquad (1)$$

where K_2 is the total cost function of plant size 2, Q is the quantity of output in appropriate units, and A_2, B_2, and C_2 are constants. M_2 is the total fixed cost which does not vary with output, and is fixed at 150. Since plant size 2 is the optimum plant size, $K_2(Q)$ is tangent to $K_{LR}(Q)$ where

$$\frac{d\phi_2}{dQ} = \frac{d\phi_{LR}}{dQ} = 0$$

$K_2(Q)$ is the total cost function of plant size 2, $K_{LR}(Q)$ is the long-run total cost function, and ϕ_2 and ϕ_{LR} refer to the average cost of plant size 2 and the long-run cost respectively. At this point of tangency,

$$\phi_2 = \frac{K_2}{Q} = A_2 Q^2 - B_2 Q + C_2 + \frac{150}{Q} \qquad (2)$$

$$\frac{d\phi_2}{dQ} = 2A_2 Q - B_2 - \frac{150}{Q^2} = 0 \qquad (3)$$

At $Q = 5$ these equations reduce to

$$\phi_2 = 25A_2 - 5B_2 + C_2 + 30 \qquad (4)$$

$$\frac{d\phi_2}{dQ} = 10A_2 - B_2 - 6 = 0 \qquad (5)$$

Set $A_2 = 1$; then from (5)

$$10 - 6 = B_2 \qquad B_2 = 4$$

Substituting $A_2 = 1$ and $B_2 = 4$ into (1) yields

$$Q^3 - 4Q^2 + C_2 Q + 150 = 225$$

and solving this equation for C_2 at $Q = 5$ gives $C_2 = 10$. Thus the cost function of plant size 2 is

$$K_2 = Q^3 - 4Q^2 + 10Q + 150$$

At this point, consider the long-run total cost and the long-run average cost functions temporarily. It would be expected that the long-run total cost function has the general form

$$K_{LR} = A_{LR}Q^3 - B_{LR}Q^2 + C_{LR}Q \tag{6}$$

Note that in the long-run total cost function, there is no fixed cost. The long-run total cost function begins at zero for zero quantity of output. It also has the property of increasing at a decreasing rate initially and then increasing at an increasing rate. The long-run average cost function is

$$\phi_{LR} = \frac{K_{LR}}{Q} = A_{LR}Q^2 - B_{LR}Q + C_{LR} \tag{7}$$

At $Q = 5$, ϕ_{LR} is at its minimum; that is

$$\frac{d\phi_{LR}}{dQ} = 2A_{LR}Q - B_{LR} = 0$$

Then $10A_{LR} = B_{LR}$. At $Q = 5$, the long-run average cost is

$$\phi_{LR} = 25A_{LR} - 5B_{LR} + C_{LR} = 45 \tag{8}$$

Substituting $B_{LR} = 10A_{LR}$ gives

$$\phi_{LR} = 25A_{LR} - 50A_{LR} + C_{LR} = 45$$

or $-25A_{LR} = 45 - C_{LR}$. Multiplying through by -1 gives

$$A_{LR} = \frac{C_{LR} - 45}{25}$$

Now consider a smaller plant of size 1 whose short-run fixed cost is 100. Assume that the total cost of plant size 1 is tangent to the long-run total cost curve at the quantity $Q = 2$. The short-run total cost function of plant size 1 is of the form

$$K_1 = A_1Q^3 - B_1Q^2 + C_1Q + 100 \tag{9}$$

with an average cost function of

$$\phi_1 = \frac{K_1}{Q} = A_1Q^2 - B_1Q + C_1 + \frac{100}{Q} \tag{10}$$

At $Q = 2$,

$$\frac{d\phi_1}{dQ} = \frac{d\phi_{LR}}{dQ}$$

or

$$2A_1Q - B_1 - \frac{100}{Q^2} = 2A_{LR}Q - B_{LR}$$

It was established earlier that $B_{LR} = 10A_{LR}$; making this substitution and letting $Q = 2$ gives

$$4A_1 - B_1 - 25 = 4A_{LR} - 10A_{LR}$$

Letting $A_1 = 5$,

$$B_1 + 5 = 6A_{LR} \qquad (11)$$

Now assume a large plant of size 3 whose total cost curve is tangent to the long-run total function at the quantity of 6 units. Assume that the total fixed cost of plant size 3 is 180, and that the total cost of producing the 6 units is 276. The average total cost for the 6 units of output is therefore $^{276}\!/_6 = 46$. The total cost function of plant size 3 is of the form

$$K_3 = K_3(Q) = A_3 Q^3 - B_3 Q^2 + C_3 Q + 180 \qquad (12)$$

The average cost of production of plant size 3 is

$$\phi_3 = A_3 Q^2 - B_3 Q + C_3 + \frac{180}{Q} = 46 \qquad (13)$$

At $Q = 6$, the short-run average cost function is tangent to the long-run average cost function; that is

$$\frac{d\phi_3}{DQ} = \frac{d\phi_{LR}}{dQ}$$

which means

$$2A_3 Q - B_3 - \frac{180}{Q^2} = 2A_{LR}Q - B_{LR}$$

Substituting $B_{LR} = 10A_{LR}$ and $Q = 6$,

$$12A_3 - B_3 - 5 = 2A_{LR}$$

Letting $A_3 = 1$,

$$7 - B_3 = 2A_{LR} \qquad (14)$$

Multiplying (14) by 3 yields

$$21 - 3B_3 = 6A_{LR} \qquad (15)$$

Combining (11) and (15),

$$21 - 3B_3 = B_1 + 5$$

If $B_1 = 1$, then $B_3 = 5$. Now at $Q = 2$,

$$K_1 = 5Q^3 - Q^2 + C_1 Q + 100 = 108$$

Solving this equation for C_1 yields $C_1 = -14$. The total cost function of plant size 1 is

$$K_1 = 5Q^3 - Q^2 - 14Q + 100 \qquad (16)$$

The total cost function of plant size 3, at $Q = 6$, is

$$K_3 = Q^3 - 5Q^2 + C_3Q + 180 = 276$$

This equation yields $C_3 = 10$, thus giving the total cost function of plant size 3:

$$K_3 = Q^3 - 5Q^2 + 10Q + 180 \qquad (17)$$

From equation (14),

$$7 - B_3 = 2A_{LR}$$
$$A_{LR} = 1$$

Since $B_{LR} = 10A_{LR}$, $B_{LR} = 10$. Since at $Q = 5$,

$$K_{LR} = Q^3 - 10Q^2 + C_{LR}Q = 225$$

$C_{LR} = 70$, and the required long-run total cost function is

$$K_{LR} = Q^3 - 10Q^2 + 70Q \qquad (18)$$

The cost functions as developed thus far are

$$K_{LR} = Q^3 - 10Q^2 + 70Q \qquad (19)$$
$$K_1 = 5Q^3 - Q^2 - 14Q + 100 \qquad (20)$$
$$K_2 = Q^3 - 4Q^2 + 10Q + 150 \qquad (21)$$
$$K_3 = Q^3 - 5Q^2 + 10Q + 180 \qquad (22)$$

The short-run total cost curve of plant size 1 is tangent to the long-run total cost curve at $Q = 2$; thus at $Q = 2$,

$$K_{LR} = K_1$$

or

$$2^3 - 10(2^2) + 70(2) = 5(2^3) - 2^2 - 14(2) + 100$$
$$108 = 108$$

Economic theory holds that the long-run marginal cost is equal to the short-run marginal cost at the quantity at which the total functions are tangent, i.e.,

$$\frac{dK_{LR}}{dQ} = \frac{dK_1}{dQ} \qquad \text{at} \qquad Q = 2$$

$$\frac{dK_{LR}}{dQ} = 3Q^2 - 20Q + 70$$

Substituting $Q = 2$, the long-run marginal cost is found to be

$$\frac{dK_{LR}}{dQ} = 3(2^2) - 20(2) + 70 = 42$$

The marginal cost of plant size 1 is

$$\frac{dK_1}{dQ} = 15Q^2 - 2Q - 14$$

which at $Q = 2$ is

$$\frac{dK_1}{dQ} = 15(2^2) - 2(2) - 14 = 42$$

At $Q = 5$, $K_{LR} = K_2$, i.e.,

$$5^3 - 10(5^2) + 70(5) = 5^3 - 4(5^2) + 10(5) + 150$$
$$225 = 225$$

It is also required that

$$\frac{dK_{LR}}{dQ} = \frac{dK_2}{dQ} \qquad \text{at} \qquad Q = 5$$

$$3(5^2) - 20(5) + 70 = 3(5^2) - 8(5) + 10$$

$$45 = 45$$

$$\frac{dK_{LR}}{dQ} = \frac{dK_2}{dQ}$$

The short-run total cost function of plant size 3 is tangent to the long-run total cost, i.e.,

$$K_{LR} = K_3 \qquad \text{at} \qquad Q = 6$$
$$6^3 - 10(6^2) + 70(6) = 6^3 - 5(6^2) + 10(6) + 180$$
$$276 = 276$$

Similarly it is required that

$$MC_{LR} = MC_3 \qquad \text{at} \qquad Q = 6$$

that is

$$\frac{dK_{LR}}{dQ} = \frac{dK_3}{dQ} \qquad \text{at} \qquad Q = 6$$

$$3(6^2) - 20(6) + 70 = 3(6^2) - 10(6) + 10$$

$$58 = 58$$

$$\frac{dK_{LR}}{dQ} = \frac{dK_3}{dQ} \qquad \text{at} \qquad Q = 6$$

In this development of the relationship between the long-run cost curve and its various short-run cost curves, only the techniques of mathematics developed up to this point have been used. This discussion employed techniques of algebraic manipulation, analytic geometry (in that the function types for application were chosen to conform to certain generally accepted economic principles), and the application of derivatives in analyzing the relationships among the long-run and short-run cost functions. In the development of this section, arbitrary values are assigned to the parameters A, B, and C. Actually, this is a problem involving 12 equations and 12 unknowns. The use of arbitrary values is for the purpose of shortening the necessary explanation.

In a later chapter, after partial derivatives have been discussed, the problem of long-run and short-run cost functions and their relationships will be considered using the envelope theory, parametric substitution, and partial derivatives.

THE NEOCLASSICAL MACROECONOMIC MODEL

The neoclassical macroeconomic model is built upon several important fundamental assumptions. From these assumptions, through a process of deductive reasoning, one can arrive at the equilibrium values of several of the macroeconomic variables.

1. The neoclassical theory of aggregate economics assumes perfect competition in both the input market and the output market. This implies that, in the output market, the firm's demand function is such that

$$P = MR \quad \text{where} \quad MR = \frac{dR}{dQ}$$

or price is equal to marginal revenue for all quantities. This means that the demand curve facing the firm is perfectly elastic.

2. Each firm is assumed to pursue a goal of profit maximization which requires that the price of the output be equal to the marginal cost of production, i.e.,

$$P = MC \quad \text{where} \quad MC = \frac{dC}{dQ}$$

Marginal cost of production MC may be viewed as the ratio of the increment to total labor cost due to the addition of one more unit of labor, divided by the increment in output from that last unit of labor, or

$$MC = \frac{W}{MPP_L} \quad \text{or} \quad MC = \frac{W}{dQ/dL}$$

where W is the wage rate and MPP_L is the marginal physical productivity of labor. To maximize profit on the input side of the market, the firm will hire labor up to the point where wages are equal to the value of marginal product

$$W = P \cdot MPP_L \qquad \text{or} \qquad W = P \frac{dQ}{dL}$$

Dividing both sides of either of these equations by P,

$$\frac{W}{P} = MPP_L \qquad \text{or} \qquad \frac{W}{P} = \frac{dQ}{dL}$$

which is to say that the real wage rate W/P is equal to the marginal physical product. This statement indicates that the employment of labor is a function of the real wage rate W/P, the money wage rate W deflated by the price level. It is important to establish the connection between the condition of profit maximization on the output side

$$MC = MR$$

with the condition of profit maximization on the input side

$$W = P \cdot MPP_L$$

Dividing this equation by MPP_L yields

$$\frac{W}{MPP_L} = P$$

but earlier W/MPP_L was defined as MC. So the profit maximizing behavior in the input market really is the act of establishing $MC = P$ or $MC = MR$ under pure competition.

3. The neoclassicists assume that the total product function is a function of the employment of labor, $Q = f(L)$, and further they assume that the production function is such that

$$\frac{dQ}{dL} > 0 \qquad \frac{d^2Q}{dL^2} < 0$$

This means that while the total product function is a positively sloped function, the rate of increase of that function is declining.

4. The supply of labor is assumed to be positively sloped and functionally dependent upon the real wage rate; that is

$$L = g\left(\frac{W}{P}\right)$$

where L is the quantity of labor supplied, and

$$\frac{dL}{d(W/P)} > 0$$

5. In order to determine the price level, the money wage level, and the several other variables, the neoclassical quantity theory of money is also needed. This is a statement of the demand behavior of cash balance, and may be stated as

$$m = k(PQ)$$

where m is the cash balance demanded, and k is the proportion of the money value of goods and services over which the economy wishes to hold command in the form of cash balances.

Combining all of these elements, the neoclassicists developed their macroeconomic model to determine the level of employment of labor, the real wage rate, the money wage rate, the price level, and the level of output of goods and services.

To illustrate the process of the neoclassical approach to the macro-economic problem, assume the following numerical example:

1. $Q = f(L) = 20L - L^2$ (production function)

   $MPP_L = \dfrac{dQ}{dL} = 20 - 2L$ (marginal product of labor)

2. $\dfrac{W}{P} = 2L$ (supply of labor)

Since in the labor market the real wage rate, W/P, and the amount of labor employed, L, are determined by the demand for labor, dQ/dL, and the supply of labor, solve by establishing the equality

$$20 - 2L = 2L$$

$$L = 5$$

At $L = 5$

$$\frac{W}{P} = 10$$

3. When $L = 5$, the output of the economy may be determined by substitution into the production function

$$Q = 20(5) - 5^2 = 100 - 25 = 75$$

4. At this point certain parameters of the demand function for money must be assumed. Let the demand for money

$$m = k(PQ)$$

be of the form

$$100 = \tfrac{1}{3}(P75)$$

where $m = 100$, and $k = \tfrac{1}{3}$. This gives the price level $P = 4$.

5. With the price level established at $P = 4$, it is evident that the money wage rate must be 40 if the real wage rate, already determined to be 10, is to hold.

This numerical example of the neoclassical model, then, has used assumed parameters for the quantity theory of money,

$$m = 100 \qquad k = \tfrac{1}{3}$$

and has developed the following values:

labor:	$L = 5$
quantity:	$Q = 75$
wage rate:	$W = 40$
price:	$P = 4$
real wage rate:	$W/P = 10$

MARGINAL PROPENSITY
TO CONSUME AND TO SAVE

In the discussion of national income theory, certain identities are accepted. It is accepted that the recipients of national income dispose of it in one of two ways: they either consume it or save it. This relationship is represented symbolically by the equation

$$Y = C + S$$

An increment in income is disposed of in the same manner, by either consuming that increment or saving it, or a combination of both. Thus a change in national income results in a change in consumption and a change in saving:

$$\Delta Y = \Delta C + \Delta S$$

Dividing both sides of the equation by ΔY gives

$$\frac{\Delta Y}{\Delta Y} = \frac{\Delta C}{\Delta Y} + \frac{\Delta S}{\Delta Y} \qquad 1 = \frac{\Delta C}{\Delta Y} + \frac{\Delta S}{\Delta Y}$$

Taking the limiting values of the two ratios in the right-hand member of the last equation, as ΔY approaches zero, results in

$$1 = \frac{dC}{dY} + \frac{dS}{dY}$$

The expression dC/dY is the marginal propensity to consume. It is the rate of change in consumption relative to change in the level of national income. The value of dC/dY is usually assumed to be positive but less than 1. The permissible range of the marginal propensity to consume is, therefore, from 0 to 1 but exclusive of 0 and 1.

The second expression in the right-hand member of the last equation is the marginal propensity to save. It is the rate of change of saving relative to change in the level of national income. Since the sum of the marginal propensity to consume and the marginal propensity to save is equal to 1, the marginal propensity to save equals 1 minus the marginal propensity to consume:

$$\frac{dS}{dY} = 1 - \frac{dC}{dY}$$

Because it is assumed that the value of the marginal propensity to consume ranges between 0 and 1, marginal propensity to save must also be positive and less than 1.

In Chapter 3, the determination of the equilibrium level of national income was discussed and a consumption function of the form

$$C = 100 + 0.6\,Y$$

was used in connection with it. Since the marginal propensity to consume is the first derivative of the consumption function,

$$MPC = \frac{dC}{dY} = 0.6$$

Furthermore, since consumption plus saving is equal to the level of income

$$Y = C + S$$

saving must be equal to income minus consumption, or

$$S = Y - C$$

Therefore, the savings function can be derived from the assumed consumption function by subtracting that function from income, Y:

$$S = Y - (100 + 0.6\,Y)$$
$$S = Y - 100 - 0.6\,Y$$
$$S = -100 + 0.4\,Y$$

Marginal propensity to save is the first derivative of the savings functio n with respect to income. Therefore,

$$MPS = \frac{dS}{dY} = 0.4$$

The calculated values of the marginal propensities to consume and to save are

$$MPC = \frac{dC}{dY} = 0.6 \qquad MPS = \frac{dS}{dY} = 0.4$$

The sum of the marginal propensity to consume and the marginal propensity to save is equal to $0.6 + 0.4 = 1$.

A principle of some importance in the study of national income analysis is the concept of the multiplier. On the simplest level, abstracting out all complications, the multiplier can be defined as the reciprocal of the marginal propensity to save. The usual formulation is

$$k = \frac{1}{\dfrac{dS}{dY}} = \frac{1}{1 - \dfrac{dC}{dY}}$$

where k is the multiplier.

AN ANALYSIS OF INCOME TAXATION AND GOVERNMENT EXPENDITURES

Consider a Keynesian model which includes government expenditures and taxation. The vital element of Keynesian models is the requirement that income is determined by the flow of the product market for a short-run equilibrium. One can start with the following basic conditions:

$$C = C_0 + C(Y_d) \qquad \text{(the consumption function)} \qquad (1)$$

$$T = T_0 + T(Y) \qquad \text{(the taxation function)} \qquad (2)$$

The equilibrium condition for the product market in the Keynesian analysis would require

$$Y = C_0 + C(Y_d) + I_0 + G_0 \qquad (3)$$

or alternatively,

$$Y = Y_d + T = Y_d + T_0 + T(Y) \qquad (4)$$

where Y is income, Y_d is disposable income, G_0 is government expenditure, and I_0 is investment. Notice that I_0 and C_0 are autonomous expenditures, T_0 is the fixed component of the tax structure, and G_0 is an exogenous variable.

Now consider the effect on income of changes in government expenditure G. In this case, government expenditure is a variable rather than an exogenously determined constant (G_0). To examine the effect of changes in government expenditure on income, the national income Y and the disposable income Y_d must be differentiated with respect to G. Disposable income is defined by

$$Y_d = C_0 + C(Y_d) + I_0 + G - T_0 - T(Y)$$

where C_0, I_0, and T_0 are all constants. Differentiating gives

$$\frac{dY_d}{dG} = \frac{dC_0}{dG} + \frac{d}{dG}[C(Y_d)] + \frac{dI_0}{dG} + \frac{dG}{dG} - \frac{dT_0}{dG} - \frac{d}{dG}[T(Y)]$$

On the right-hand side, the process of differentiation will reduce the first, the third, and the fifth terms to zero, since C_0, I_0, and T_0 are all constants. The differentiation yields

$$\frac{dY_d}{dG} = \frac{dC}{dY_d} \cdot \frac{dY_d}{dG} + 1 - \frac{dT}{dY} \cdot \frac{dY}{dG}$$

Note that

$$\frac{dC}{dY_d} = c = \text{marginal propensity to consume}$$

and

$$\frac{dT}{dY} = t = \text{marginal rate of taxation}$$

Making these substitutions, write

$$\frac{dY_d}{dG} = c\frac{dY_d}{dG} + 1 - t\frac{dY}{dG} \tag{5}$$

Equation (4) states that

$$Y = Y_d + T = Y_d + T_0 + T(Y)$$

Differentiating this function with respect to G yields

$$\frac{dY}{dG} = \frac{dY_d}{dG} + \frac{d}{dG}[T(Y)] = \frac{dY_d}{dG} + \frac{dT}{dY}\frac{dY}{dG}$$

$$\frac{dY}{dG} = \frac{dY_d}{dG} + t\frac{dY}{dG}$$

Rearranging gives

$$\frac{dY_d}{dG} = (1 - t)\frac{dY}{dG} \tag{6}$$

Equation (5) may be written as

$$\frac{dY_d}{dG} = \frac{1 - t\dfrac{dY}{dG}}{1 - c} \tag{7}$$

Equating (6) and (7) and simplifying gives

$$\frac{dY}{dG}[1 - c + ct] = 1$$

$$\frac{dY}{dG} = \frac{1}{1 - c + ct} \qquad (8)$$

Macroeconomic theory holds that

$$1 - c = s = \text{marginal propensity to save}$$

Equation (8), then, may be alternatively stated as

$$\frac{dY}{dG} = \frac{1}{s + (1 - s)t} < \frac{1}{s}$$

This clearly shows that if the government increases its expenditures, with taxes remaining fixed, the effect on national income is less than the multiplier, $1/s$.

Next consider a change in T_0, the fixed component of taxation. Again the first fundamental relations are

$$Y_d = C_0 + C(Y_d) + I_0 + G_0 - T - T(Y) \qquad (1)$$

$$Y = Y_d + T + T(Y) \qquad (2)$$

To measure the effect of the change in the fixed component of the tax on the level of national income, differentiate (1) and (2) with respect to T:

$$\frac{dY_d}{dT} = \frac{dC_0}{dT} + \frac{d}{dT}[C(Y_d)] + \frac{dI_0}{dT} + \frac{dG_0}{dT} - \frac{dT}{dT} - \frac{d}{dT}[T(Y)]$$

$$\frac{dY_d}{dT} = \frac{dC}{dY_d} \cdot \frac{dY_d}{dT} - 1 - \frac{dT(Y)}{dY} \frac{dY}{dT}$$

$$\frac{dY_d}{dT} = c\frac{dY_d}{dT} - 1 - t\frac{dY}{dT}$$

$$\frac{dY_d}{dT} = \frac{-1 - t\dfrac{dY}{dT}}{1 - c} \qquad (3)$$

Differentiating (2) with respect to T gives

$$\frac{dY}{dT} = \frac{dY_d}{dT} + \frac{dT}{dT} + \frac{d}{dT}[T(Y)]$$

$$\frac{dY}{dT} = \frac{dY_d}{dT} + 1 + \frac{dT(Y)}{dY}\frac{dY}{dT} = \frac{dY_d}{dT} + 1 + t\frac{dY}{dT} \qquad (4)$$

Solving (4) for dY_d/dT yields

$$\frac{dY_d}{dT} = (1 - t)\frac{dY}{dT} - 1 \tag{5}$$

Equating expressions (3) and (5) gives

$$\frac{-1 - t(dY/dT)}{1 - c} = (1 - t)\frac{dY}{dT} - 1$$

Solving this equation for dY/dT yields

$$\frac{dY}{dT} = \frac{c}{c(1 - t) - 1} = \frac{1 - s}{(1 - s)(1 - t) - 1} = \frac{1 - s}{t(s - 1) - s}$$

or

$$-\frac{dY}{dT} = \frac{1 - s}{s + t(1 - s)} < \frac{1 - s}{s} \tag{6}$$

Equation (6) shows that as the fixed component of the tax is reduced, the effect on national income is less than the multiplier. When dY/dG and dY/dT are compared, it is apparent that the effect on the national income of an increase in government expenditure is greater than the effect of a decrease in the fixed component of the tax.

As yet a third way of viewing the national income model, consider a change in the tax rate $T(Y)$. For simplicity, consider that the tax rate is the same for all levels of income, i.e.,

$$T = T_0 + tY$$

Start from the same two original propositions,

$$Y_d = C_0 + C(Y_d) + I_0 + G_0 - T_0 - tY \tag{1}$$

$$Y = Y_d + T_0 + tY \tag{2}$$

Differentiating (1) with respect to t gives

$$\frac{dY_d}{dt} = c\frac{dY_d}{dt} - t\frac{dY}{dt} - Y$$

Solving for dY_d/dt gives

$$\frac{dY_d}{dt} = \frac{-t\dfrac{dY}{dt} - Y}{1 - c} \tag{3}$$

Differentiating (2) with respect to t gives

$$\frac{dY}{dt} = \frac{dY_d}{dt} + t\frac{dY}{dt} + Y$$

Solving for dY_d/dt gives

$$\frac{dY_d}{dt} = (1 - t)\frac{dY}{dt} - Y \qquad (4)$$

Equating (3) and (4) gives

$$\frac{-t\dfrac{dY}{dt} - Y}{1 - c} = (1 - t)\frac{dY}{dt} - Y$$

Solving for dY/dt gives

$$\frac{dY}{dt}[1 - c + ct] = -cY$$

$$-\frac{1}{Y}\frac{dY}{dt} = \frac{c}{(1 - c) + ct} = \frac{1 - s}{s + (1 - s)t} < \frac{1 - s}{s}$$

The effect of a change for this case is similar to that of a change in the fixed component. The difference is that there is a proportional change in Y which is a multiple of the change in the tax rate.

PROBLEMS

1. The utility function is given; graph it and the marginal utility and show graphically that the marginal utility is negatively sloped:
   (a) $U = 4Q - Q^2$ (c) $U = 20Q - 20Q^2$
   (b) $U = 16Q - 4Q^2$

2. Given two utility functions, find the equilibrium quantity for the marginal utilities.
   (a) $U = 5Q - \frac{1}{4}Q^2$ $U = 8Q - Q^2$
   (b) $U = 4Q - \frac{1}{2}Q^2$ $U = 2Q - \frac{1}{6}Q^2$
   (c) $U = 8Q - \frac{2}{3}Q^2$ $U = 6Q - \frac{1}{3}Q^2$

3. Find the consumer equilibrium, given the utility functions and the budget equation, and check:
   (a) $U_A = 18Q_A - Q_A^2$ $U_B = 32Q - 2Q_B^2$ $Q_A + 2Q_B = 20$
   (b) $U_A = 10Q_A - Q_A^2$ $U_B = 30Q_B - 4Q_B^2$ $2Q_A + 3Q_B = 40$
   (c) $U_A = 20Q_A - Q_A^2$ $U_B = 40Q_B - 2Q_B^2$ $Q_A + Q_B = 50$
   (d) $U_A = 4Q_A - Q_A^2$ $U_B = 4Q_B - 2Q_B^2$ $Q_A + 4Q_B = 6$

4. Define elasticity of demand, explain when demand is elastic, inelastic, and unitary, and show these conditions graphically.

5. Use the point elasticity formula and the arc elasticity formula, and compare the results for the following:

(a) $p_1 = \$100.01$ $q_1 = 9999$ (c) $p_1 = \$50$ $q_1 = 200$
    $p_2 = \$100.00$ $q_2 = 10,000$ $p_2 = \$40$ $q_2 = 250$
(b) $p_1 = \$1.00$ $q_1 = 9$ (d) $p_1 = \$10$ $q_1 = 100$
    $p_2 = \$0.99$ $q_2 = 10$ $p_2 = \$5$ $q_2 = 400$

6. Use derivatives to find the elasticity of demand for the following:

(a) $q = 100 - 4p$ at $p = 9$ (c) $q = 400 - 8p$ at $p = 40$
(b) $q = 250 - 5p$ at $p = 25$ (d) $q = 50 - p$ at $p = 10$

7. Use the arc formula on problem 6 by adding ± 1 to the given p to get 2 prices. Compare the results.

8. Using rules of derivatives, derive the following formulas for the evaluation of elasticities, if

$$q = f(p)$$

and if x and y are single-valued functions of p, where

$$e_q = \frac{p}{q}\frac{dq}{dp}$$

is the notation:

(a) If $q = x \pm y$, then

$$e_q = e_{x \pm y} = \left(\frac{1}{x \pm y}\right)[xe_x \pm ye_y]$$

(b) If $q = xy$, then

$$e_q = e_{xy} = e_x + e_y$$

(c) If $q = x/y$, then

$$e_q = e_{x/y} = e_x - e_y$$

(d) If $q = x + k$, where k is a constant, then

$$e_q = e_{x+k} = \frac{x}{x + k}e_x$$

(e) If $q = kx$, where k is a constant, then

$$e_q = e_{kx} = e_x$$

(f) If $q = kx + c$, where k and c are constants, then

$$e_q = e_{kx+c} = \frac{kx}{kx + c}$$

(g) If $q = kx^c$ where k and c are constants, then

$$e_q = e_{kx^c} = c$$

9. Find the elasticity for the following, and draw conclusions:

(a) $q = \dfrac{12}{p}$ $p = 4, p = 6, p = 2$

(b) $q = \dfrac{16}{p}$ $p = 4, p = 8, p = 2$

(c) $q = \dfrac{1}{p}$ $p = 1, p = \frac{1}{4}$

10. Find the elasticity for the following:

(a) $q = 10{,}000 - p^2$ at $p = 10, 50, 90$
(b) $q = 160 - 4p^2$ at $p = 5, 10, 15$
(c) $q = \dfrac{1000}{p^3}$ at $p = 2, 4, 8$
(d) $q = \dfrac{3125}{p^5}$ at $p = 1, 3, 5$

11. If perfect competition exists, what is the elasticity of the demand curve? What relations are true about perfect competition? Find the elasticity of the following demand curves:

(a) $p = 10$ (b) $p = 7000$

12. Define elasticity of supply. Find the elasticity of the following supply curves, and draw conclusions:
(a) $q = -40 + p$ at $p = 10, 20, 30$
(b) $q = 8$ at $p = 2, 4$
(c) $q = p^{1/2}$ at $p = 1, 4$
(d) When is the supply curve elastic and when is it inelastic?

13. Given the demand function, find the cross elasticity for each price and determine what type of relation exists between the goods; also find income elasticity:
(a) $Q_x = -5P_x - P_1 - 2P_2 + 3P_3 + 4P_4 + 0.1Y$
     $P_x = 2, P_1 = 4, P_2 = 10, P_3 = 6, P_4 = 8, Y = 100$
(b) $Q_x = -4P_x - P_1 - 2P_2 + 6P_3 + 0.25Y$
     $P_x = 10, P_1 = 50, P_2 = 30, P_3 = 25, Y = 1000$

14. Find total revenue and marginal revenue for the following:

(a) $q = 10 - p$

(b) $q = 50 - \frac{1}{2}p^2$

(c) $q = \dfrac{500}{p + 10}$

(d) $q = 20 - 4p$

(e) $q = \dfrac{40}{p + 5} - 5$

15. Given the demand function, graph total revenue and marginal revenue, and show the range of elasticity:

(a) $q = 20 - 2p$

(b) $q = 18 - p$

(c) $q = \dfrac{20}{p + 5}$

(d) $q = \dfrac{4}{p + 1} - 1$

16. What is the relationship between marginal revenue and elasticity; between total revenue and elasticity?

17. Given the relationships

$$MR = P\left(1 - \frac{1}{e}\right) \qquad e = \frac{P}{P - MR}$$

what can be substituted for P? What type of market exists when $MR = AR$ is always true?

18. Given the demand curve $q = a - bp$, what are the axis-intercepts, and what is the elasticity at each intercept?

19. If a monopolist can impose price discrimination, and if $MR_1 = MR_2$ and $e_1 > e_2$, what must be true?

20. Graph total cost, marginal cost, average cost, and the derivative of marginal cost:
    (a) $C = 1000 + 25x - 5x^2 + x^3$
    (b) $C = \frac{1}{8}x^2 + 2x + 10$
    (c) $C = x^3 - 2x^2 + 9x + 650$

21. Graph the following curves: total fixed cost, total variable cost, and total cost. Then graph the following curves directly below, showing their relationship: average fixed cost, average variable cost, average total cost, and marginal cost.

22. Use the profit maximization rule $MC = MR$ to find the quantity produced for maximum profit:
    (a) $C = x^3 - 2x^2 + 4x + 50$ $p = 112 - 4x$
    (b) $C = 2x^3 - 4x^2 + 4x + 20$ $p = 24 - 3x$
    (c) $C = 4x^3 - 24x^2 + 60x + 120$ $p = 180 - 6x$

23. Define elasticity of cost. Graph total cost, marginal cost, and average cost, and show the ranges of elasticity.

24. If the curve for supply of variable input is given by $p = f(q)$ and $f'(q) > 0$, find total variable cost, marginal cost, and the relationships between marginal cost and elasticity.

25. Find MPC and MPS for the following:
    (a) $C = 500 + 0.5Y$
    (b) $C = 450 + 0.76Y$
    (c) $C = 250 + 4Y^{\frac{1}{2}}$ at $Y = 25, 64, 100$
    (d) $C = 650 - 2Y^{\frac{1}{2}} + 0.8Y$ at $Y = 25, 100$

26. Give a verbal explanation of the multiplier. Let

$$\frac{dC}{dY} = x$$

and carry out the division $1/(1 - x)$ to obtain an infinite series.

27. Find the multipliers for the following:

    (a) $\dfrac{dC}{dY} = 0.5$ (c) $\dfrac{dC}{dY} = 0.75$

    (b) $\dfrac{dS}{dY} = 0.2$ (d) $\dfrac{dS}{dY} = 0.1$

28. Use the infinite series found for $1/(1 - x)$ if

$$x = \frac{dC}{dY}$$

and verify its

$$\text{sum} = \frac{1}{1 - x}$$

for the following:

    (a) $\dfrac{dC}{dY} = 0.8$ (b) $\dfrac{dC}{dY} = 0.4$

29. Verify the following where K is the multiplier:

(a) $\dfrac{dS}{dC} = \dfrac{dY}{dC} \cdot \dfrac{1}{K}$

(c) $\dfrac{dC}{dY} = 1 - \dfrac{1}{K}$

(b) $\dfrac{dC}{dY} + \dfrac{dC}{dS} = K - \dfrac{1}{K}$

(d) $\left(\dfrac{dC}{dY}\right)^2 = \dfrac{dS}{dY} + \dfrac{dC}{dY} - \dfrac{1}{K}\dfrac{dC}{dY}$

30. If G is government expenditure, D is government deficit, Y is national income, and t is a time, what conclusions can be drawn from

$$\frac{dY}{dt} = \frac{dG}{dt} + \frac{dD}{dt}$$

when $dY/dt = 0$?

7

DIFFERENTIATION OF TRANSCENDENTAL FUNCTIONS

In Chapter 4 the rules of differentiation of some algebraic functions were discussed. The task of this chapter is to examine the rules of differentiation of two additional types of functions: the logarithmic and the exponential functions.

DIFFERENTIATION OF LOGARITHMIC FUNCTIONS

In Chapter 3 it was mentioned that the natural logarithm of a number N is the power to which the base e is raised to obtain N. It was suggested that the base e is the limiting value of the function

$$\lim_{x \to 0} (1 + x)^{1/x} = e = 2.71828$$

approximately to the fifth place. It is beyond the scope of this book to show rigorously the existence of the limit e, but it can be shown intuitively that the limit of e is somewhere between 2 and 3, and that as x becomes progressively smaller, e approaches the number 2.71828.

Natural logarithmic functions are those functions in which y is the natural logarithm of a variable x. For example,

$$y = \ln (2x^2 + 3x)$$

is a logarithmic function in which y is the natural logarithm of $2x^2 + 3x$. The differentiation of this type of function is the subject matter of this section. The rule of differentiation of natural logarithmic functions will be stated; proof of the rule will be shown; and then the differentiation of logarithmic functions of various types will be discussed. Let $y = \ln x$. Then

$$\frac{dy}{dx} = \frac{1}{x}$$

If y is the natural logarithm of x, then the first derivative of y with respect to x is the reciprocal of x, or $1/x$.

To prove this rule, assume a function

$$y = \ln x \tag{1}$$

When x changes by an amount Δx, the function becomes

$$y + \Delta y = \ln (x + \Delta x) \tag{2}$$

Take the difference between the original value of the function (1) and the new value of the function (2) and subtract (1) from (2); the result is

$$\Delta y = \ln (x + \Delta x) - \ln x$$

When the natural logarithm of the first number is subtracted from the natural logarithm of the second, it is the same as the natural logarithm of the ratio of the first to the second. So Δy can be expressed yet another way, as

$$\Delta y = \ln \left(\frac{x + \Delta x}{x}\right) = \ln \left(1 + \frac{\Delta x}{x}\right) \tag{3}$$

Equation (3) now shows the amount of change in y as a consequence of the change in x. To measure the rate of change in y, Δy, to the change in x, Δx, divide Δx into both sides of (3).

$$\frac{\Delta y}{\Delta x} = \frac{1}{\Delta x} \ln \left(1 + \frac{\Delta x}{x}\right)$$

Now multiply both sides of the equation by x/x:

$$\frac{\Delta y}{\Delta x} = \frac{1}{x} \cdot \frac{x}{\Delta x} \ln \left(1 + \frac{\Delta x}{x}\right) \tag{4}$$

Since

$$\frac{x}{\Delta x} \ln \left(1 + \frac{\Delta x}{x}\right) = \ln \left(1 + \frac{\Delta x}{x}\right)^{x/\Delta x}$$

equation (4) can be rewritten into the form

$$\frac{\Delta y}{\Delta x} = \frac{1}{x} \ln \left(1 + \frac{\Delta x}{x}\right)^{x/\Delta x} \tag{5}$$

The expression

$$\left(1 + \frac{\Delta x}{x}\right)^{x/\Delta x}$$

in (5) will approach the value e as Δx approaches zero. Therefore, taking the limit of (5),

$$\lim_{\Delta x \to 0} \frac{\Delta y}{\Delta x} = \frac{dy}{dx} = \frac{1}{x} \ln e$$

Since $\ln e = 1$,

$$\frac{dy}{dx} = \frac{1}{x} \tag{6}$$

It appears therefore that (6) is the derivative of (1), and the proof agrees with the verbal statement of the rule of differentiation of the function $y = \ln x$.

The process of using the rule of natural logarithmic differentiation in deriving the first derivatives of logarithmic functions of various types will be illustrated by several examples.

Let $y = \ln (6x^2 + x + 5)$. The composite function rule can be used to say

$$y = \ln u \quad \text{and} \quad u = 6x^2 + x + 5$$

Then

$$\frac{dy}{du} = \frac{1}{u} \quad \frac{du}{dx} = 12x + 1$$

$$\frac{dy}{dx} = \frac{dy}{du} \cdot \frac{du}{dx} = \frac{1}{u}(12x + 1)$$

$$\frac{dy}{dx} = \frac{12x + 1}{u} = \frac{12x + 1}{6x^2 + x + 5}$$

Let $y = \ln x - \ln x^2$.

$$\frac{dy}{dx} = \frac{d}{dx} \ln x - \frac{d}{dx} \ln x^2$$

$$= \frac{1}{x} - \frac{2x}{x^2} = \frac{1}{x} - \frac{2}{x} = -\frac{1}{x}$$

The third example of natural logarithmic differentiation requires a slight manipulation of the function, using the rules of logarithms. Let

$$y = \ln \sqrt{1 - x^2}$$

This can be rewritten using a fractional exponent, resulting in

$$y = \ln (1 - x^2)^{\frac{1}{2}}$$

which is the same as

$$y = \frac{1}{2} \ln (1 - x^2)$$

Differentiating gives

$$\frac{dy}{dx} = \frac{1}{2} \left[\frac{\frac{d}{dx}(1 - x^2)}{(1 - x^2)} \right] = -\frac{2x}{2[1 - x^2]} = \frac{x}{x^2 - 1}$$

The following example also involves a little manipulation of the function to simplify it before proceeding with the differentiation. Suppose the function to be differentiated to be

$$y = \ln \sqrt{\frac{x^3 - x^2}{x^2 + 5}}$$

First remove the radical sign by using a fractional exponent:

$$y = \ln \left(\frac{x^3 - x^2}{x^2 + 5}\right)^{\frac{1}{2}}$$

Since the natural log of the square root of any quantity is one-half the natural log of the quantity, write

$$y = \frac{1}{2} \ln \left(\frac{x^3 - x^2}{x^2 + 5}\right)$$

This can be further rearranged into the form

$$y = \frac{1}{2}[\ln (x^3 - x^2) - \ln (x^2 + 5)]$$

Differentiating yields

$$\frac{dy}{dx} = \frac{1}{2} \left[\frac{\dfrac{d}{dx}(x^3 - x^2)}{x^3 - x^2} - \frac{\dfrac{d}{dx}(x^2 + 5)}{x^2 + 5} \right]$$

$$= \frac{1}{2} \left(\frac{3x^2 - 2x}{x^3 - x^2} - \frac{2x}{x^2 + 5}\right) = \frac{(x^2 + 5)(3x - 2) - (2x)(x^2 - x)}{2(x^2 - x)(x^2 + 5)}$$

$$= \frac{x^3 + 15x - 10}{2x^4 - 2x^3 + 10x^2 - 10x}$$

More examples are given below.

1. $y = (2x^3 - 3x^2 + 2)[\ln (6x^2 + 2x - 1)]$. Here there is a product of two functions, one an algebraic polynomial and the other a natural logarithm of a polynomial. To find the derivative of this function, one must use the rule for the product of two functions.

$$\frac{dy}{dx} = \left[\frac{d}{dx}(2x^3 - 3x^2 + 2)\right][\ln (6x^2 + 2x - 1)]$$

$$+ (2x^3 - 3x^2 + 2)\left[\frac{d}{dx}\ln (6x^2 + 2x - 1)\right]$$

$$= (6x^2 - 6x)[\ln (6x^2 + 2x - 1)]$$

$$+ (2x^3 - 3x^2 + 2)\left[\dfrac{\dfrac{d}{dx}(6x^2 + 2x - 1)}{6x^2 + 2x - 1}\right]$$

$$= (6x^2 - 6x)[\ln(6x^2 + 2x - 1)]$$

$$+ (2x^3 - 3x^2 + 2)\left[\dfrac{12x + 2}{6x^2 + 2x - 1}\right]$$

$$= \dfrac{24x^4 - 32x^3 - 6x^2 + 24x + 4}{6x^2 + 2x - 1} + (6x^2 - 6x)[\ln(6x^2 + 2x - 1)]$$

2. $y = \dfrac{x^2 + x - 10}{\ln(2x^2 + 3x)}$

In this case the problem involves a quotient of two functions, and accordingly, the rule for the quotients of functions in finding the derivative must be used.

$$\frac{dy}{dx} = \dfrac{\left[\dfrac{d}{dx}(x^2 + x - 10)\right][\ln(2x^2 + 3x)] - \left[\dfrac{d}{dx}\ln(2x^2 + 3x)\right][x^2 + x - 10]}{[\ln(2x^2 + 3x)]^2}$$

$$= \dfrac{(2x + 1)[\ln(2x^2 + 3x)] - \dfrac{4x + 3}{2x^2 + 3x}(x^2 + x - 10)}{[\ln(2x^2 + 3x)]^2}$$

$$= \dfrac{(2x + 1)[\ln(2x^2 + 3x)] - \dfrac{4x^3 + 7x^2 - 37x - 30}{2x^2 + 3x}}{[\ln(2x^2 + 3x)]^2}$$

3. $y = 3x^2 - x^3 + \ln(x^3 - 3x^2 - x - 10)$

In this example, the first two terms on the right-hand side are simple algebraic power functions and the last term is a natural logarithmic function.

$$\frac{dy}{dx} = 6x - 3x^2 + \dfrac{3x^2 - 6x - 1}{x^3 - 3x^2 - x - 10}$$

$$= \dfrac{-3x^5 + 15x^4 - 15x^3 + 27x^2 - 66x - 1}{x^3 - 3x^2 - x - 10}$$

4. Certain functions which are not expressed in logarithmic form may be converted to logarithmic form and the rules for differentiating natural logarithmic functions may then be applied. Given

$$y = (x - 5)(3x + 2)$$

find dy/dx by the logarithmic method. First take the natural logarithm of both sides of the equation and write

$$\ln y = \ln \left[(x - 5)(3x + 2)\right]$$

This step is legitimate because numbers which are equal to each other will have natural logarithms which will also be equal. By logarithmic Law I from Chapter 2, the function may be rewritten in the form

$$\ln y = \ln (x - 5) + \ln (3x + 2)$$

The left-hand side of this equation is a natural log of y, and since what is desired is dy/dx, in effect the composite function rule can be used to write

$$\frac{1}{y}\frac{dy}{dx} = \frac{1}{x - 5} + \frac{3}{3x + 2} = \frac{6x - 13}{3x^2 - 13x - 10}$$

To find dy/dx, multiply both sides of the equation by y to get

$$\frac{dy}{dx} = \left(\frac{6x - 13}{3x^2 - 13x - 10}\right)[(x - 5)(3x + 2)]$$

$$\frac{dy}{dx} = \frac{(6x - 13)(3x^2 - 13x - 10)}{3x^2 - 13x - 10} = 6x - 13$$

To verify this result, use the technique of differentiating the product of two functions:

$$y = (x - 5)(3x + 2)$$

$$\frac{dy}{dx} = (3x + 2) + 3(x - 5) = 6x - 13$$

5. Given

$$y = (x^2 + x - 5)^{(2x - \sqrt{x - 1})}$$

find dy/dx. Take the natural logarithm of both sides of the equation:

$$\ln y = (2x - \sqrt{x - 1})[\ln (x^2 + x - 5)]$$

Differentiate both sides of the equation with respect to x:

$$\frac{1}{y}\frac{dy}{dx} = \left[\left(2 - \frac{1}{2\sqrt{x - 1}}\right)\right][\ln (x^2 + x - 5)] + (2x - \sqrt{x - 1})\left[\frac{2x + 1}{x^2 + x - 5}\right]$$

Multiply both sides of the equation by y:

$$\frac{dy}{dx} = \left\{\left[\left(2 - \frac{1}{2\sqrt{x - 1}}\right)\right][\ln (x^2 + x - 5)] \right.$$

$$\left. + (2x - \sqrt{x - 1})\left[\frac{2x + 1}{x^2 + x - 5}\right]\right\}(x^2 + x - 5)^{(2x - \sqrt{x - 1})}$$

6. Given

$$y = \frac{(x - 1)(x + 2)}{(x - 3)(x + 4)}$$

find dy/dx. Take the natural logarithm of both sides:

$$\ln y = \ln \left[\frac{(x - 1)(x + 2)}{(x - 3)(x + 4)}\right]$$

$$\ln y = \ln (x - 1) + \ln (x + 2) - \ln (x - 3) - \ln (x + 4)$$

Differentiate both sides with respect to x:

$$\frac{1}{y}\frac{dy}{dx} = \frac{1}{x - 1} + \frac{1}{x + 2} - \frac{1}{x - 3} - \frac{1}{x + 4}$$

Multiply both sides of the equation by y:

$$\frac{dy}{dx} = \left[\frac{1}{x - 1} + \frac{1}{x + 2} - \frac{1}{x - 3} - \frac{1}{x + 4}\right]\left[\frac{(x - 1)(x + 2)}{(x - 3)(x + 4)}\right]$$

Simplifying gives

$$\frac{dy}{dx} = \frac{-10[2x + 1]}{[(x - 3)(x + 4)]^2}$$

$$\frac{dy}{dx} = \frac{-10[2x + 1]}{x^4 + 2x^3 - 23x^2 - 24x + 144}$$

DIFFERENTIATION OF EXPONENTIAL FUNCTIONS

This topic will be treated in the same format as the last section, with a statement of the rule for differentiation followed by its proof and a few examples of technique.

The derivative of an exponential function of the form

$$y = e^v \tag{1}$$

(where v is a differentiable function of x) is the product of itself, i.e., e^v, times the derivative of v with respect to x. To prove the rule, first take the natural logarithm of both sides of the equation (1):

$$\ln y = v \ln e \tag{2}$$

Since $\ln e = 1$, equation (2) reduces to

$$\ln y = v$$

Now differentiate both sides of the equation with respect to v:

$$\frac{1}{y}\cdot\frac{dy}{dx}=\frac{dv}{dx}$$

Multiplying both sides of the equation by y yields

$$\frac{dy}{dx}=y\frac{dv}{dx}$$

Since $y=e^v$,

$$\frac{dy}{dx}=e^v\frac{dv}{dx}$$

To illustrate the process of differentiating exponential functions, the derivatives of a few examples will be found.

1. $y=e^{2x-x^2}$

$$\frac{dy}{dx}=e^{2x-x^2}\frac{d}{dx}(2x-x^2)$$

$$=(2-2x)e^{2x-x^2}$$

2. $y=e^{3nx}$

$$\frac{dy}{dx}=\left[\frac{d}{dx}(3nx)\right]e^{3nx}$$

$$=3ne^{3nx}$$

3. $y=be^{ax}$

$$\frac{dy}{dx}=\left[\frac{d}{dx}(ax)\right]be^{ax}$$

$$=abe^{ax}$$

4. $y=16e^{3x^2-6x+5}$

Let $u=3x^2-6x+5$

$$\frac{du}{dx}=6x-6$$

$$y=16e^u$$

$$\frac{dy}{du}=16e^u\frac{du}{dx}$$

$$\frac{dy}{dx}=(6x-6)[16e^{(3x^2-6x+5)}]$$

$$=96xe^{3x^2-6x+5}-96e^{3x^2-6x+5}$$

5. $y=4e^{2x^2}$

$$\frac{dy}{dx}=4\left(\frac{d}{dx}2x^2\right)(e^{2x^2})$$

$$=16xe^{2x^2}$$

6. $y=(x^3+x^2-10)e^{2x-2}$

Here the problem involves the product of the two functions

$$x^3 + x^2 - 10 \qquad e^{2x-2}$$

The derivative will employ the rule for differentiating the product of two functions.

$$\frac{dy}{dx} = (3x^2 + 2x)e^{2x-2} + (2)e^{2x-2}(x^3 + x^2 - 10)$$

$$= (3x^2 + 2x)e^{2x-2} + (2x^3 + 2x^2 - 20)e^{2x-2}$$

$$= (2x^3 + 5x^2 + 2x - 20)e^{2x-2}$$

7. $y = \ln(3x^2 + 2x) + e^{2x-2}$

$$\frac{dy}{dx} = \frac{6x + 2}{3x^2 + 2x} + 2e^{2x-2}$$

8. $y = \dfrac{3e^{4x^2-x+10}}{\ln(x^3 + 3x)}$

$$\frac{dy}{dx} = \frac{[(24x - 3)e^{4x^2-x+10}]\ln(x^3 + 3x) - \dfrac{3x^2 + 3}{x^3 + 3x}3e^{4x^2-x-10}}{[\ln(x^3 + 3x)]^2}$$

DIFFERENTIATION OF LOGARITHMIC EXPRESSIONS TO ANY BASE

The techniques of differentiating logarithmic expressions have, up to this point, been based entirely upon natural logarithms. In many cases, however, logarithmic expressions are based on the number 10, or the so-called "common" logarithm. Furthermore, logarithmic systems may be developed to any base whatever. The derivative of a natural logarithmic function may be found directly by the various techniques already discussed. But the derivative of a logarithmic function based on any base other than e must be found by somewhat different techniques.

Suppose a number N is expressed as an exponential function to the base a as well as the base e. Thus, there are two expressions for the number N:

$$N = a^y \tag{1}$$

$$N = e^x \tag{2}$$

Take the logarithm to the base a of equation (1):

$$\log_a N = y \tag{3}$$

and take the natural logarithm of equation (2):

$$\ln N = x \tag{4}$$

To establish the relationship between the logarithm to the base a and the logarithm to the base e, take the natural logarithm of (1):

$$\ln N = y \ln a \tag{5}$$

It was established in (3) that $\log_a N = y$. Solving (5) for y, write

$$y = \frac{\ln N}{\ln a} \tag{6}$$

Since $y = \log_a N$,

$$\log_a N = \frac{\ln N}{\ln a} \tag{7}$$

Conversely, the logarithm to the base a of equation (2) may be taken:

$$\log_a N = x \log_a e \tag{8}$$

Solving for x yields

$$x = \frac{\log_a N}{\log_a e} \tag{9}$$

Since it was established in equation (4) that $x = \ln N$, the relation is

$$\ln N = \frac{\log_a N}{\log_a e} \tag{10}$$

Thus a logarithm to any base may be converted to a logarithm to any other base.

Besides the natural logarithm, the other most commonly used type is the common logarithm. Suppose a number

$$M = e^x$$

is given. Take the common logarithm of both sides:

$$\log M = x \log e$$

Solving for x, find the relation

$$x = \frac{\log M}{\log e} \quad \text{or} \quad \ln M = \frac{\log M}{\log e}$$

From logarithm tables,

$$\log e = 0.4343 \quad \text{or} \quad \frac{1}{\log e} = 2.303$$

Thus
$$\ln M = 2.303 \log M$$

Differentiation of an exponential function to any base a may be derived. Let $y = a^v$ where $a > 1$ and $v = f(x)$. Take the natural logarithm of $y = a^v$:
$$\ln y = v \ln a$$

Solve for v:
$$v = \frac{\ln y}{\ln a} = \frac{1}{\ln a} \ln y$$

Differentiating with respect to y yields
$$\frac{dv}{dy} = \frac{1}{\ln a} \cdot \frac{1}{y}$$

By the inverse function rule,
$$\frac{dy}{dv} = \ln a \cdot y$$

which is to say
$$\frac{dy}{dv} = \ln a \cdot a^v$$

By the composite function rule,
$$\frac{dy}{dx} = \frac{dy}{dv}\frac{dv}{dx} = \ln a \cdot a^v \frac{dv}{dx}$$

A few examples will illustrate the application of this rule.

1. $y = 2^x$. Find dy/dx.
$$\frac{dy}{dx} = (\ln 2)(2^x)\frac{d}{dx}x = (\ln 2)(2^x)$$

2. $y = 10^{(3x^3 - 2x^2 + x - 10)}$. Find dy/dx.
$$\frac{dy}{dx} = (\ln 10)[10^{(3x^3 - 2x^2 + x - 10)}](9x^2 - 4x + 1)$$
$$= (2.303)(9x^2 - 4x + 1)[10^{(3x^3 - 2x^2 + x - 10)}]$$

3. $y = \log \dfrac{3x}{x^2 + 1}$. Find $\dfrac{dy}{dx}$.
$$y = \log 3x - \log (x^2 + 1)$$

Since $\log 3x = (\log e) \ln 3x$, and
$$\log (x^2 + 1) = (\log e) \ln (x^2 + 1)$$
$$\frac{dy}{dx} = \frac{\log e}{3x} \frac{d}{dx} 3x - \frac{\log e}{x^2 + 1} \frac{d}{dx} (x^2 + 1)$$
$$= \frac{0.4343}{x} - \frac{0.4343}{x^2 + 1} 2x = \frac{0.4343}{x} - \frac{0.8686x}{x^2 + 1}$$

4. $y = \log (3x^3 - x^2 + 2x + 10)$. Find dy/dx. First rewrite this common logarithmic function in its natural logarithmic equivalent:
$$y = (0.4343) \ln (3x^3 - x^2 + 2x + 10)$$
Now differentiation may proceed by the rules developed earlier
$$\frac{dy}{dx} = \frac{(0.4343)(9x^2 - 2x + 2)}{3x^3 - x^2 + 2x + 10}$$

5. $y = \log [(x - 1)(x^2 - x)]$. Find dy/dx. Write
$$y = (\log e) \ln [(x - 1)(x^2 - x)] \qquad \log e = 0.4343$$
$$y = \log e[\ln (x - 1) + \ln (x^2 - x)]$$
$$\frac{dy}{dx} = \log e \left(\frac{1}{x - 1} + \frac{2x - 1}{x^2 - x} \right)$$

6. $y = \log \sqrt{\dfrac{x - 1}{x^2 + 5}}$. Find $\dfrac{dy}{dx}$.

Write this common logarithmic function as a natural logarithmic function:
$$y = (\log e) \ln \sqrt{\frac{x - 1}{x^2 + 5}}$$
Employing the various well-known rules of logarithmic manipulation (and remembering that $\log e = 0.4343$, a constant), proceed step by step as follows:
$$y = (\log e) \ln \left(\frac{x - 1}{x^2 + 5} \right)^{1/2}$$
$$y = \tfrac{1}{2}(\log e)[\ln (x - 1) - \ln (x^2 + 5)]$$
At this point differentiation is easily carried out by using the methods already developed:
$$\frac{dy}{dx} = \tfrac{1}{2}(\log e) \left(\frac{1}{x - 1} - \frac{2x}{x^2 + 5} \right)$$
$$\frac{dy}{dx} = \frac{0.4343}{2} \left[\frac{-x^2 + 2x + 5}{(x - 1)(x^2 + 5)} \right]$$

TRIGONOMETRIC FUNCTIONS

In Chapter 4, certain trigonometric functions were developed and their applications in economic theory were discussed. The rules for differentiation of 6 trigonometric functions will be discussed in this section. Although we are including the rules of differentiation of trigonometric functions in this chapter in the interest of completeness, this section may be skipped by beginning students in mathematical economics without loss of continuity in the remainder of the book. Economic applications of trigonometric functions are fairly infrequent. The most important application occurs in analyzing economic problems involving regularly recurring economic variables, namely in the analysis of business cycles.

For each trigonometric function, the differentiation rule will be stated and a few examples will be presented. The statement of the rule will be in terms of a trigonometric function of v which in turn is a function of x.

Rule I

$$y = \sin v \qquad \frac{dy}{dx} = (\cos v)\frac{dv}{dx}$$

Examples:

1. $y = \sin bx$
Solution: Here $v = bx$

$$\frac{dy}{dx} = (\cos bx)\frac{d}{dx}bx = b(\cos bx)$$

2. $y = \sin (x^2 + 1)$
Solution: $v = (x^2 + 1)$

$$\frac{dy}{dx} = [\cos (x^2 + 1)]\frac{d}{dx}(x^2 + 1) = 2x[\cos (x^2 + 1)]$$

3. $y = \frac{1}{2} \sin x$
Solution: $v = x$ and $\frac{1}{2}$ is a constant.

$$\frac{dy}{dx} = (\frac{1}{2}\cos x)\frac{d}{dx}x = \frac{1}{2}\cos x$$

4. $y = \dfrac{\sin x}{x}$

Solution: This equation may be rewritten as a product of two functions:

$$y = \frac{1}{x} \sin x$$

and the rule for differentiating products of functions applied:

$$\frac{dy}{dx} = \left[(\cos x) \frac{d}{dx} x \right] \frac{1}{x} + (\sin x) \frac{d}{dx} \frac{1}{x}$$

$$= \frac{1}{x} (\cos x) - \frac{1}{x^2} (\sin x)$$

5. $y = x^2(\sin 2x)$

Solution: Again this is a product of two functions, x^2 multiplied by $\sin 2x$, where $v = 2x$.

$$\frac{dy}{dx} = 2x(\sin 2x) + x^2[\cos (2x)] \frac{d}{dx} 2x$$

$$= 2x(\sin 2x) + 2x^2[\cos (2x)]$$

6. $y = x^{\sin x}$

Solution: Take the natural logarithm of both sides:

$$\ln y = (\sin x) \ln x$$

Differentiate both sides of the equation with respect to x, keeping in mind that again the right-hand side is the product of two functions.

$$\frac{1}{y} \frac{dy}{dx} = (\cos x) \ln x + \frac{1}{x} (\sin x)$$

Multiply both sides of the equation by y:

$$\frac{dy}{dx} = x^{\sin x} \left[(\cos x) \ln x + \frac{1}{x} (\sin x) \right]$$

Rule 2

$$y = \cos v \qquad \frac{dy}{dx} = -\sin v \frac{dv}{dx}$$

Examples:

1. $y = \cos x$

Solution: $v = x$

$$\frac{dy}{dx} = (-\sin x) \frac{d}{dx} x = -\sin x$$

2. $y = a(\cos bx)$

Solution: a and b are constants and $v = bx$

$$\frac{dy}{dx} = a(-\sin bx)\frac{d}{dx}bx = ab(-\sin bx)$$
$$= -ab(\sin bx)$$

3. $y = 3(\cos 2x)$

Solution: $v = 2x$

$$\frac{dy}{dx} = 3(-\sin 2x)\frac{d}{dx}2x = -6(\sin 2x)$$

4. $y = \sqrt{\cos 2x}$

Solution: Let $u = \cos 2x$, where $v = 2x$.

$$\frac{du}{dx} = (-\sin 2x)\frac{d}{dx}2x = -2(\sin 2x)$$

Since $u = \cos 2x$,

$$y = u^{1/2} \qquad \frac{dy}{du} = \tfrac{1}{2}u^{-1/2}$$

$$\frac{dy}{dx} = \frac{du}{dx} \cdot \frac{dy}{du} = \frac{-2(\sin 2x)}{2\sqrt{u}} = -\frac{\sin (2x)}{\sqrt{\cos 2x}}$$

5. $y = (\cos x)^x$

Solution: This is an exponential of a cosine function. Proceed again step by step. Take the natural logarithm of both sides:

$$\ln y = x \ln (\cos x)$$

Differentiate both sides of the equation with respect to x:

$$\frac{1}{y}\frac{dy}{dx} = \ln (\cos x) + x\frac{-\sin x}{\cos x}$$

Multiply both sides of the equation by y:

$$\frac{dy}{dx} = y\left[\ln \cos x - x\frac{\sin x}{\cos x}\right]$$
$$= (\cos x)^x[\ln \cos x - x \tan x]$$

Rule 3

$$y = \tan v \qquad \frac{dy}{dx} = \sec^2 v\frac{dv}{dx}$$

Examples:

1. $y = \tan x$

Solution: This is a straightforward case where $v = x$:

$$\frac{dy}{dx} = (\sec^2 x) \frac{d}{dx} x = \sec^2 x$$

2. $y = \tan 2x^2$

Solution: $v = 2x^2$

$$\frac{dy}{dx} = \sec^2 2x^2 \frac{d}{dx} 2x^2 = 4x \sec^2 2x^2$$

3. $y = \tan [\ln (3x^2 - x + 10)]$

Solution: In this case $v = \ln (3x^2 - x + 10)$.

$$\frac{dy}{dx} = [\sec^2 \ln (3x^2 - x + 10)] \frac{d}{dx} \ln (3x^2 - x + 10)$$

$$= \frac{6x - 1}{3x^2 - x + 10} [\sec^2 \ln (3x^2 - x + 10)]$$

4. $y = \tan (1 - x)$

Solution: $v = 1 - x$

$$\frac{dy}{dx} = [\sec^2 (1 - x)] \frac{d}{dx} (1 - x)$$

$$= -\sec^2 (1 - x)$$

5. $y = \tan \sqrt{1 - x}$

Solution: $v = \sqrt{1 - x}$

$$\frac{dy}{dx} = [\sec^2 \sqrt{1 - x}] \frac{d}{dx} (1 - x)^{\frac{1}{2}}$$

$$= [\sec^2 \sqrt{1 - x}] \tfrac{1}{2} (1 - x)^{-\frac{1}{2}} (-1)$$

$$= - \frac{\sec^2 \sqrt{1 - x}}{2\sqrt{1 - x}}$$

6. $y = \tan \left(\dfrac{x - 1}{x + 1}\right)$

Solution: $v = \dfrac{x - 1}{x + 1}$

$$\frac{dy}{dx} = \left[\sec^2 \left(\frac{x - 1}{x + 1}\right)\right] \frac{d}{dx} \left(\frac{x - 1}{x + 1}\right)$$

$$= \left[\frac{(x + 1) - (x - 1)}{(x + 1)^2}\right] \sec^2 \left(\frac{x - 1}{x + 1}\right)$$

$$= \frac{2}{(x + 1)^2} \sec^2 \left(\frac{x - 1}{x + 1}\right)$$

7. $y = (2x + x^2)^{\tan x}$

Solution: In this case there is an exponential function whose exponent is a trigonometric function. Take the natural logarithm of both sides:

$$\ln y = (\tan x)[\ln (2x + x^2)]$$

Take the derivative of each side of the equation with respect to x:

$$\frac{1}{y}\frac{dy}{dx} = (\sec^2 x)[\ln (2x + x^2)] + \frac{2 + 2x}{2x + x^2} \tan x$$

Multiply both sides of the equation by y.

$$\frac{dy}{dx} = \left\{(\sec^2 x)[\ln (2x + x^2)] + \frac{2 + 2x}{2x + x^2} \tan x\right\}(2x + x^2)^{\tan x}$$

Rule 4

$$y = \cot v \qquad \frac{dy}{dx} = -\csc^2 v \frac{dv}{dx}$$

Examples:

1. $y = \cot x$

Solution:

$$\frac{dy}{dx} = (-\csc^2 x) \frac{d}{dx} x = -\csc^2 x$$

2. $y = \cot x^2$

Solution:

$$\frac{dy}{dx} = (-\csc^2 x^2) \frac{d}{dx} x^2 = 2x(-\csc^2 x^2)$$

$$= -2x(\csc^2 x^2)$$

3. $y = (x^2 - 1)[\cot (2x^2 - x - 10)]$

Solution: This is a product of two functions; apply the appropriate rules for the differentiation of such functions.

$$\frac{dy}{dx} = 2x[\cot (2x^2 - x - 10)]$$

$$+ [-\csc^2 (2x^2 - x - 10)](x^2 - 1)(4x - 1)$$

$$= 2x[\cot (2x^2 - x - 10)]$$

$$+ (4x^3 - x^2 - 4x + 1)[-\csc^2 (2x^2 - x - 10)]$$

4. $y = e^{(2x^2-x-1)} \cot (x^3 - 3x - 1)$

Solution: Again this is a product of two functions.

$$\frac{dy}{dx} = (4x - 1)e^{(2x^2-x-1)}\cot(x^3 - 3x - 1)$$

$$+ e^{(2x^2-x-1)}(3x^2 - 3)[-\csc^2(x^3 - 3x - 1)]$$

5. $y = \cot \sqrt[3]{x - 1}$

Solution: This differentiation may be done in two different ways. The first method is to use the composite function rule.

$$u = (x - 1)^{\frac{1}{3}}$$

$$\frac{du}{dx} = \frac{1}{3}\frac{1}{\sqrt[3]{(x - 1)^2}}$$

$$y = \cot u$$

$$\frac{dy}{du} = -\csc^2 u \frac{du}{dx}$$

$$\frac{dy}{dx} = \frac{dy}{du}\frac{du}{dx} = -\tfrac{1}{3}[(\csc^2)\sqrt[3]{(x - 1)}]\left[\frac{1}{\sqrt[3]{(x - 1)^2}}\right]$$

The second method involves the use of natural logarithms of the function. Take the natural log of both sides of the original function:

$$\ln y = \ln \cot(x - 1)^{\frac{1}{3}}$$

Differentiate both sides with respect to x:

$$\frac{1}{y}\frac{dy}{dx} = \frac{[-\csc^2 \sqrt[3]{x - 1}]\left[\frac{1}{3}\frac{1}{\sqrt[3]{(x - 1)^2}}\right]}{[\cot(x - 1)^{\frac{1}{3}}]}$$

Multiply both sides by y:

$$\frac{dy}{dx} = \frac{[-\csc^2 \sqrt[3]{x - 1}]\left[\frac{1}{3}\frac{1}{\sqrt[3]{(x - 1)^2}}\right]}{[\cot(x - 1)^{\frac{1}{3}}]} \cdot \cot \sqrt[3]{x - 1}$$

$$\frac{dy}{dx} = [-\csc^2 \sqrt[3]{x - 1}]\left[\frac{1}{3} \cdot \frac{1}{\sqrt[3]{(x - 1)^2}}\right]$$

Rule 5

$$y = \sec v \qquad \frac{dy}{dx} = \sec v \tan v \frac{dv}{dx}$$

Examples:

1. $y = \sec x$

Solution:

$$\frac{dy}{dx} = \sec x \tan x \frac{d}{dx} x = \sec x \tan x$$

2. $y = \sec ax^2$
Solution:

$$\frac{dy}{dx} = \sec ax^2 \tan ax^2 \frac{d}{dx} ax^2$$

$$= 2ax \sec ax^2 \tan ax^2$$

3. $y = (x^3 - 2x^2 - x + 1)[\sec (x^2 - 5)]$
Solution: This is the product of an algebraic polynomial and a trigonometric function.

$$\frac{dy}{dx} = (3x^2 - 4x - 1)[\sec (x^2 - 5)]$$

$$+ [2x \sec (x^2 - 5) \tan (x^2 - 5)](x^3 - 2x^2 - x + 1)$$

4. $y = \dfrac{\sec (3x^2 - x - 1)}{\sin (x^2 + 1)}$

Solution: This is the quotient of two trigonometric functions.

$$\frac{dy}{dx} = \frac{[(6x - 1) \sec (3x^2 - x - 1) \tan (3x^2 - x - 1)] \sin (x^2 + 1)}{[\sin (x^2 + 1)]^2}$$

$$- \frac{[2x \cos (x^2 + 1)][\sec (3x^2 - x - 1)]}{[\sin (x^2 + 1)]^2}$$

Rule 6

$$y = \csc v \qquad \frac{dy}{dx} = -\csc v \cot v \frac{dv}{dx}$$

Examples:
1. $y = \csc x$

Solution:

$$\frac{dy}{dx} = -\csc x \cot x \frac{d}{dx} x = -\csc x \cot x$$

2. $y = \csc 2x^2$

Solution:

$$\frac{dy}{dx} = (-\csc 2x^2)(\cot 2x^2)\frac{d}{dx}2x^2$$
$$= -4x(\csc 2x^2)(\cot 2x^2)$$

3. $y = \dfrac{\csc 2x^2}{\sin (x - 1)}$

Solution: This problem may be approached by two methods. By the first method, the equation is treated simply as a quotient of two functions.

$$\frac{dy}{dx} = \frac{[(-4x)(\csc 2x^2)(\cot 2x^2)][\sin (x - 1)]}{[\sin (x - 1)]^2}$$
$$- \frac{[\cos (x - 1)](\csc 2x^2)}{[\sin (x - 1)]^2}$$
$$= \frac{(-4x)(\csc 2x^2)(\cot 2x^2)}{\sin (x - 1)} - \frac{[\cos (x - 1)][\csc 2x^2]}{[\sin (x - 1)]^2}$$
$$= \frac{(-4x)(\csc 2x^2)(\cot 2x^2)}{\sin (x - 1)} - \frac{\csc 2x^2 \cot (x - 1)}{\sin (x - 1)}$$
$$= \frac{-\csc 2x^2[4x(\cot 2x^2) + \cot (x - 1)]}{\sin (x - 1)}$$

The second method is to take the natural log of both sides. Take the natural log:

$$\ln y = \ln \csc 2x^2 - \ln \sin (x - 1)$$

Differentiate with respect to x:

$$\frac{1}{y}\frac{dy}{dx} = \frac{(-4x)(\csc 2x^2)(\cot 2x^2)}{\csc 2x^2} - \frac{\cos (x - 1)}{\sin (x - 1)}$$

Multiply both sides by y:

$$\frac{dy}{dx} = \left[\frac{(-4x)(\csc 2x^2)(\cot 2x^2)}{\csc 2x^2} - \frac{\cos (x - 1)}{\sin (x - 1)}\right]\left[\frac{\csc 2x^2}{\sin (x - 1)}\right]$$
$$= \frac{(-4x)(\csc 2x^2)(\cot 2x^2)}{\sin (x - 1)} - \frac{(\csc 2x^2)[\cot (x - 1)]}{\sin (x - 1)}$$
$$= \frac{-\csc 2x^2[4x(\cot 2x^2) + \cot (x - 1)]}{\sin (x - 1)}$$

ECONOMIC APPLICATIONS OF DIFFERENTIATION OF TRANSCENDENTAL EXPRESSIONS

Economic functions of various types may be represented by a variety of appropriate mathematical functions. The problem of selecting a specific mathematical function to represent a particular economic relationship is considered in that branch of economics called *econometrics*. In econometrics, masses of economic data are examined, various statistical techniques are applied, and finally a mathematical function which seems most accurately to describe the relationships among the data is developed.

For example, H. Schultz, in his famous volume *The Theory and Measurement of Demand*, derived the demand for wheat per capita in the United States for the period from 1921 to 1937, using annual data. If Q represents the quantity demanded annually of wheat in bushels, p is the price of wheat, and t is time in years with $1928 = 0$, the equation is

$$\ln Q = 1.0802 - 0.2143 \ln p - 0.00358t - 0.00163t^2 \qquad (1)$$

If this demand function is applied to the year 1930, t can be assigned the specific value $t = 2$ since 1930 is two years later than 1928. When $t = 2$, the equation becomes

$$\ln Q = 1.06652 - 0.2143 \ln p \qquad (2)$$

Now take the derivative of both sides of the equation with respect to p,

$$\frac{1}{Q}\frac{dQ}{dp} = -\frac{0.2143}{p} \qquad (3)$$

Multiply both sides of the equation by p,

$$\frac{p}{Q}\frac{dQ}{dp} = -0.2143 \qquad (4)$$

The expression $(p/Q)(dQ/dp)$ is the price elasticity of demand. Thus the price elasticity of demand for wheat as calculated by Schultz was approximately -0.2143.

To calculate the slope of the demand curve for wheat in 1930, solve equation (2) for Q in terms of p:

$$Q = \frac{e^{1.06652}}{p^{0.2143}} \qquad (5)$$

This shows an inverse relationship between quantity demanded of wheat and its price. The slope of this demand function (5) is

$$\frac{dQ}{dp} = -\frac{0.2143e^{1.06652}}{p^{1.2143}}$$

As expected, the demand curve is negatively sloped.

The second example demand function is assumed to be of the form

$$Q = \frac{80}{e^{2p}} \quad \text{or} \quad Q = 80e^{-2p}$$

The slope of this demand curve is

$$\frac{dQ}{dp} = -160e^{-2p} = -\frac{160}{e^{2p}}$$

Consider a demand curve whose equation is

$$Q = \frac{p^2}{e^{4p+1}} = p^2 e^{-4p-1}$$

The slope of this demand function is given by dQ/dp. Find the required slope by

$$\frac{dQ}{dp} = 2pe^{-4p-1} + (-4)e^{(-4p-1)}p^2$$

$$= \frac{2p}{e^{4p+1}} - \frac{4p^2}{e^{4p+1}} = \frac{2(p - 2p^2)}{e^{4p+1}}$$

In Chapter 4, an equation which represented a business cycle was developed; it was in the form

$$y = 200 + 50 \sin \frac{\pi}{6} t$$

where y is the level of net national product in appropriate units and t is time in years. The rate of change of net national product with respect to time is given by the derivative of y with respect to t:

$$\frac{dy}{dt} = \left[50 \cos \frac{\pi}{6} t \right] \frac{d}{dt} \frac{\pi}{6} t$$

$$= 50 \frac{\pi}{6} \cos \frac{\pi}{6} t$$

It was shown earlier that the business cycle represented by this business cycle function had a duration of 12 years. The cycle is on the upswing from $t = 0$ to $t = 3$. In this range, the level of economic activities is expected to be rising as a function of time. Thus at $t = 2$, for example, it would be expected that dy/dt of the function is positive. The rate of change of the economic activity relative to time at $t = 2$ can be measured by substituting

$t = 2$ into the derivative function, namely,

$$\frac{dy}{dt} = 50\,\frac{\pi}{6}\cos\frac{\pi}{6}t$$

$$\frac{dy}{dt} = 50\,\frac{\pi}{6}\cos\frac{\pi}{6}2 = 50\,\frac{\pi}{6}\cos\frac{\pi}{3}$$

The numerical value of π is 3.14, accurate to 2 decimal places, and

$$\cos\frac{\pi}{3} = \cos(60°)$$

Making these substitutions,

$$\frac{dy}{dt} = (50)\,\frac{3.14}{6}\cos(60°)$$

$$\cos(60°) = \tfrac{1}{2}$$

$$\frac{dy}{dt} = (50)(0.523)(0.50) = 13.075$$

This is the rate of change of y relative to $t = 2$. This rate of change is positive, because the business cycle is on the upswing, and y is increasing when $t = 2$.

Figure 4-25 and Table 4-1 showed that when $t = 3$, y is at its maximum value of 250. Such a maximum point of a function has the property that the first derivative at that point is equal to zero and the second derivative is negative. At $t = 3$, then,

$$\frac{dy}{dt} = 50\,\frac{\pi}{6}\cos\frac{3\pi}{6} = 50\,\frac{\pi}{6}\cos\frac{\pi}{2}$$

$$= 50\,\frac{\pi}{6}\cos(90°) = 50\,\frac{\pi}{6}(0)$$

To determine that the business cycle function is indeed at its maximum value, the second derivative of the function must be evaluated at $t = 3$. The second derivative is

$$\frac{d^2y}{dt^2} = 50\,\frac{\pi}{6}\left(-\sin\frac{\pi}{6}t\right)\frac{d}{dt}\frac{\pi}{6}t$$

$$= 50\left(\frac{\pi}{6}\right)^2\left(-\sin\frac{3\pi}{6}\right)$$

$$= 50\left(\frac{\pi}{6}\right)^2[-\sin(90°)]$$

since sin $(90°) = 1$

$$\frac{d^2y}{dt^2} = -50\left(\frac{\pi}{6}\right)^2$$

The second derivative is negative, so y is at its maximum when $t = 3$.

Now consider the rate of change of this business cycle function when $t = 8$. Again referring back to Figure 4-25 and Table 4-1, when $t = 8$, the function is decreasing. Then it would be expected that dy/dt is negative. The derivative at $t = 8$ is

$$\frac{dy}{dt} = 50\,\frac{\pi}{6}\cos\frac{8\pi}{6}$$

$$= (50)(0.523)[\cos(\tfrac{4}{3}\pi)]$$

$$= (50)(0.523)[\cos(240°)]$$

$$= (50)(0.523)[-\cos(60°)]$$

$$= (50)(0.523)(-0.50)$$

$$= -13.075$$

PROBLEMS

1. Show that if

$$e = \lim_{x \to 0} (1 + x)^{1/x}$$

then

$$e = \lim_{z \to \infty} \left(1 + \frac{1}{z}\right)^{z}$$

Expand $[1 + (1/z)]^z$ by the binomial theorem. Simplify the expansion to obtain the form $[1 - (n/z)]$ and apply $\lim_{z \to \infty}$ to obtain the series for e. Calculate the value of the series.

2. Use problem 1 to show that $2 < e < 3$, if

$$\frac{1}{n!} < \frac{1}{2^m - 1}$$

is given.

3. If

$$e = \lim_{n \to \infty} \left(1 + \frac{1}{n}\right)^{n}$$

what does e^x equal, and what is the series for e^x? Using the series for e^x, find the value of $e^{1/2}$ and e^2.

4. Find dy/dx for the following:

(a) $y = \ln 4x^4$

(b) $y = \ln (8x^3 + 6x + 7)$

(c) $y = \ln (x^3 + x^2)^{1/6}$

(d) $y = \ln [(x^4 + 3x^2)^4(5x^6 + 4x)^3]$

(e) $y = \ln [(x^2 + 1)^{10}(7x^5 + 5x^7)^6]$

(f) $y = \ln \sqrt[8]{x^{1/2}} - x$

(l) $y = \ln \left(\dfrac{2x^5 - \sqrt{x + 2}}{\sqrt{3x + 1}}\right)$

(g) $y = \ln (3x^2 + 6x + 6)$

(m) $y = \ln (x + \sqrt{1 + x^2})$

(h) $y = (\ln 5x^8)^5$

(n) $y = 3x^2(\ln 6x^2) - 7x^2(\ln x)$

(i) $y = (\ln 4x)^3$

(o) $y = x[\ln (\ln 2x^2)]$

(j) $y = \ln \left(\dfrac{x^4 + 3x^2 + 5}{x^2 - x + 1}\right)$

(p) $y = [\ln (\ln 10x^3)]^4$

(k) $y = \ln \left(\dfrac{7x^2 - 9}{x^3 + 4x + 7}\right)$

(q) $y = \dfrac{1}{x}(\ln 8x^3)^4$

5. Use logarithms to find dy/dx for the following:

(a) $y = \sqrt[3]{\dfrac{(x^2 - 2)(3 - x)}{(4x + 1)(2x^2 + 3x + 1)}}$

(b) $y = x^x$

(c) $y = x^{\ln x}$

(d) $y = (x^2 + 2x)\sqrt[4]{(x^3 - x + 1)}$

(e) $y = \dfrac{x^6 + x^3 + 1}{\sqrt{2x^2 + 1}}$

6. If elasticity

$$e = \frac{x}{y} \cdot \frac{dy}{dx}$$

show that

$$e = \frac{d(\ln y)}{d(\ln x)}$$

7. Derive the formula

$$\frac{d}{dx}(\log_a U) = \frac{1}{U}\log_a e \frac{du}{dx}$$

where U is a differentiable function of x. Find dy/dx for the following:

(a) $y = \log_2 (6x^3 + 6x^2 + 6x + 1)$

(b) $y = \log_7 \dfrac{3x^2 + 1}{1 - 3x^2}$

(c) $y = \log_{11} [(x^2 + 1)^4 (7x + 1)^6]$

(d) $y = \log_5 \left(\dfrac{x^2 + 2}{x^4 + 4}\right)^3$

(e) $y = (\log_3 2x^2)^3$

8. If $y = e^x$, use the inverse function and the rule for the inverse function of a derivative to prove that

$$\frac{d}{dx}(e^x) = e^x$$

9. By using $a^u = e^{u \ln a}$, prove that

$$\frac{d}{dx}(a^u) = a^u \ln a \frac{du}{dx}$$

where a is a constant and u is a differentiable function of x. Find the derivatives of the following:

(a) $y = 4^x$

(b) $y = 6^{x^2 + 2x + 1}$

(c) $y = 18x^3 \cdot 6^{3x^2}$

(d) $y = 3^{-2x^2 - 1/x}$

(e) $y = 5^{-x}$

10. Find dy/dx:

(a) $y = e^{-x}$

(b) $y = e^{6x + 2}$

(c) $y = e^{3x^2 + 9x}$

(d) $y = e$

(e) $y = x^2 e^{3x^3 - 2x^2}$

(f) $y = e^{e^{nx}}$

(g) $y = e^{1/x}$

(h) $y = e^{e^{x^2}}$

(i) $y = \dfrac{e^x - e^{-x}}{e^x + e^{-x}}$

(j) $y = e^x \ln x$

11. Use mathematical induction to prove:

(a) $\dfrac{d^n}{dx^n}(xe^x) = (x + n)e^x$

(b) $\dfrac{d^n}{dx^n}(x^{n-1} \ln x) = \dfrac{(n - 1)!}{x}$

(c) $\dfrac{d^n}{dx^n}(xe^{-x}) = (-1)^n(x - n)e^{-x}$

12. Verify the following:

(a) $\dfrac{d^2y}{dx^2} - 3\dfrac{dy}{dx} - 10y = 0$ for $y = e^{5x}, e^{-2x}$

(b) $\dfrac{d^2y}{dx^2} - 7\dfrac{dy}{dx} + 12y = 0$ for $y = e^{4x}, e^{3x}$

(c) $\dfrac{d^4y}{dx^2} - 5\dfrac{d^2y}{dx^2} + 4y = 0$ for $y = e^{x}, e^{-x}, e^{2x}, e^{-2x}$

(d) $\dfrac{d^2y}{dx^2} - 2\dfrac{dy}{dx} + y = 0$ for $y = e^{x}, xe^{x}$

(e) Draw conclusions about the differential equations when $y = e^{mx}$ is a root.

13. If e^{ix} is defined as

$$e^{ix} = \cos x + i \sin x$$

find $\sin x$ and $\cos x$ in terms of e^{ix}. Use this result and the trigonometric identities to prove:

(a) $\dfrac{d}{dx}(\sin x) = \cos x$

(b) $\dfrac{d}{dx}(\cos x) = -\sin x$

(c) $\dfrac{d}{dx}(\tan x) = \sec^2 x$

(d) $\dfrac{d}{dx}(\cot x) = -\csc^2 x$

(e) $\dfrac{d}{dx}(\sec x) = \sec x \tan x$

(f) $\dfrac{d}{dx}(\csc x) = -\csc x \cot x$

(g) If $y = \sin u$ where u is a differentiable function of x, what is dy/dx? Apply this to the other derivatives.

14. Find the elasticity:

(a) $y = e^{x}$

(b) $y = e^{-x^2}$

(c) $y = e^{x^2+x+1}$

(d) $y = x^{n}e^{ax+b}$

(e) $y = e^{ax}$

15. The hyperbolic functions are defined as

$$\sinh u = \tfrac{1}{2}(e^u - e^{-u}) \qquad \cosh u = \tfrac{1}{2}(e^u + e^{-u})$$

where u is a function of x. The other four hyperbolic functions can be derived from $\sinh u$ and $\cosh u$. Find $\tanh u$, $\coth u$, $\mathrm{sech}\ u$, $\mathrm{csch}\ u$. Verify the following:

(a) $\cosh^2 u - \sinh^2 u = 1$

(c) $\dfrac{d}{dx}(\cosh u) = \sinh u \dfrac{du}{dx}$

(b) $\dfrac{d}{dx}(\sinh u) = \cosh u \dfrac{du}{dx}$

(d) $\dfrac{d}{dx}(\tanh u) = \mathrm{sech}^2 u \dfrac{du}{dx}$

(e) $\dfrac{d}{dx}(\coth u) = -\mathrm{csch}^2 u \dfrac{du}{dx}$

(f) $\dfrac{d}{dx}(\mathrm{sech}\ u) = -\mathrm{sech}\ u \tanh u \dfrac{du}{dx}$

(g) $\dfrac{d}{dx}(\mathrm{csch}\ u) = -\mathrm{csch}\ u \coth u \dfrac{du}{dx}$

(h) $\sinh(-x) = -\sinh x$

(i) $\cosh(-x) = \cosh x$

16. Graph the six hyperbolic functions by following the definitions

$$\sinh x = \tfrac{1}{2}(e^x - e^{-x}) \qquad \cosh x = \tfrac{1}{2}(e^x + e^{-x})$$

17. Using the definitions

$$x = \sinh y = \tfrac{1}{2}(e^y - e^{-y}) \qquad x = \cosh y = \tfrac{1}{2}(e^y + e^{-y})$$

show that

(a) $\operatorname{arcsinh} x = \ln(x + \sqrt{x^2 + 1})$ \qquad for all x

(b) $\operatorname{arccosh} x = \ln(x + \sqrt{x^2 - 1})$ \qquad for \quad $x \geq 1$

(c) $\operatorname{arctanh} x = \dfrac{1}{2}\ln\dfrac{1 + x}{1 - x}$ \qquad for \quad $x^2 < 1$

(d) $\operatorname{arccoth} x = \dfrac{1}{2}\ln\dfrac{x + 1}{x - 1}$ \qquad for \quad $x^2 > 1$

(e) $\operatorname{arcsech} x = \ln\dfrac{1 + \sqrt{1 - x^2}}{x}$ \qquad for \quad $0 < x \leq 1$

(f) $\operatorname{arccsch} x = \ln\left(\dfrac{1}{x} + \dfrac{\sqrt{1 + x^2}}{|x|}\right)$ \qquad for \quad $x \neq 0$

18. Using problems 13 and 15, find dy/dx:

(a) $y = \sin 4x - \cos 5x$

(f) $y = \sinh \left(\dfrac{x}{4} \right)$

(b) $y = \tan 4_x$

(g) $y = \cosh^2 x$

(c) $y = \cot (x^5)$

(h) $y = \ln (\sinh x)$

(d) $y = x^3 \cos x$

(i) $y = x^2 \tanh x$

(e) $y = \dfrac{\sin x}{x}$

(j) $y = \operatorname{sech} (3x^2)$

19. Find dy/dx; use problems 13 and 15.

(a) $y = e^{\sin x}$

(c) $y = e^{x^2} \cos^3 2x$

(b) $y = xe^{\cosh x}$

(d) $y = \cos (e^{4x^2})$

20. If $e^{iy} = \cos y + i \sin y$, verify:

(a) $|e^{iy}| = 1, |e^{x+iy}| = e^x$

(b) $e^{x+i(y+2\pi)} = e^{x+iy}$

(c) $2 \sin y \cos y = \sin 2y$

(d) $\sin^2 y + \cos^2 y = 1$

(e) $e^{i(\pi/2)} = i, e^{i\pi} = -1, e^0 = 1, e^{i(3\pi/2)} = -i$

(f) $e^{x+i(y+\pi)} = -e^{x+iy}$

(g) $\overline{e^{(x+iy)}} = \overline{(e^{x+iy})}$

8
PARTIAL DIFFERENTIATION

In a function of two or more variables

$$z = f(x, y)$$

x and y can vary independently of each other, and each variation in either x or y, or both, will result in a new value of z. If x, y, and z are treated as the axes of a rectangular coordinate system, the function will trace out a three-dimensional surface.

Suppose that the amount of capital used is measured along the x-axis, the amount of labor employed along the y-axis, and the amount of output, corn, along the z-axis. The xy plane will be made up of points representing various combinations of labor and capital. Corresponding to each combination of labor and capital there will be a given amount of the output, corn, measured by the vertical height on the z-axis.

As another example of a three-dimensional function, one can measure the consumption of food on the x-axis, and the consumption of clothing on the y-axis. Then the z-axis can be used to represent the various levels of satisfaction associated with the varying combinations of food and clothing consumed.

These relationships can be seen in Figure 8-1, which represents a three-dimensional surface, with two cross sections shown.

If the function $z = f(x, y)$ is continuous, then a small change in one or both of the independent variables will result in a small change in z. A function $z = f(x, y)$ is defined as continuous if when $x = a$, and $y = b$, $z = f(a, b)$. Or in terms of limits

$$\lim_{\substack{x \to a \\ y \to b}} f(x, y) = f(a, b)$$

Then the function z is continuous in x and in y in the neighborhood where $x = a$ and $y = b$.

PARTIAL DERIVATIVES

One of the independent variables of the function $z = f(x, y)$ can be held constant by assigning a specific value to it, and the rate of change of the

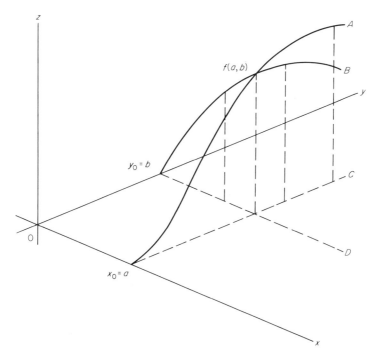

FIGURE 8-1   A Surface with Two Cross Sections Shown

function can then be measured with respect to the other variable only. For example, y can be assigned a specific value so that it becomes the constant

$$y = y_0 = b$$

Holding the value $y = b$, one can move on the xy plane along the line bD, parallel to the x-axis and perpendicular to the y-axis at $b = y_0$. Then as x increases, z will increase or decrease as specified by the function. The measurement of the rate of change of z with respect to x while y remains constant is called the *partial derivative* of z with respect to x, and is symbolized by

$$\frac{\partial z}{\partial x} = \text{partial derivative of } z \text{ with respect to } x$$

Alternatively, it may be desired to hold x constant at some value $x = x_0 = a$, and treat z as a function of y. Then, geometrically, the movement will be on the xy plane along a line aC parallel to the y-axis and perpendicular to the x-axis at the point where $x_0 = a$. Then z will vary as y changes in value. The measure of the rate of change of z with respect to y, while x is held constant at some value, is called the partial derivative of z with respect to y, and is symbolized by

$$\frac{\partial z}{\partial y} = \text{partial derivative of } z \text{ with respect to } y$$

The partial derivatives are derived from the following relationships:

$$\frac{\partial z}{\partial x} = \lim_{\Delta x \to 0} \frac{f(x + \Delta x, y_0) - f(x, y_0)}{\Delta x}$$

$$\frac{\partial z}{\partial y} = \lim_{\Delta y \to 0} \frac{f(x_0, y + \Delta y) - f(x_0, y)}{\Delta y}$$

Partial derivatives are denoted by

$$\frac{\partial z}{\partial x} = f_x(x, y) = \frac{\partial}{\partial x} f(x, y) = f_x = z_x$$

$$\frac{\partial z}{\partial y} = f_y(x, y) = \frac{\partial}{\partial y} f(x, y) = f_y = z_y$$

Consider a few examples of partial derivatives. In each case, the object is to find the partial derivatives of the dependent variable with respect to each of the independent variables.

1. $z = x^2 + 2xy + y^5$

$$\frac{\partial z}{\partial x} = 2x + 2y$$

is the partial derivative of z with respect to x, treating y as a constant. If $y = 2$ and $x = 3$, the value of the partial derivative will be

$$\frac{\partial z}{\partial x} = 2(3) + 2(2) = 10$$

This means that in the neighborhood where $x = 3$ and $y = 2$, the rate of change of z with respect to x is equal to 10.

$$\frac{\partial z}{\partial y} = 2x + 5y^4$$

is the partial derivative of z with respect to y, treating x as a constant. If $y = 2$ and $x = 3$, then the value of the partial derivative will be

$$\frac{\partial z}{\partial y} = 2(3) + 5(2^4) = 86$$

This means that in the neighborhood where $x = 3$ and $y = 2$, the rate of change of z with respect to y is equal to 86.

2. $z = ax^2 + bxy + cy^2 + dx + ey + f$

$$\frac{\partial z}{\partial x} = 2ax + by + d$$

$$\frac{\partial z}{\partial y} = bx + 2cy + e$$

3. $z = x^3 + x^2y + y^2 - 10x + 8y + 6$

$$\frac{\partial z}{\partial x} = 3x^2 + 2xy - 10$$

$$\frac{\partial z}{\partial y} = x^2 + 2y + 8$$

4. $z = xy^2 + \dfrac{5}{x} - \dfrac{6}{y^2}$

$$\frac{\partial z}{\partial x} = y^2 - \frac{5}{x^2}$$

$$\frac{\partial z}{\partial y} = 2xy + \frac{12}{y^3}$$

5. Let the utility function of the consumption of good A and good B be represented by the function

$$U = 2e^{6Q_aQ_b}$$

where U is utility, Q_a is the quantity of good A consumed, and Q_b is the quantity of good B consumed. Then the marginal utility of good A is the partial derivative of U with respect to good A, and the marginal utility of good B is the partial derivative of U with respect to good B.

$$\frac{\partial U}{\partial Q_a} = 12Q_b e^{6Q_aQ_b} \qquad \text{(marginal utility of good } A)$$

$$\frac{\partial U}{\partial Q_b} = 12Q_a e^{6Q_aQ_b} \qquad \text{(marginal utility of good } B)$$

6. Given a production function

$$Q = f(a, b, c, d)$$
$$= 6a + 10b + 8c + 4d - 0.6a^2 - 0.4b^2 - 0.5c^2 - 0.25d^2$$

$$\frac{\partial Q}{\partial a} = 6 - 1.2a \qquad \text{(marginal product of factor } a\text{)}$$

$$\frac{\partial Q}{\partial b} = 10 - 0.8b \qquad \text{(marginal product of factor } b\text{)}$$

$$\frac{\partial Q}{\partial c} = 8 - c \qquad \text{(marginal product of factor } c\text{)}$$

$$\frac{\partial Q}{\partial d} = 4 - 0.5d \qquad \text{(marginal product of factor } d\text{)}$$

TOTAL DIFFERENTIAL

In the case of a function involving three variables, partial derivatives give the rate of change of the dependent variable with respect to each of the independent variables, while the other independent variable is treated as a constant. The total differential provides a linear approximation of the amount of change in the dependent variable when both of the independent variables change by a small amount.

If z is the quantity of corn produced, x is the amount of capital used in corn production on a particular farm, and y is the amount of labor employed in corn production, then the function $z = f(x, y)$ is the production function of corn. The amount of change in corn output associated with a given small change in the amount of capital used is $(\partial z/\partial x)\,\Delta x$. In the same way, the amount of change in corn production due to a small amount of change in the use of labor is $(\partial z/\partial y)\,\Delta y$.

The total amount of change in corn output can be thought of as the sum of the increments or decrements in corn output due to changes in both x and y.

$$\Delta z = \frac{\partial z}{\partial x}\Delta x + \frac{\partial z}{\partial y}\Delta y$$

If $\Delta z = dz, \Delta x = dx, \Delta y = dy$, then the equation for Δz can be rewritten as

$$dz = \frac{\partial z}{\partial x}dx + \frac{\partial z}{\partial y}dy$$

This expression gives the amount of change in z due to small amounts of change in both x and y.

Consider a few examples of finding the values of the total differentials of a few functions of several variables.

1. $z = 6x^3 + 4y^2$

$$\frac{\partial z}{\partial x} = 18x^2$$

$$\frac{\partial z}{\partial y} = 8y$$

$$dz = 18x^2\, dx + 8y\, dy$$

Let $x = 2$ and $y = 3$ be the point at which the individual partial derivatives and the total differential of the function are to be evaluated. Let $dx = 1$, and $dy = 1$.

$$\frac{\partial z}{\partial x} = f_x(x) = f_x(2) = 18(2^2) = 72$$

$$\frac{\partial z}{\partial x} = f_y(y) = f_y(3) = 8(3) = 24$$

$$dz = \frac{\partial z}{\partial x}\, dx + \frac{\partial z}{\partial y}\, dy = 72(1) + 24(1) = 96$$

2. $z = x^2 - 4xy + 3y^2$

$$\frac{\partial z}{\partial x} = 2x - 4y$$

$$\frac{\partial z}{\partial y} = -4x + 6y$$

Let $x = 4$ and $y = 5$. Let $dx = 0.5$ and $dy = 0.5$.

$$dz = \frac{\partial z}{\partial x}\, dx + \frac{\partial z}{\partial y}\, dy$$

$$\frac{\partial z}{\partial x} = f_x(x, y) = f_x(4, 5) = 2(4) - 4(5) = -12$$

$$\frac{\partial z}{\partial y} = f_y(x, y) = f_y(4, 5) = (-4)(4) + 6(5) = 14$$

$$dz = (-12)(0.5) + 14(0.5) = -6 + 7 = 1$$

DIFFERENTIATION OF IMPLICIT FUNCTIONS

Suppose an implicit function

$$f(x, y) = 0$$

is given. In this function, x is defined as an implicit function of y, and y as an implicit function of x. When a third variable z is introduced and z is set equal to the implicit function $f(x, y)$, there is a new relationship

$$z = f(x, y)$$

Differentiating this new function with respect to x yields

$$\frac{dz}{dx} = \frac{\partial f}{\partial x} + \frac{\partial f}{\partial y}\frac{dy}{dx}$$

in which y is considered a function of x. Now let y be a specific function of x, satisfying the original equation

$$f(x, y) = 0$$

Then $z = 0$ and $dz = 0$. From these relationships, it appears that

$$\frac{\partial f}{\partial x} + \frac{\partial f}{\partial y}\frac{dy}{dx} = 0$$

$$\frac{\partial f}{\partial y}\frac{dy}{dx} = -\frac{\partial f}{\partial x}$$

Therefore,

$$\frac{dy}{dx} = \frac{-(\partial f/\partial x)}{\partial f/\partial y} = -\frac{\partial f/\partial x}{\partial f/\partial y}$$

Differentiating the function

$$z = f(x, y)$$

with respect to y,

$$\frac{dz}{dy} = \frac{\partial f}{\partial y} + \frac{\partial f}{\partial x}\frac{dx}{dy}$$

where x is a function of y. Now let x be a specific function of y, satisfying the original implicit function

$$f(x, y) = 0$$

Then $z = 0$ and $dz = 0$. Therefore,

$$\frac{\partial f}{\partial y} + \frac{\partial f}{\partial x}\frac{dx}{dy} = 0$$

$$\frac{\partial f}{\partial x}\frac{dx}{dy} = -\frac{\partial f}{\partial y}$$

Solving for dx/dy,

$$\frac{dx}{dy} = \frac{-(\partial f/\partial y)}{\partial f/\partial x} = -\frac{\partial f/\partial y}{\partial f/\partial x}$$

The method of differentiating implicit functions is useful, because occasion-ally a function will be found in an implicit form that is difficult or impossible to convert to an explicit function. In such a case, if differentiation is desired, it is best carried out by the method just discussed.

Here are some examples of the differentiation of implicit functions.

1. $f(x, y) = 2x^2 - xy + y^2$

$$\frac{dy}{dx} = -\frac{4x - y}{-x + 2y} = \frac{y - 4x}{2y - x}$$

$$\frac{dx}{dy} = -\frac{-x + 2y}{4x - y} = \frac{x - 2y}{4x - y}$$

2. $f(x, y) = x^3 + 4x^2y^2 + 2y^4$

$$\frac{dy}{dx} = -\frac{3x^2 + 8xy^2}{8x^2y + 8y^3} = \frac{-3x^2 - 8xy^2}{8x^2y + 8y^3}$$

$$\frac{dx}{dy} = -\frac{8x^2y + 8y^3}{3x^2 + 8xy^2} = \frac{-8x^2y - 8y^3}{3x^2 + 8xy^2}$$

3. $f(x, y) = x^3 - y^3 + 4xy$

$$\frac{dy}{dx} = -\frac{3x^2 + 4y}{-3y^2 + 4x} = \frac{-3x^2 - 4y}{4x - 3y^2}$$

$$\frac{dx}{dy} = -\frac{-3y^2 + 4x}{3x^2 + 4y} = \frac{3y^2 - 4x}{3x^2 + 4y}$$

4. Let the utility of the consumption of two goods x and y be denoted by U, and let U be some constant.

$$U = f(x, y) = c$$

This is an indifference curve, whose slope is

$$\frac{dy}{dx} = -\frac{f_x}{f_y} = -\frac{\text{marginal utility of } x}{\text{marginal utility of } y}$$

where f_x is the partial derivative of the utility function with respect to x, or the marginal utility of x; and f_y is the partial derivative of U with respect to y, or the marginal utility of y.

In indifference curve analysis, it is shown that consumer equilibrium is attained when the slope of the indifference curve is equal to the slope of the budget line. The equation of a budget line is

$$P_xQ_x + P_yQ_y = M$$

where P_x is the price of commodity x, P_y is the price of y, Q_x and Q_y are the quantities of x and y respectively, and M is the amount of the budget to be spent on x and y. The budget line can be rewritten as

$$Q_y = \frac{M}{P_y} - \frac{P_x}{P_y} Q_x$$

The slope of the budget line is now given by the derivative of Q_y with respect to Q_x, i.e.,

$$\frac{d(Q_y)}{d(Q_x)} = -\frac{P_x}{P_y}$$

The slope of the budget line is therefore the negative of the ratio of the price of x to the price of y. Consumer equilibrium is defined as

$$-\frac{f_x}{f_y} = -\frac{P_x}{P_y}$$

This formulation of the equilibrium position of a consumer by indifference curve analysis shows that the consumer will achieve his utility maximizing equilibrium by equating the ratio of the marginal utility of x to the marginal utility of y, to the ratio of the price of x to the price of y.

PARTIAL DERIVATIVES OF HIGHER ORDER

The first-order partial derivatives of the function $z = f(x, y)$ have been shown to be

$$\frac{\partial z}{\partial x} = f_x(x, y) \qquad \text{and} \qquad \frac{\partial z}{\partial y} = f_y(x, y)$$

The second-order partial derivatives of z in respect to x are

$$\frac{\partial}{\partial x}\left(\frac{\partial z}{\partial x}\right) = \frac{\partial^2 z}{\partial x^2} = f_{xx}(x, y)$$

$$\frac{\partial}{\partial y}\left(\frac{\partial z}{\partial x}\right) = \frac{\partial^2 z}{\partial y \, \partial x} = f_{yx}(x, y)$$

The second-order partial derivatives of z in respect to y are

$$\frac{\partial}{\partial y}\left(\frac{\partial z}{\partial y}\right) = \frac{\partial^2 z}{\partial y^2} = f_{yy}(x, y)$$

$$\frac{\partial}{\partial x}\left(\frac{\partial z}{\partial y}\right) = \frac{\partial^2 z}{\partial x \, \partial y} = f_{xy}(x, y)$$

Consider the two direct second-order partial derivatives

$$\frac{\partial^2 z}{\partial x^2} = f_{xx}(x, y) \qquad \frac{\partial^2 z}{\partial y^2} = f_{yy}(x, y)$$

Since the first partial derivative $\partial z/\partial x$ measures the rate of change of z with respect to x while y is treated as a constant, the second partial derivative $\partial^2 z/\partial x^2$ measures the slope of the first partial derivative. If z is output produced, with x the labor input and y the capital input, then $\partial z/\partial x$ is the marginal physical productivity of labor. Thus $\partial^2 z/\partial x^2$ gives the rate of change of labor's marginal physical productivity with changes in labor.

Similarly $\partial z/\partial y$ measures the marginal physical productivity of capital and $\partial^2 z/\partial y^2$ measures the rate of change of marginal physical productivity of capital with respect to changes in the amount of capital used.

The second-order mixed partial derivatives are $\partial^2 z/\partial y\,\partial x$ and $\partial^2 z/\partial x\,\partial y$. In general $\partial z/\partial x$ and $\partial z/\partial y$ are both functions of x and y. In words, then, $\partial^2 z/\partial y\,\partial x$ measures the rate of change of $\partial z/\partial x$ with respect to y and $\partial^2 z/\partial x\,\partial y$ measures the rate of change of $\partial z/\partial y$ with respect to x. Provided the first-order partial derivatives are continuous, the second-order mixed partial derivatives are equal, that is,

$$\frac{\partial^2 z}{\partial y\,\partial x} = \frac{\partial^2 z}{\partial x\,\partial y}$$

Since the second-order mixed partial derivatives are equal, there are three distinct second-order partial derivatives:

$$f_{xx}(x, y), f_{xy}(x, y) = f_{yx}(x, y), f_{yy}(x, y)$$

The following section gives some examples of second-order partial derivatives.

1. $$z = 3x^4 - y^3 + 2x^2 y^2 - 3y^3 x + y$$

$$\frac{\partial z}{\partial x} = 12x^3 + 4xy^2 - 3y^3$$

$$\frac{\partial^2 z}{\partial x^2} = 36x^2 + 4y^2$$

$$\frac{\partial^2 z}{\partial y\,\partial x} = 8xy - 9y^2$$

$$\frac{\partial z}{\partial y} = -3y^2 + 4x^2 y - 9y^2 x + 1$$

$$\frac{\partial^2 z}{\partial y^2} = -6y + 4x^2 - 18yx$$

$$\frac{\partial^2 z}{\partial x\,\partial y} = 8xy - 9y^2$$

Notice that

$$\frac{\partial^2 z}{\partial y\, \partial x} = \frac{\partial^2 z}{\partial x\, \partial y}$$

2. $$z = 2x^2 + xy^2 + 3y^3$$

$$\frac{\partial z}{\partial x} = 4x + y^2$$

$$\frac{\partial^2 z}{\partial x^2} = 4$$

$$\frac{\partial^2 z}{\partial y\, \partial x} = 2y$$

$$\frac{\partial z}{\partial y} = 2xy + 9y^2$$

$$\frac{\partial^2 z}{\partial y^2} = 2x + 18y$$

$$\frac{\partial^2 z}{\partial x\, \partial y} = 2y$$

Again notice that

$$\frac{\partial^2 z}{\partial y\, \partial x} = \frac{\partial^2 z}{\partial x\, \partial y}$$

HOMOGENEOUS FUNCTIONS

The class of equations (or more precisely identities) called *homogeneous functions* is especially useful in economic theory. A homogeneous function is defined as a function whose value is changed by the factor of k^p when the independent variables are changed by the factor of k. That is, a homogeneous function is such that if

$$z = f(x, y)$$

then

$$f(kx, ky) = k^p f(x, y)$$

where p is the degree of homogeneity.

Homogeneous functions of various degrees will be illustrated in this section, and economic applications will be shown where appropriate.

Homogeneity of Degree Zero

Let

$$z = f(x, y) = \frac{x}{y}$$

If the independent variables x and y are changed by the same proportion k, the value of the function will be

$$f(kx, ky) = \frac{kx}{ky} = k^0 \cdot \frac{x}{y} = \frac{x}{y}$$

Here, when the values of the independent variables are changed by a factor k, the value of the function is changed by the amount k^0. This means that the value of the function will remain unchanged, because $k^0 = 1$. A function of this type is called a homogeneous function of degree zero. For such a function,

$$z = f(x, y) = f(kx, ky)$$

Let P be the price, Q the quantity demanded of a good, and Y the income of the consumer. The demand function is given as

$$Q = f(P, Y) = \frac{Y}{aP}$$

If the consumer's income rises k times and the price of the good rises k times, the quantity demanded will be

$$Q = f(kP, kY) = \frac{kY}{akP} = k^0 \cdot \frac{Y}{aP} = \frac{Y}{aP} = k^0 \cdot f(Y, P) = f(Y, P)$$

This means that the quantity demanded is unchanged when both the income and the price change by the same proportion k. A consumer who behaves in such a way is said to have no money illusion.

Consider the case of a commodity x for which the quantity demanded Q_x is a function of its price P_x and the price of a second good P_y. Let such a demand function be

$$Q_x = f(P_x, P_y) = \frac{30P_y}{P_x}$$

If the price of x and the price of y were both doubled, the quantity demanded of x would be unchanged, since

$$f(2P_x, 2P_y) = \frac{2(30)P_y}{2P_x} = 2^0 \cdot \frac{30P_y}{P_x} = 2^0 \cdot f(P_x, P_y) = f(P_x, P_y) = Q_x$$

When the relative prices of x and y are unchanged, the consumer's demand for x remains unchanged.

Homogeneity of Degree One

Equations such as

$$z = f(x, y) = x + y \qquad z = f(x, y) = x^{0.5}y^{0.5} \qquad z = f(x, y) = x^d y^{1-d}$$

are integral rational equations of degree 1 in x and y (see Chapter 2.) In such functions, if the independent variables are changed by the same proportion k, the value of the function will also be changed by the proportion k. If

$$f(x, y) = x + y$$

then

$$f(kx, ky) = kx + ky = k(x + y) = kf(x, y)$$

If

$$f(x, y) = x^{0.5}y^{0.5}$$

then

$$f(kx, ky) = (kx)^{0.5} = k^{0.5}x^{0.5}k^{0.5}y^{0.5}$$
$$= k(x^{0.5}y^{0.5}) = kf(x, y)$$

If

$$f(x, y) = x^d y^{1-d}$$

then

$$f(kx, ky) = (kx)^d(ky)^{1-d} = k^d x^d k^{1-d}y^{1-d} = k(x^d y^{1-d}) = kf(x, y)$$

These are examples of homogeneous equations of degree 1. They are also called *linearly* homogeneous functions.

When a production function is homogeneous and of degree 1, certain very important relationships may be deduced. The well-known Cobb-Douglas production function is linear and homogeneous. It is represented by a function such as

$$Q = f(L, C) = aL^b C^{1-b}$$

where Q is the output, L is labor, C is capital, a and b are constants. In this case, if the amount of labor and capital employed in production were to be changed by some proportion k, output would increase by that same proportion k.

$$f(kL, kC) = a(kL)^b(kC)^{1-b} = ak^b L^b k^{1-b}C^{1-b} = kaL^b C^{1-b}$$
$$= kf(L, C)$$

Assume, for illustrative purposes, the following values for the constants:

$$a = 1.5 \qquad b = 0.75 \qquad k = 2$$

With these values of the constants, the initial output will be

$$Q = f(L, C) = 1.5L^{0.75}C^{0.25} \tag{1}$$

When labor and capital are both doubled, output will be

$$\begin{aligned} f(2L, 2C) &= 1.5(2L)^{0.75}(2C)^{0.25} \\ &= 1.5(2^{0.75})L^{0.75}(2^{0.25})C^{0.25} \\ &= (2)1.5L^{0.75}C^{0.25} \\ &= 2f(L, C) \end{aligned}$$

The result is that output is exactly doubled.

If the output defined by equation (1) is held at the level of Q_0, the function defines an isoquant along whose locus are the various combinations of labor and capital yielding the output Q_0. The equation of such an isoquant will be

$$1.5L^{0.75}C^{0.25} = Q_0 \tag{2}$$

If capital is plotted on the ordinate and labor on the abscissa, equation (2) can be rewritten so that C becomes the dependent variable and L the independent variable. To do so, first raise to the 4th power each term of (2) and write

$$(1.5)^4 L^3 C = Q_0^4 \tag{3}$$

Solve (3) for C:

$$C = \frac{Q_0^4}{1.5^4 L^3} \tag{4}$$

The slope of the isoquant representing $Q = Q_0$ in the capital-labor plane is

$$\frac{dC}{dL} = -\frac{3Q_0^4}{(1.5)^4 L^4}$$

But from (3),

$$Q_0^4 = (1.5)^4 L^3 C$$

Make this substitution:

$$\frac{dC}{dL} = -\frac{3[(1.5)^4 L^3 C]}{(1.5)^4 L^4} = -\frac{3C}{L} \tag{5}$$

Of course, the slope of the isoquant may also be derived by implicit differentiation:

$$\frac{dC}{dL} = -\frac{\partial f/\partial L}{\partial f/\partial C} = -\frac{1.125L^{-0.25}C^{0.25}}{0.375L^{0.75}C^{-0.75}} = \frac{MPP_L}{MPP_C} \tag{6}$$

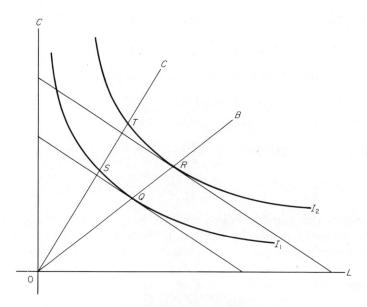

FIGURE 8-2   Slopes of Isoquants Developed from a Linearly Homo-geneous Production Function

Simplify:

$$\frac{dC}{dL} = -\frac{3C}{L} \tag{7}$$

Equations (5) and (7) are expressions of the derivative of the isoquant for $Q = Q_0$ in Figure 8-2, with capital as the ordinate and labor as the abscissa. Equation (6) is the general expression for the derivative of any among the family of isoquants arising from the production function

$$Q = 1.5L^{0.75}C^{0.25}$$

Now assume that equation (1) gives the production function, from which any number of isoquants may be specified by assuming different values for Q, so that

$$Q = Q_0, Q = Q_1, Q = Q_2, \ldots, Q = Q_n$$

The production budget is given by the relation

$$P_LL + P_CC = M$$

where P_L is the price of labor, P_C is the price of capital, and M is the production budget. A whole family of production budget lines may be defined by assuming different values of M such that

$$M = M_0, M = M_1, M = M_2, \ldots, M = M_n$$

Assume the following values:

$$P_L = 3 \qquad P_C = 1 \qquad M = 140$$

The production budget equation then becomes

$$3L + C = 140$$
$$C = 140 - 3L \tag{8}$$

Given the production function (1) and the budget equation (8), the equilibrium level of production is defined by a system of two equations.

$$\frac{MPP_L}{P_L} = \frac{MPP_C}{P_C}$$

$$P_L L + P_C C = M$$

From the given data,

$$MPP_L = \frac{\partial Q}{\partial L} = \frac{1.125 C^{0.25}}{L^{0.25}}$$

$$MPP_C = \frac{\partial Q}{\partial C} = \frac{0.375 L^{0.75}}{C^{0.75}}$$

In Figure 8-2, the points of the isoquants intersected by the lines OB and OC will have the same slope. Point Q on isoquant I_1 will have the same slope as point R on isoquant I_2, and along OC, point S on I_1 and point T on I_2 will have the same slope.

Yet another interesting characteristic of the linearly homogeneous production function is that if the factors of production such as labor and capital were paid their marginal products, the total product would be exhausted. Assume that the production function is

$$Q = 1.5 L^{0.75} C^{0.25}$$

Then the marginal product of labor is

$$MPP_L = \frac{\partial Q}{\partial L} = 0.75(1.5 L^{-0.25} C^{0.25})$$

If L amount of labor is hired, the total wage bill will be wages times L

$$\text{Wage bill} = 0.75(1.5 L^{-0.25} C^{0.25})L$$
$$= 0.75(1.5 L^{0.75} C^{0.25})$$

The wage bill is shown to be 75 percent of the total output. Given that same production function, the marginal productivity of capital is

$$MPP_C = \frac{\partial Q}{\partial C} = 0.25(1.5 L^{0.75} C^{-0.75})$$

With the employment of C amount of capital, the capital share of the total product is

$$\text{Capital share} = 0.25(1.5L^{0.75}C^{-0.75})C$$
$$= 0.25(1.5L^{0.75}C^{0.25})$$

For equilibrium, the relations are

$$\frac{1.125C^{0.25}}{3L^{0.25}} = \frac{0.375L^{0.75}}{C^{0.75}} \tag{9}$$

$$C = 140 - 3L \tag{10}$$

Multiplying both sides of equation (9) by $3L^{0.25}C^{0.75}$ gives

$$1.125C = 1.125L$$

which is

$$C = L \tag{11}$$

Solving (11) simultaneously with (10) yields

$$L = 35 \quad \text{and} \quad C = 35$$

Now assume that while the prices of labor and capital remain constant, the production budget is increased from 140 to 280. The production budget equation will become

$$C = 280 - 3L \tag{12}$$

The solution of (11) with (12) will yield

$$L = 70 \quad \text{and} \quad C = 70$$

Given a linear homogeneous production function, if the ratio of the prices of labor and capital do not change, the ratio in which labor and capital are to be combined will remain unchanged as the production budget is increased or decreased. The two equilibrium positions are points Q and R of Figure 8-2. Point Q corresponds to a production budget of $M = 140$. At that point the amount of labor employed is 35 and the amount of capital is 35, and the slope of the budget line and the slope of the isoquant I_1 are equal. When the budget is increased to 280, the new budget line retains the same slope because of the assumption that the price of labor and the price of capital remain the same. The new budget line is tangent to isoquant I_2 at point R. The slope of I_2 at R must be equal to the slope of the budget line. Therefore the slope of I_1 at Q and the slope of I_2 at R must be equal. As a matter of fact, on all conceivable isoquants derived from a linearly homogeneous production function, the slopes at the points intersected by the line OA must all be equal. This is so because the measure of the slope of the isoquants arising from the production function

$$Q = 1.5L^{0.75}C^{0.25}$$

is

$$\frac{dC}{dL} = -\frac{3C}{L}$$

Then for $C = 35$ and $L = 35$

$$\frac{dC}{dL} = -3$$

For $C = 2(35) = 70$ and $L = 2(35) = 70$

$$\frac{dC}{dL} = -3$$

If the initial combination of labor and capital were, say, $L = 20$ and $C = 10$, the slope of the isoquant would be

$$\frac{dC}{dL} = \frac{-3(10)}{20} = -1.5$$

If labor and capital were both increased to $2\frac{1}{2}$ times these values, the new values

$$L = 2.5(20) = 50 \qquad C = 2.5(10) = 25$$

would result in a higher isoquant. The slope of the new isoquant corresponding to $L = 50$ and $C = 25$ would be

$$\frac{dC}{dL} = \frac{-3(25)}{50} = -1.5$$

The capital share amounts to 25 percent of the total output; the combined returns received by labor and capital will equal the total output. This relationship, in which total product is exhausted when the factors of production are paid their marginal products, is usually spoken of as the *adding up theorem* of marginal productivity theory. The *adding up theorem* is based on an important mathematical relationship called *Euler's theorem* (discussed in the section after the following one).

Homogeneity of Degrees Higher than One

Consider the following functions:

1. $z = f(x, y) = xy$
   $f(kx, ky) = kxky = k^2xy = k^2f(x, y)$

This is a homogeneous function of degree 2.

2. $z = f(x, y) = x^2y$
$f(kx, ky) = (kx)^2(ky) = k^3(xy) = k^3f(x, y)$

This is a homogeneous function of degree 3.

3. $u = f(x, y, z) = x^3y^3z - x^2y^2z^3 + xy^3z^3 - y^2z^5$
$f(kx, ky, kz) = (kx)^3(ky)^3(kz) - (kx)^2(ky)^2(kz)^3$
$\qquad + (kx)(ky)^3(kz)^3 - (ky)^2(kz)^5$
$\qquad = k^7(x^3y^3z) - k^7(x^2y^2z^3) + k^7(xy^3z^3) - k^7(y^2z^5)$
$\qquad = k^7(x^3y^3z - x^2y^2z^3 + xy^3z^3 - y^2z^5)$
$\qquad = k^7f(x, y, z)$

This is a homogeneous function of degree 7.

Homogeneous functions of degrees greater than 1 may be used to represent cases in production function in which the returns to scale are increasing, i.e., when output rises by a greater proportion than a given proportionate increase in all the inputs. As an illustration, assume production processes in which the quantity of output, Q, is some function of the amount of labor employed, L, and the amount of capital used, C.

4. $Q = f(L, C) = 2LC$

Tripling the amount of L and the amount of C gives

$$f(3L, 3C) = 2(3L)(3C) = 3^2(2LC) = 3^2f(L, C)$$

As the inputs were multiplied by 3, output increased by $3^2 = 9$ times. This is clearly a case of increasing returns to scale.

5. Consider a production function which is homogeneous of degree 4

$$Q = f(L, C) = L^2C^2 + L^3C$$

Tripling the use of labor and capital,

$$f(3L, 3C) = (3L)^2(3C)^2 + (3L)^3(3C)$$
$$= 3^4(L^2C^2) + 3^4(L^3C)$$
$$= 3^4(L^2C^2 + L^3C)$$
$$= 3^4f(L, C)$$

While the inputs were multiplied by 3, the output was increased by a factor of 3^4. Again this case illustrates a case of increasing returns to scale.

In order to round out the picture of the various possible patterns of returns to scale, this example shows the case in which a homogeneous function of a degree less than 1 can illustrate the case of diminishing returns to scale.

6. Consider the production function

$$Q = f(L, C) = \frac{L^{3/2}}{C}$$

Suppose both labor and capital are increased by a factor of 4.

$$f(4L, 4C) = \frac{(4L)^{3/2}}{4C} = 4^{1/2}\left(\frac{L^{3/2}}{C}\right) = 4^{1/2}f(L, C)$$

As inputs are increased four times, output in this case increases only by a factor of $\sqrt{4} = 2$. Since output is increasing at a lower rate than are the inputs, this is a case of decreasing returns to scale.

EULER'S THEOREM

Euler's theorem is developed from the special properties of the homogeneous functions. It states essentially that given a homogeneous function of degree p, if each independent variable is multiplied by the partial derivative of the function with respect to that variable, the sum of these products will equal the original function multiplied by p, the degree of homogeneity. Symbolically, this means that given the function $z = f(x, y)$, then

$$\frac{\partial f}{\partial x} \cdot x + \frac{\partial f}{\partial y} \cdot y = pz$$

The properties of Euler's theorem can be illustrated with a few examples.

1. $z = x^2 + 2xy + y^2$

This is a homogeneous function of degree $p = 2$. By Euler's theorem the relationship is

$$\frac{\partial z}{\partial x} \cdot x + \frac{\partial z}{\partial y} \cdot y = 2z$$

In this particular problem

$$\frac{\partial z}{\partial x} = 2x + 2y$$

$$\frac{\partial z}{\partial x} \cdot x = (2x + 2y)x = 2x^2 + 2xy \tag{1}$$

$$\frac{\partial z}{\partial y} = 2x + 2y$$

$$\frac{\partial z}{\partial y} \cdot y = (2x + 2y)y = 2xy + 2y^2 \tag{2}$$

Now add relations (1) and (2) to get

$(2x^2 + 2xy) + (2xy + 2y^2)$

$$= 2x^2 + 4xy + 2y^2 = 2(x^2 + 2xy + y^2) \quad (3)$$

The final expression of equation (3) is precisely $p \cdot z$, which establishes Euler's relation

$$\frac{\partial z}{\partial x} \cdot x + \frac{\partial z}{\partial y} \cdot y = pz$$

2. $z = u^3 + uxy + x^2y + y^3$

Here the relationship involves three independent variables and a homogeneous equation of degree 3. Thus $p = 3$.

$$\frac{\partial z}{\partial u} = 3u^2 + xy$$

$$\frac{\partial z}{\partial u} \cdot u = (3u^2 + xy)u = 3u^3 + uxy \quad (1)$$

$$\frac{\partial z}{\partial x} = uy + 2xy$$

$$\frac{\partial z}{\partial x} \cdot x = (uy + 2xy)x = uxy + 2x^2y \quad (2)$$

$$\frac{\partial z}{\partial y} = ux + x^2 + 3y^2$$

$$\frac{\partial z}{\partial y} \cdot y = (ux + x^2 + 3y^2)y = uxy + x^2y + 3y^3 \quad (3)$$

Add (1), (2), and (3),

$(3u^3 + uxy) + (uxy + 2x^2y) + (uxy + x^2y + 3y^3)$

$$= 3u^3 + 3uxy + 3x^2y + 3y^3$$
$$= 3(u^3 + uxy + x^2y + y^3)$$

Again the result is that the sum of the partial derivatives with respect to each independent variable multiplied by their respective independent variables is equal to the degree of homogeneity of the original equation, (in this case $p = 3$) multiplied by the original function.

To prove the general proposition of Euler's theorem, consider the homogeneous function

$$f(kx, ky) = k^p f(x, y)$$

First differentiate the left-hand side implicitly with respect to k.

$$\frac{\partial f(kx, ky)}{\partial k} = \frac{\partial f(kx, ky)}{\partial kx} \cdot \frac{\partial kx}{\partial k} + \frac{\partial f(kx, ky)}{\partial ky} \cdot \frac{\partial ky}{\partial k}$$

$$= x \cdot \frac{\partial f(kx, ky)}{\partial kx} + y \cdot \frac{\partial f(kx, ky)}{\partial ky}$$

$$= x f_{kx} + y f_{ky}$$

Since k may assume any value, set $k = 1$. Then for the left-hand member,

$$x f_x + y f_y = x \frac{\partial f}{\partial x} + y \frac{\partial f}{\partial y} \tag{1}$$

Differentiating the right-hand side gives

$$p k^{p-1} f(x, y)$$

Again since $k = 1$, $k^{p-1} = 1$, and the right-hand member becomes

$$p f(x, y) \tag{2}$$

Equating (1) and (2) yields the general result,

$$x \frac{\partial f}{\partial x} + y \frac{\partial f}{\partial y} = p f(x, y)$$

Economic Applications of Euler's Theorem

In connection with the linearly homogeneous function, the various implications of the Cobb-Douglas type of production function were discussed. In the case of a linearly homogeneous production function such as the Cobb-Douglas, the payment of the marginal product to each factor exactly exhausts the total output.

Now consider a production in which there are increasing returns to scale, so that the degree of homogeneity is greater than 1. Suppose the production function in question is of the form

$$Q = C^2 + 4CL + L^2$$

where Q is total output and C and L represent the amount of capital and labor employed respectively. This production function is a homogeneous function of degree 2, for increasing both factors of production by the same proportion, k, will increase total output by a factor of k^2, so that

$$f(kC, kL) = (kC)^2 + 4(kC)(kL) + (kL)^2$$
$$= k^2 C^2 + 4k^2 CL + k^2 L^2 = k^2 (C^2 + 4CL + L^2)$$

In this case the marginal product of capital will be

$$\frac{\partial Q}{\partial C} = 2C + 4L$$

Then capital's share of the output of the economy will be

$$\frac{\partial Q}{\partial C} C = (2C + 4L)C = 2C^2 + 4CL$$

The wage rate is the marginal product of labor, namely

$$\frac{\partial Q}{\partial L} = 4C + 2L$$

and the total amount of wages paid is the wage rate multiplied by the amount of labor employed, or

$$\frac{\partial Q}{\partial L} L = (4C + 2L)L = 4CL + 2L^2$$

The total amount of claims against the national product is the sum of the returns due capital and the total wages which must be paid, or

$$\frac{\partial Q}{\partial C} C + \frac{\partial Q}{\partial L} L = (2C^2 + 4CL) + (4CL + 2L^2)$$

$$= 2C^2 + 8CL + 2L^2$$

$$= 2(C^2 + 4CL + L^2)$$

Clearly in this case the total of claims upon the national product is twice as large as the total output of the economy. This results from the fact that the original production function is a homogeneous function of degree 2. This is a production function with increasing returns to scale. In such an event, either capital holders will develop some monopsonistic power in their purchases of labor services and force labor to accept a rate of return less than the marginal product of labor, or labor may form a powerful union, exert monopolistic power in the selling of labor services, and thereby force capital to accept a rate of return less than its marginal product.

Under these circumstances, several interesting economic observations might be made. First, there are increasing returns to scale. Due to this fact, there will be a tendency for firms to increase in size. But secondly, if each factor is to be paid exactly at the rate of its marginal productivity, there will be an insufficiency of resources to pay all factors. As a result, thirdly, there will be a tendency for labor and capital to organize and for each to try to force the other to accept a rate of return less than its marginal productivity. These are the classic conditions under which bilateral monopoly struggles will generally develop. It is a well-known theorem of economics that under bilateral monopoly, the solution of the division of output will be indeterminate. The solution will depend upon the relative bargaining strengths of the respective power groups.

Now consider a production function

$$Q = f(C, L) = C^{1/4}L^{1/4}$$

This production function is homogeneous of degree $\frac{1}{2}$, for if both capital and labor were increased by a proportion k, the output would increase only by the factor of $k^{1/2}$, which may be shown by the following relation

$$f(kC, kL) = (kC)^{1/4}(kL)^{1/4} = k^{1/2}(C^{1/4}L^{1/4})$$

Given a production function of this type, the returns to scale are clearly decreasing. What then would be the result of paying each factor its marginal product? The marginal product of capital is

$$\frac{\partial Q}{\partial C} = \frac{1}{4}C^{-3/4}L^{1/4}$$

The total of returns to capital is equal to the marginal product of capital times the amount of capital used, namely

$$\frac{\partial Q}{\partial C}C = (\frac{1}{4}C^{-3/4}L^{1/4})C = \frac{1}{4}(C^{1/4}L^{1/4})$$

The marginal product of labor is the partial derivative of output with respect to labor,

$$\frac{\partial Q}{\partial L} = \frac{1}{4}C^{1/4}L^{-3/4}$$

The total of returns to labor is the product of labor's marginal product times the amount of labor employed,

$$\frac{\partial Q}{\partial L}L = (\frac{1}{4}C^{1/4}L^{-3/4})L = \frac{1}{4}(C^{1/4}L^{1/4})$$

The sum of the claims by labor and capital is given by

$$\frac{\partial Q}{\partial C}C + \frac{\partial Q}{\partial L}L = \frac{1}{4}(C^{1/4}L^{1/4}) + \frac{1}{4}(C^{1/4}L^{1/4}) = \frac{1}{2}(C^{1/4}L^{1/4})$$

In this case, the payment of marginal product to each factor results in a total payment to capital and labor of only $\frac{1}{2}$ of the total output. A surplus results. Thus in the case of decreasing returns to scale, payment of its marginal product to each factor will not exhaust the output.

A Geometric Interpretation of Euler's Theorem and its Applications

Given a linear homogeneous (production) function, Euler's theorem states that

$$Q = K\frac{\partial Q}{\partial K} + L\frac{\partial Q}{\partial L}$$

for the two-variable case. In non-mathematical terms, this states that a linear homogeneous function can be written as the sum of the products of the independent variables and the first partial derivatives of the function with respect to those independent variables. When Euler's theorem is applied to production theory in economics, it is also known as the "adding-up theorem." That is, if conditions of constant returns to scale exist, and if each factor of input is paid its marginal product, the total product will be completely depleted by the apportionment. For example, under conditions of constant returns to scale, the quantity produced will be tripled if the amounts of capital and labor used are tripled (assuming that capital and labor are the only factors of production).

A three-dimensional graph with quantity, capital, and labor axes would be ideal for interpreting Euler's theorem, but since a three-dimensional representation of such a graph is difficult to draw and interpret, a two-dimensional graph is provided in Figure 8-3. The axes of the graph represent quantity and capital.

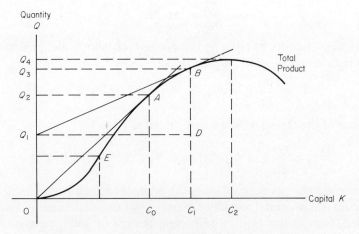

FIGURE 8-3   A Geometric Demonstration of Euler's Theorem

Consider production at the point B. The line segment Q_1B is tangent at B, so

$$\frac{\partial Q}{\partial K} = \frac{dQ_B}{dK} = \frac{BD}{Q_1D} = \frac{BD}{OC_1} = \frac{Q_1Q_3}{OC_1}$$

$$K = OC_1$$

$$K\frac{\partial Q}{\partial K} = OC_1 \cdot \frac{Q_1Q_3}{OC_1} = Q_1Q_3$$

The total product at B is

$$TP = Q = BC_1 = OQ_3$$

Using Euler's theorem,

$$Q = L\frac{\partial Q}{\partial L} + K\frac{\partial Q}{\partial K}$$

$$OQ_3 = Q_1Q_3 + L\frac{\partial Q}{\partial L}$$

$$L\frac{\partial Q}{\partial L} = OQ_3 - Q_1Q_3 = OQ_1$$

or

$$OQ_3 = Q_1Q_3 + OQ_1$$

Consider production at point C. This is the point of maximum output, and

$$\frac{\partial Q}{\partial K} = 0$$

Thus

$$Q = K(0) + L\frac{\partial Q}{\partial L} \qquad \text{or} \qquad \frac{Q}{L} = \frac{\partial Q}{\partial L}$$

In terms of economics, when the marginal physical product of capital is zero, the average physical product of labor equals the marginal physical product of labor. Also the corresponding statement can be made when

$$\frac{\partial Q}{\partial L} = 0$$

then

$$\frac{Q}{K} = \frac{\partial Q}{\partial K}$$

At the point A, where the line OA is tangent to the curve, average physical product of capital is at its maximum. The marginal physical product will take on its maximum at point E, the point of inflection. Remember that this is only a cross-section of the problem.

Assume that the production function is

$$Q = cK^aL^B$$

where c is some constant.

$$\frac{\partial Q}{\partial K} = acK^{a-1}L^B \qquad \frac{\partial Q}{\partial L} = BcK^aL^{B-1}$$

Using Euler's theorem

$$Q = K\frac{\partial Q}{\partial K} + L\frac{\partial Q}{\partial L}$$

$$Q = K(acK^{a-1}L^B) + L(BcK^aL^{B-1})$$

$$Q = acK^aL^B + BcK^aL^B$$

$$Q = cK^aL^B(a + B)$$

The values of a and B will determine the nature of the returns to scale. If $a + B < 1$, then

$$cK^aL^B > cK^aL^B(a + B)$$

which indicates decreasing returns to scale. If $a + B = 1$, then

$$cK^aL^B = cK^aL^B(a + B)$$

which indicates constant returns to scale. If $a + B > 1$, then

$$cK^aL^B < cK^aL^B(a + B)$$

indicating increasing returns to scale.

RELATIONSHIP OF CONSTANT RETURNS TO SCALE AND MARGINAL PRODUCTIVITY

The famous neoclassical growth model can be stated as follows: *if the condition of pure competition exists, and each factor of input receives a return equal to the value of its marginal product, then the returns to scale are constant.* Let

$$R_K = P\frac{\partial Q}{\partial K} \qquad R_L = P\frac{\partial Q}{\partial L}$$

be given, where R_K and R_L are the returns paid to capital and labor respectively, P is the price of the output, and $\partial Q/\partial K$ and $\partial Q/\partial L$ are the marginal products of capital and labor respectively. Let the production function be given as $Q = Q(K, L)$. The rule of additivity (Euler's theorem) shows that the total output is the sum of the marginal products multiplied by their respective amounts of input, i.e.,

$$Q = K\frac{\partial Q}{\partial K} + L\frac{\partial Q}{\partial L}$$

Take the differential of the production function:

$$dQ = \frac{\partial Q}{\partial K}\,dK + \frac{\partial Q}{\partial L}\,dL$$

Divide by Q

$$\frac{dQ}{Q} = \frac{\partial Q}{\partial K}\frac{dK}{Q} + \frac{\partial Q}{\partial L}\frac{dL}{Q}$$

Since

$$\frac{\partial Q}{\partial K}\frac{dK}{Q}\cdot\frac{K}{K} = \frac{\partial Q}{\partial K}\frac{dK}{Q}$$

$$\frac{\partial Q}{\partial L}\frac{dL}{Q}\cdot\frac{L}{L} = \frac{\partial Q}{\partial L}\frac{dL}{Q}$$

the result is unchanged, so that

$$\frac{dQ}{Q} = \frac{\partial Q}{\partial K}\frac{dK}{Q}\frac{K}{K} + \frac{\partial Q}{\partial L}\frac{dL}{Q}\frac{L}{L}$$

$$\frac{dQ}{Q} = \frac{\partial Q}{\partial K}\frac{K}{Q}\frac{dK}{K} + \frac{\partial Q}{\partial L}\frac{L}{Q}\frac{dL}{L}$$

Now consider the factors

$$\frac{\partial Q}{\partial K}\frac{K}{Q} \quad \text{and} \quad \frac{\partial Q}{\partial L}\frac{L}{Q}$$

Observe that

$$\frac{\partial Q}{\partial K}\frac{K}{Q} = \frac{\partial(\ln Q)}{\partial(\ln K)} = E_K$$

$$\frac{\partial Q}{\partial L}\frac{L}{Q} = \frac{\partial(\ln Q)}{\partial(\ln L)} = E_L$$

Thus

$$\frac{dQ}{Q} = \frac{\partial(\ln Q)}{\partial(\ln K)}\frac{dK}{K} + \frac{\partial(\ln Q)}{\partial(\ln L)}\frac{dL}{L}$$

or

$$\frac{dQ}{Q} = E_K \frac{dK}{K} + E_L \frac{dL}{L}$$

Notice that dQ/Q, dK/K, and dL/L are the proportional rates of growth of quantity, capital, and labor respectively for a given period of time. The elasticity of output with respect to capital, E_K, is that proportion of output paid to capital; similarly, E_L is the proportion of output paid to labor.

If the proportional rate of growth of output is 10 percent, the proportional growth rates of labor and capital must be 10 percent each. Thus the result would be constant returns to scale. Thus if X represents the proportional growth rates

$$E_K = A \qquad E_L = B$$

the following equation results:

$$X = AX + BX = (A + B)X \qquad \text{where} \qquad X = \frac{dQ}{Q} = \frac{dK}{K} = \frac{dL}{L}$$

Thus $A + B = 1$. That is, the sum of the elasticities of output with respect to the inputs must equal 1 for the case of constant returns to scale. In the case of increasing returns to scale, $A + B$ would be greater than 1 and an element of monopoly would be present, but this would contradict the original assumption of pure competition.

The equation

$$\frac{dQ}{Q} = E_K \frac{dK}{K} + E_L \frac{dL}{L}$$

can now be rewritten as

$$\frac{dQ}{Q} = A \frac{dK}{K} + B \frac{dL}{L}$$

If A and B are constants, and initial conditions are not considered, the solution of this differential equation is

$$Q = CK^A L^B$$

or

$$Q = CK^A L^{1-A} = CK^{1-B} L^B \qquad \text{if} \qquad A + B = 1$$

where C is some constant that must be determined from the initial condition. This equation is the general Cobb-Douglas production function.

The converse of the previous model can be stated as follows: *if conditions of pure competition and constant returns to scale exist, then each factor of input will receive a return equal to the value of its marginal product.* Since the condition of constant returns to scale is given, the production function will be linear homogeneous (of degree 1) and

$$E_K + E_L = 1$$

Note that this relationship can be derived from Euler's theorem by dividing the production function

$$Q = K \frac{\partial Q}{\partial K} + L \frac{\partial Q}{\partial L}$$

by Q. Taking the differential of the production function yields

$$dQ = \frac{\partial Q}{\partial K} dK + \frac{\partial Q}{\partial L} dL$$

Divide by dQ,

$$1 = \frac{\partial Q}{\partial K} \frac{dK}{dQ} + \frac{\partial Q}{\partial L} \frac{dL}{dQ}$$

Using the fact that

$$E_K + E_L = \frac{K}{Q} \frac{\partial Q}{\partial K} + \frac{L}{Q} \frac{\partial Q}{\partial L} = 1$$

Set the two equations equal

$$\frac{K}{Q} \frac{\partial Q}{\partial K} + \frac{L}{Q} \frac{\partial Q}{\partial L} = \frac{\partial Q}{\partial K} \frac{dK}{dQ} + \frac{\partial Q}{\partial L} \frac{dL}{dQ}$$

$$\left(\frac{K}{Q} - \frac{dK}{dQ} \right) \frac{\partial Q}{\partial K} = \left(\frac{dL}{dQ} - \frac{L}{Q} \right) \frac{\partial Q}{\partial L}$$

$$\frac{(K/Q) - (dK/dQ)}{(dL/dQ) - (L/Q)} = \frac{\partial Q/\partial L}{\partial Q/\partial K} = \frac{MP_L}{MP_K} = \frac{P_L}{P_K} = \frac{R_L}{R_K} = MRTS_{L \text{ for } K}$$

Note that P_L and P_K are the market demand prices and R_L and R_K are supplier's returns. Recall that the marginal product of labor divided by the marginal product of capital is the marginal rate of technical substitution of labor for capital.

Some other relations can be derived from the market price equation.

$$\frac{(K/Q) - (dK/dQ)}{(dL/dQ) - (L/Q)} = \frac{P_L}{P_K}$$

$$P_K \left(\frac{K}{Q} \right) - P_K \frac{dK}{dQ} = P_L \frac{dL}{dQ} - P_L \left(\frac{L}{Q} \right)$$

$$P_K \left(\frac{K}{Q} \right) + P_L \frac{L}{Q} = P_K \frac{dK}{dQ} + P_L \frac{dL}{dQ}$$

$$\frac{P_K K + P_L L}{Q} = P_K \frac{dK}{dQ} + P_L \frac{dL}{dQ}$$

Notice that if the prices, P_K and P_L, are fixed, then

$$\frac{P_K K + P_L L}{Q}$$

is the average cost, and

$$P_K \frac{dK}{dQ} + P_L \frac{dL}{dQ}$$

is the marginal cost. That is, the budget or cost function is

$$C = P_K K + P_L L$$

Thus, average cost and marginal cost are equal for all outputs, and average cost is constant. (This can be verified by use of differential equations.) Therefore,

$$P = \frac{C}{Q} = \frac{P_K K + P_L L}{Q}$$

where P is the price corresponding to the constant average cost. Recall the following equation:

$$1 = \frac{\partial Q}{\partial K} \frac{dK}{dQ} + \frac{\partial Q}{\partial L} \frac{dL}{dQ}$$

Multiply through by P to obtain

$$P = P \frac{\partial Q}{\partial K} \frac{dK}{dQ} + P \frac{\partial Q}{\partial L} \frac{dL}{dQ}$$

Since

$$\frac{\partial Q / \partial L}{\partial Q / \partial K} = \frac{P_L}{P_K} \quad \text{then} \quad \frac{\partial Q}{\partial L} = \left(\frac{P_L}{P_K}\right) \frac{\partial Q}{\partial K}$$

Substitute into the equation for $\partial Q / \partial L$:

$$P = P \frac{\partial Q}{\partial K} \frac{dK}{dQ} + P \frac{P_L}{P_K} \frac{\partial Q}{\partial K} \frac{dL}{dQ}$$

Now multiply through by P_K:

$$PP_K = PP_K \frac{\partial Q}{\partial K} \frac{dK}{dQ} + PP_L \frac{\partial Q}{\partial K} \frac{dL}{dQ}$$

Factoring out the term $P(\partial Q / \partial K)$ from the right-hand member of the above equation leads to

$$PP_K = \left(P_K \frac{dK}{dQ} + P_L \frac{dL}{dQ}\right) P \frac{\partial Q}{\partial K}$$

Now the expression within the parentheses on the right-hand side of this equation is really an expression for the marginal cost of production. Under pure competition, marginal cost is equated with the product price; thus P, the product price, may be substituted for the expression within the parentheses. Make that substitution:

$$PP_K = P \cdot \frac{\partial Q}{\partial K}$$

Dividing through by P gives

$$P_K = P \frac{\partial Q}{\partial K}$$

which says that the price of capital is equal to the value of the marginal product of capital. By similar analysis it is apparent that

$$P_L = P \frac{\partial Q}{\partial L}$$

Note that

$$\frac{P_K}{\partial Q/\partial K} = \frac{P_L}{\partial Q/\partial L} = MC = P$$

Since the returns paid to capital and labor were defined at the beginning of this section as

$$R_K = P \frac{\partial Q}{\partial K} \qquad R_L = P \frac{\partial Q}{\partial L}$$

it is clear that each factor of input will receive a return equal to the value of its marginal physical product under conditions of constant returns to scale and pure competition.

THE THEORY OF LONG-RUN TOTAL COST

A series of short-run cost functions and the long-run cost function were developed in Chapter 6, and their various properties were examined. In this section, the envelope technique involving parametric substitutions and partial derivatives will be used to show, in more general and abstract terms, the relationship between short-run cost functions and the long-run cost function.

Suppose a family of short-run total cost functions which are dependent upon varying plant sizes are given. Then the problem to be solved is the determination of a long-run total cost function from the given short-run total cost functions. This long-run total cost curve would be the minimum cost for the various levels of output over the range of the varying plant sizes.

If the levels of fixed inputs are represented by a parameter t upon which the different plant sizes will depend, then increasing plant sizes would be represented by increasing values of the parameter t. Mathematically, the parameter t will be an independent variable in the equations of cost, of the production function, and of the expansion path. Thus, the number of possible options will depend upon the values over which t may range.

Stated in terms of explicit functions, the production function is

$$Q = f(K, L, t)$$

the cost equation is

$$C = P_K \cdot K + P_L \cdot L + g(t)$$

and the expansion path function is

$$p(K, L, t) = 0$$

where Q = output, K = capital, L = labor, and P_K and P_L are the respective prices. The function $g(t)$ is the fixed cost, and it increases with increasing plant sizes. By eliminating the variables K and L in the cost function, the total cost may be expressed as a function of output and parameter t:

$$C = h(Q, t) + g(t)$$

This cost equation will define the family of short-run total cost curves by letting the values of t vary.

The long-run total cost curve will be derived from the family of short-run cost curves by the method of envelopes. A long-run curve that is tangent to each short-run curve at a point and that will not intersect any of the short-run curves will be found. This process will yield a long-run total cost function which will be the minimum cost of production over the range of varying plant sizes. Thus, if a particular quantity to be produced is given, then the total cost which is the minimum should be selected by computing the total cost for each of the possible plant sizes. Or, mathematically, the long-run total cost curve is the locus of points of minimum cost for the family of short-run curves.

The *envelope* of a family of curves is a curve that is tangent to each member of the family. The theory of envelopes is developed as follows: Let f be an implicit function, $f(x, y, t) = 0$, and let t be a parameter such that $x = x(t)$ and $y = y(t)$. For a point of tangency

$$\frac{\partial f}{\partial x}\frac{dx}{dt} + \frac{\partial f}{\partial y}\frac{dy}{dt} + \frac{\partial f}{\partial t} = 0 \qquad (1)$$

On a member of the family of curves, t is a constant, so that

$$\frac{\partial f}{\partial x} dx + \frac{\partial f}{\partial y} dy = 0$$

is the differential. The slope for a member of the family is

$$\frac{dy}{dx} = -\frac{\partial f/\partial x}{\partial f/\partial y}$$

The slope of the envelope is

$$\frac{dy}{dx} = \frac{dy/dt}{dx/dt}$$

The points of tangency are found by equating the slopes:

$$\frac{dy/dt}{dx/dt} = -\frac{\partial f/\partial x}{\partial f/\partial y}$$

or

$$\frac{\partial f}{\partial x}\frac{dx}{dt} + \frac{\partial f}{\partial y}\frac{dy}{dt} = 0 \qquad (2)$$

From equations (1) and (2) it can be seen that

$$\frac{\partial f}{\partial t} = 0$$

Thus the envelope can be found by solving the equations

$$f(x, y, t) = 0 \qquad \frac{\partial f}{\partial t} = 0$$

simultaneously.

As an application of this theory to the economic problem stated earlier in this section, the family of short-run cost curves can be written with parameters in an implicit form:

$$f(C, Q, t) = h(Q, t) + g(t) - C = 0$$

Now take the partial derivative of f with respect to t and set it equal to zero:

$$\frac{\partial f}{\partial t} = 0$$

Solving the two equations simultaneously eliminates the parameter, t, and cost, C, can be expressed as a function of quantity, i.e., $C = \phi(Q)$.

For these examples, assume that each of the short-run total cost functions is in the form of a cubic equation. The cubic will be as follows:

$$SRTC = aQ^3 - bQ^2 + cQ + d$$

where a, b, c, and d are all positive constant coefficients and $b^2 < 3ac$. Or, expressed as a function,

$$SRTC = f(Q) + d$$

where $f(Q)$ is the total variable cost (*TVC*) and d is the total fixed cost (*TFC*). The assumption that each of the short-run total cost functions is a cubic of the given form will provide the required properties of cost functions.

Since the long-run total cost function is to be derived from the family of short-run total cost functions, the long-run total cost function will also be a cubic equation. It will have the form

$$LRTC = AQ^3 - BQ^2 + CQ$$

where the coefficients A, B, and C are all positive constants, and

$$B^2 < 3AC$$

Notice that

$$LRTC = f(Q)$$

Since the definition of the long-run total cost function states that all inputs are variable, no fixed cost appears in this cubic equation. The cubic equation of long-run total cost will originate at the origin whereas the cubics of the various short-run total cost functions will originate along the cost axis at the value of their fixed cost, as is shown in Figure 8-4.

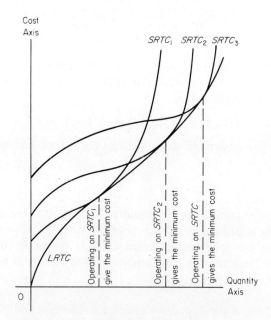

FIGURE 8-4 Relation Between Long-Run Total Cost and Short-Run Total Costs

Suppose that a family of short-run total cost functions can be expressed in the following form with the range of the parameter t determining the number of short-run curves and their respective plant sizes:

$$SRTC = aQ^3 - bQ^2 + (e - ft)Q + dt^2$$

where d, e, and f are constants and

$$(e - ft) = C > 0$$

for the range of t. Now by the method of envelopes

$$\phi(Q, t) = SRTC = aQ^3 - bQ^2 + (e - ft)Q + dt^2$$

$$\frac{\partial \phi}{\partial t} = -fQ + 2\,dt = 0$$

$$t = \frac{f}{2d}\,Q$$

Substitute for t and express the function as long-run total cost, $LRTC$:

$$LRTC = aQ^3 - bQ^2 + \left[e - f\left(\frac{f}{2d}\right)Q\right]Q + d\left(\frac{f}{2d}\,Q\right)^2$$

$$= aQ^3 - bQ^2 + eQ - \frac{f^2}{2d}Q^2 + \frac{f^2}{4d}Q^2$$

$$= aQ^3 - \left[b + \frac{f^2}{2d} - \frac{f^2}{4d}\right]Q^2 + eQ = AQ^3 - BQ^2 + CQ$$

where the conditions previously stated must hold.

If a number of short-run total cost functions and their respective plant sizes are given, the long-run total cost function is to be found, then the problem should be solved by the method illustrated in the following example:

$$SRTC_1 = 0.009Q^3 - 0.5Q^2 + 17Q + 10 \qquad \text{for } t = 1$$
$$SRTC_2 = 0.009Q^3 - 0.5Q^2 + 15Q + 40 \qquad \text{for } t = 2$$
$$SRTC_3 = 0.009Q^3 - 0.5Q^2 + 13Q + 90 \qquad \text{for } t = 3$$

The equation of the family of short-run curves expressed with the parameter t, then, is

$$SRTC = 0.009Q^3 - 0.5Q^2 + (19 - 2t)Q + 10t^2$$

Now, proceeding by the method of envelopes

$$\frac{\partial \phi}{\partial t} = -2Q + 20t = 0$$

$$t = \tfrac{1}{10}Q$$

Substituting into the equation of $LRTC$,

$$LRTC = 0.009Q^3 - 0.5Q^2 + (19 - \tfrac{2}{10}Q)Q + \frac{Q^2}{10}$$

$$= 0.009Q^3 - [0.5 + 0.2 - 0.1]Q^2 + 19Q$$

$$= 0.009Q^3 - 0.6Q^2 + 19Q$$

which satisfies the conditions for a long-run total cost function.

It is worth noting that long-run average cost is the envelope of the short-run average costs. This is true since the long-run average cost is the long-run total cost divided by the output, and also since the long-run average cost is tangent to each of the short-run average costs. However, the long-run marginal cost is *not* the envelope of the short-run marginal cost functions. This is true since marginal cost is found by taking the derivative of total cost and also by the definition of the long-run marginal cost as the locus of points on the short-run marginal cost which represent the optimum output for each plant size.

PROBLEMS

1. Evaluate the following limits:

   (a) $\lim_{(x,y) \to (2,1)} (xy - 4x + 2y + 4)$

   (b) $\lim_{(x,y) \to (1,2)} (x^2 y - y^2 x + 3x + y + 2)$

   (c) $\lim_{(x,y) \to (0,0)} \left(\dfrac{4x - 3y}{3x - 4y} \right)$

2. The iterated limits

$$\lim_{x \to x_0} \lim_{y \to y_0} f(x,y) = \lim_{y \to y_0} \lim_{x \to x_0} f(x,y)$$

   must be equal if

$$\lim_{(x,y) \to (x_0,y_0)} f(x,y)$$

   is to exist. Check the three cases for the following:

   (a) $\lim_{(x,y) \to (0,0)} \left(\dfrac{x - y}{x + y} \right)$

   (b) $\lim_{(x,y) \to (1,-2)} \left(\dfrac{x + y + 5}{3x - 2y + 3} \right)$

(c) $\displaystyle\lim_{(x,y)\to(1,\pi)} 13x^6 \cos\left(\frac{y}{x^2}\right)$

3. Check the continuity of the following functions:

(a) $z = \dfrac{x^3 + y^3}{x^2 + y^2}$ at (a, b)

(b) $z = \dfrac{x^2 + 3xy + 4y^2 + y + 2}{3x - 2y}$ at $(0, 0)$

(c) $z = \begin{vmatrix} \dfrac{x - y}{x + y} & \text{if } (x, y) \neq (0, 0) \quad \text{at } (0, 0) \\ 0 & \text{if } (x, y) = (0, 0) \end{vmatrix}$

4. Find $\Delta z/\Delta x$ and $\Delta z/\Delta y$ for the following:

(a) $z = 2xy + 3x + 4y + 1$ (c) $z = 3x^2 + y^3 x^3$

(b) $z = x^2 - 2xy + 2y^2$ (d) $z = x^3 y + x^2 y^2 + xy^3$

5. Apply $\displaystyle\lim_{\Delta x \to 0} \frac{\Delta z}{\Delta x}$ and $\displaystyle\lim_{\Delta y \to 0} \frac{\Delta z}{\Delta y}$

    to the equations in problem 4.

6. Find $\dfrac{\partial z}{\partial x}$ and $\dfrac{\partial z}{\partial y}$:

(a) $z = 6x^2 + 4y^2 + 3x - 10y + 2$

(b) $z = x^3 y + 2x^4 + y^5$ (i) $z = \ln\left(\dfrac{x^2 + y^2}{xy}\right)$

(c) $z = xy + x^4 y^2 + y\sqrt{x}$ (j) $z = x^4 y^5 5^{x^2 + y^2}$

(d) $z = x^2 y e^{x^2 + y^2 + 4xy}$ (k) $z = x^2 y^3 \ln(x^3 y^2)$

(e) $z = e^{-x + y^2 x^3 + y - 1}$ (l) $z = \sqrt[3]{x^4 + y^5}$

(f) $z = \ln(x^2 + y^2)$ (m) $z = \dfrac{2x - y}{x + y}$

(g) $z = x^2 e^{xy}$ (n) $z = \sqrt{2xy^2}\, e^{-xy}$

(h) $z = x^{x^2 y}$ (o) $z = e^{y^2 - xy} \ln(4x + x^2 y)$

7. If $z = xy$, $\Delta x = dx$, and $\Delta y = dy$, find Δz, dz (the total differential), and $\Delta z - dz$. Interpret this problem geometrically.

8. Find the total differential:

(a) $z = 3x^2 + 4xy - y^2$ (c) $z = x^4y + x^2y^3 + y^5$

(b) $z = xy - 6x - 5y + 1$ (d) $z = x^2 - 7x + y^3 - 12$

9. Evaluate Δz and dz if $\Delta x = dx$ and $\Delta y = dy$:

(a) $z = 3x^2 + 2y - 6$ $x = 2$ $y = 1$ $dx = dy = 1$

(b) $z = x^3y + y^3x$ $x = 1$ $y = 1$ $dx = dy = 0.1$

(c) $z = x^2 - y^2 + 2xy$ $x = 4$ $y = 1$ $dx = 0.01$

    $dy = 0.02$

10. Use logarithms to find $\partial z/\partial x$ and $\partial z/\partial y$:

(a) $z = \dfrac{\sqrt{(x + y)(4y - x)}}{(x - y)(4x + 2)}$

(b) $z = (x^2 - 9)^4(y^4 + 16)^5(xy + 4)^6$

(c) $z = \dfrac{x^2 + xy + y^2}{(x^2 + y^2)^3}$

11. Find $\partial z/\partial x$ and $\partial z/\partial y$ for these implicit functions:

(a) $x^2 + y^2 + z^2 + xy + xz + yz + x + y + z = 0$

(b) $x^2z + y^2z + z^2yx = 0$

(c) $3x - 4z + 2y - 7xyz + 1 = 0$

(d) $xyz + x^2y^2z^2 + x - y = 0$

(e) $z^2 + xy + z + zy - 6 = 0$

Hint: Use $\dfrac{\partial F}{\partial x} + \dfrac{\partial F}{\partial z} \cdot \dfrac{\partial z}{\partial x} = 0$

12. Find dy/dx and dx/dy for the following:

(a) $f(x, y) = x^2 + y^2 - 25$

(b) $f(x, y) = x^2 - y^2 - 625$

(c) $f(x, y) = x^2y^2 + xye^{xy}$

(d) $f(x, y) = x^3 - y^3 + x^2 - y^2 + x - y - 1$

(e) $f(x, y) = x^5y - x^3y^3 + xy^5$

13. Find dz/dt:

(a) $z = 4x^2y^2$ $x = (t^2 + 2)^2$ $y = (2t^2 + t)^{1/3}$

(b) $z = e^{x^2+y^2}$ $x = te^{t^2}$ $y = e^t - e^{-t}$

(c) $z = x^3 - y^2$ $x = t^4e^{t-1}$ $y = 4t^2 \ln (2t + 1)$

14. If $F(x, y, z) = 0$, prove the following:

(a) $\dfrac{\partial z}{\partial x} = \dfrac{-F_x}{F_y}$

(b) $\dfrac{\partial x}{\partial y} \cdot \dfrac{\partial z}{\partial x} \cdot \dfrac{\partial y}{\partial z} = -1$

15. Verify the following:

(a) If $Z = f(x^2y)$, prove that

$$x \frac{\partial z}{\partial x} = 2y \frac{\partial z}{\partial y}$$

(b) If $Z = f(x^{2n}y^n)$, prove by induction that

$$x \frac{\partial z}{\partial x} = 2y \frac{\partial z}{\partial y}$$

16. Use the total differential to find the approximate value:

(a) $\sqrt{(6.02)^2 + (7.98)^2}$ $z = \sqrt{x^2 + y^2}$

(b) $\sqrt{(2.98)^2 + (2.01)^2 + (6.01)^2}$ $w = \sqrt{x^2 + y^2 + z^2}$

17. For a function of two variables $Z = f(x, y)$, the partial elasticities are defined as

$$Ex = \frac{x}{z} \frac{\partial z}{\partial x} \qquad Ey = \frac{y}{z} \frac{\partial z}{\partial y}$$

Find the elasticities for the following:

(a) $Z = Kx^by^{1-b}$ (c) $Z = x^3 + y^3$
(b) $Z = x^2y^2e^{xy}$ (d) $Z = e^{(x^2-2y^2)}$

18. Find the consumer equilibrium, given the utility function and the budget constraint:

(a) $U = x^2 + y^2 + z^2$ $Qx + 2Qy + 3Qz = 120$
(b) $U = x^3y^2z + 12x - 7y + 2z$ $2Qx + 7Qy + 6Qz = 200$

19. Find the marginal productivity for each factor, where P is the total product, and C, L, and R are factors of production:

(a) $P = 200 + 3L - 2C^2 + 7CL^2e^{CR} - 4R^3C$
(b) $P = 350\,CLR - 2C\ln(LR) - 2\sqrt{CR}\,e^{-2CL} + R^3 - \tfrac{1}{2}L^4$

20. Find the price and income elasticity for the following:

    (a) $q = 100 - 0.6p^5 + 0.7y$

    (b) $q = 650 - 0.3p^2 + 0.6y + 0.4py$

    (c) $q = 500 - 0.3p^3 + 0.5y + 0.1py$ $p = 10, y = 100$

    (d) $q = 100 + 0.5p^2 - 0.2y + 0.5py$ $p = 10, y = 100$

21. Find the partial derivative of the order indicated.

    (a) $Z = 4x^3 + 6y^2 + 7x^4y^2 + y$ f_{xx}

    (b) $Z = e^{x^2+xy}$ f_{xxx}

    (c) $Z = y^2e^{x^2+y^3}$ f_{yyy}

    (d) $Z = x^3y^2 + x^2y^3 + y$ f_{xyx}

    (e) $Z = \ln(x^2y)$ f_{yy}

    (f) $Z = x^3 + y^2 + x$ f_{xy}, f_{yx}

    (g) $Z = x^3e^x$ f_{xyx}

    (h) $Z = x^2 \ln(xy)$ f_{yxx}

    (i) $Z = x^2y + xy^2$ f_{yxx}

    (j) $Z = x^3y^2$ f_{yxxx}

22. Evaluate the partial derivatives as indicated:

    (a) $Z = 5x^3 + 4x^2y^2 + 9y^3$ $f_{xy}(1, -1)$

    (b) $Z = e^{x^2y}$ $f_{yxx}(0, 0)$

    (c) $Z = \ln(x^2 + y^2)$ $f_{xx}(-3, -4)$

    (d) $Z = x^2e^{xy}$ $f_{yy}(1, 0)$

    (e) $Z = 2x^2 + 3xy + y^2 + 6x - 5y - 17$ $f_{xyx}(2, 6)$

23. A function is Laplacian if it satisfies the partial differential equation

$$\frac{\partial^2 F}{\partial x^2} + \frac{\partial^2 F}{\partial y^2} = 0$$

Check the following functions:

    (a) $F(x, y) = 2x - 2xy + 2y + 1$

    (b) $F(x, y) = \ln(x^2 + y^2)$

24. An exact differential is of the form

$$P(x, y)\, dx + Q(x, y)\, dy$$

if and only if

$$\frac{\partial P}{\partial y} = \frac{\partial Q}{\partial x}$$

Check whether the following are exact:

(a) $(2x + 3) dx + (2y + 3) dy = 0$

(b) $(16x^2 + x + 1 + y) dx - (y^5 + y^3 - y - x + 1) dy = 0$

(c) $(8x^3y - x^2 - 4y^2 + x - 5) dx + (y^3 - 8xy + 2x^4 + 2) dy = 0$

25. Check the following functions for homogeneity, and find the degree:

(a) $Z = \dfrac{x^2 - y^2}{x^2 + y^2}$

(f) $Z = \dfrac{x}{x^2 + y^2}$

(b) $Z = x^2y^3 \ln \left(\dfrac{x}{y}\right)$

(g) $Z = \sqrt[3]{x^2y}$

(c) $Z = x^4 + y^4$

(h) $Z = \dfrac{x - y}{y}$

(d) $Z = x^2y^2 + xy\sqrt{xy}$

(i) $Z = \dfrac{x + y + \sqrt{xy}}{\sqrt{x^4}}$

(e) $Z = 4x^2 + 2xy - y^2$

(j) $Z = x^5y + x^3y^3 + x^2y^4 + y^6$

26. If $f(x, y, z)$ is a function with continuous partial derivatives and satisfies

$$f(Kx, Ky, Kz) = K^n f(x, y, z)$$

then prove

$$x \frac{\partial f}{\partial x} + y \frac{\partial f}{\partial y} + z \frac{\partial f}{\partial z} = nf$$

27. If $f(x, y)$ is homogeneous of degree 2, then prove that

$$x^2 \frac{\partial^2 f}{\partial x^2} + 2xy \frac{\partial^2 f}{\partial x \, \partial y} + y^2 \frac{\partial^2 f}{\partial y^2} = 2f$$

Factor this result and verify with

$$f(x, y) = xy \ln \left(\frac{y}{x}\right)$$

28. Verify for the homogeneous function $Z = Kx^ay^b$:

(a) $x \dfrac{\partial z}{\partial x} + y \dfrac{\partial z}{\partial y} = (a + b)Z$

(b) $x^2 \dfrac{\partial^2 z}{\partial x^2} + 2xy \dfrac{\partial^2 z}{\partial x \, \partial y} + y^2 \dfrac{\partial^2 z}{\partial y^2} = (a + b)(a + b - 1)Z$

29. If a function $f(x, y)$ is homogeneous of degree n, prove

$$x^2 \frac{\partial^2 f}{\partial x^2} + 2xy \frac{\partial^2 f}{\partial x \, \partial y} + y^2 \frac{\partial^2 f}{\partial y^2} = n(n - 1)f$$

30. Given the Cobb-Douglas function

$$Q = 10L^{0.6}C^{0.4}$$

and the budget constraint

$$6L + 4C = 100$$

find the equilibrium level of production and the returns received by labor and capital.

31. Apply Euler's theorem to these homogeneous functions:

(a) $Q = 3L^2 + 2CL - C^2$ if $K = 2$

(b) $Q = L^3C^2R^1 - C^4R^2 + R^6$ if $K = 3$

(c) $Q = L^3C^2 \ln \left(\dfrac{L}{C} \right)$ if $K = 4$

(d) $Q = \dfrac{LC}{C^4 + L^4}$ if $K = 2$

32. If $Z = \Theta(u, v)$, $u = f(x, y)$, and $v = g(x, y)$, and if

$$\frac{\partial u}{\partial x} = \frac{\partial v}{\partial y} \qquad \frac{\partial u}{\partial y} = - \frac{\partial v}{\partial x}$$

then prove that

(a) $\dfrac{\partial^2 u}{\partial x^2} + \dfrac{\partial^2 u}{\partial y^2} = \dfrac{\partial^2 v}{\partial x^2} + \dfrac{\partial^2 v}{\partial y^2} = 0$

(b) $\dfrac{\partial^2 \Theta}{\partial x^2} + \dfrac{\partial^2 \Theta}{\partial y^2} = \left\{ \left(\dfrac{\partial u}{\partial x} \right)^2 + \left(\dfrac{\partial v}{\partial x} \right)^2 \right\} \left(\dfrac{\partial^2 \Theta}{\partial u^2} + \dfrac{\partial^2 \Theta}{\partial v^2} \right)$

33. Verify the following:

(a) If

$$Z = x^n f \left(\frac{y}{x} \right)$$

prove

$$x \frac{\partial f}{\partial x} + y \frac{\partial f}{\partial y} = nZ$$

(b) If

$$Z = f(x + ay) + g(x - ay)$$

show that

$$\frac{\partial^2 z}{\partial x^2} = \frac{1}{a^2} \frac{\partial^2 z}{\partial y^2}$$

(c) If

$$f\left(\frac{x}{y}, \frac{z}{y}\right) = 0$$

show that

$$x\frac{\partial z}{\partial x} + y\frac{\partial z}{\partial y} = z$$

(d) If

$$Z = x^3y^2$$

show that

$$xyf_{yxxx} - xf_{xxx} - f_{xx} - yf_{yy} + f_y = 0$$

(e) If

$$Z = f\left(\frac{x-y}{y}\right)$$

show that

$$x\frac{\partial z}{\partial x} + y\frac{\partial z}{\partial y} = 0$$

9

MAXIMA AND MINIMA
OF FUNCTIONS

The concept of *rationality* in economic theory is the idea that behavior is directed toward predetermined goals, and that it tends to maximize or minimize some quantity. It is assumed that the members of a household try to maximize the total utility from their consumption of goods within a given expenditure of money; that workers try to maximize the income received from their work; that an industrial firm seeks to maximize its output for a given expenditure on the various factors of production, or to minimize the cost of producing a certain output; that a business firm tries to maximize its profits.

The assumption of rationality is at the same time essential to the structure of economic theory (a systematic analysis of irrational behavior would be by definition impossible) and open to serious questions. There is widespread debate today about the objectives of rational behavior. Does the consumer really allocate his budget among the many items he buys in such a way as to maximize its utility? Does he have sufficient information to pattern his economic decisions in this direction? Does the worker actually try to maximize his money income, or is he concerned with a complex combination of objectives including "psychic income" as well?

With respect to the objectives of business firms, there is a significant body of literature emphasizing the complex nature of the conflicting goals and objectives of businesses. The simple imperative that businesses maximize their profits is thought to be an oversimplification of a complex of many objectives.

A discussion of the merits of such literature is beyond the scope of this text. This chapter is concerned with the mechanics of optimizing behavior, and is based on accepting the assumption of rationality as an operational guide to economic theory.

FUNCTIONS OF ONE VARIABLE

A function such as

$$y = x^3 - 4x^2 + 5$$

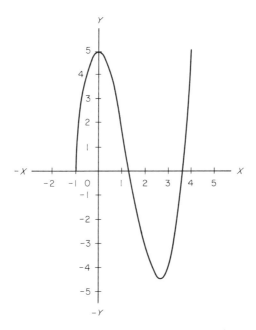

FIGURE 9-1 Curve with a Relative Maximum
Point and a Relative Minimum Point

has a range of increasing values, a range of decreasing values, and another range of increasing values. This function is illustrated in Figure 9-1. Between the increasing portion and the decreasing portion of the function, it must reach some maximum value. Between the decreasing and the increasing portions the function must reach a minimum point. When the function is increasing, its derivative is positive; when it is decreasing, its derivative is negative. When a function is at either a maximum or a minimum, it has a stationary value. The derivative of a function at its maximum or its minimum is zero. It is a *necessary* condition of a maximum or a minimum of the function that its derivative at that point be equal to zero. To find this stationary point, therefore, the first derivative of the function must be found, set equal to zero, and the value or values of the independent variable found which will satisfy the resulting equation. For the equation considered here, the procedure is as follows:

$$\frac{dy}{dx} = 3x^2 - 8x = 0$$

The first derivative is in quadratic form. Solution by the quadratic formula shows that the first derivative will assume a value of zero when $x = 0$ and again when $x = 2.66$.

Two values of the independent variable x at which the function will have a derivative of zero and assume stationary values have been identified. This information merely suggests that when $x = 0$, the function is at either a maximum or a minimum; and that when $x = 2.66$, the function is again at either a maximum or a minimum. The condition

$$\frac{dy}{dx} = 0$$

is a necessary condition for the identification of a maximum or a minimum, but it is in itself insufficient to identify precisely which of the stationary values the function has achieved.

To specify whether a value of x at which

$$\frac{dy}{dx} = 0$$

obtains is a maximum or a minimum, it is necessary to evaluate the value of the second derivative at that point. If the second derivative is negative, then a maximum point has been identified. If the second derivative is positive, then the point in question is a minimum. The condition that the second derivative must be negative for a maximum or positive for a minimum is called the *sufficient* condition for either the maximum or the minimum. Conditions for the maximum and the minimum are summarized as

	Maximum	*Minimum*
Necessary condition	$\dfrac{dy}{dx} = 0$	$\dfrac{dy}{dx} = 0$
Sufficient condition	$\dfrac{d^2y}{dx^2} < 0$	$\dfrac{d^2y}{dx^2} > 0$

In the function,

$$y = x^3 - 4x^2 + 5$$

the first derivative has been shown to be zero when $x = 0$ and when $x = 2.66$. To identify whether a maximum or a minimum is attained at $x = 0$ and at $x = 2.66$, the second derivative of the function must be evaluated at $x = 0$ and at $x = 2.66$.

$$\frac{d^2y}{dx^2} = 6x - 8$$

Substitute $x = 0$ into $6x - 8$,

$$\frac{d^2y}{dx^2} = f''(x) = f''(0) = 6(0) - 8 = -8$$

The value of the second derivative when $x = 0$ is -8, a negative value. The function, therefore, is at a maximum when $x = 0$. The maximum value of the function is found by substituting the value of $x = 0$ into the original function.

$$y = f(x) = f(0) = 0^3 - 4(0^2) + 5 = 5$$

When the function is at its maximum, its value is 5.

To determine the nature of the stationary value of the function when $x = 2.66$, substitute this value of the independent variable into the equation for the second derivative.

$$\frac{d^2y}{dx^2} = f''(x) = f''(2.66) = 6(2.66) - 8 = 7.96$$

Since the value of the second derivative is positive, the function is at a minimum when x is 2.66.

Consider an average cost function

$$AC = 20 - 8Q + Q^2$$

shown graphically in Figure 9-2. To find the minimum point of the average cost function, take its derivative, set it equal to zero, and solve for the

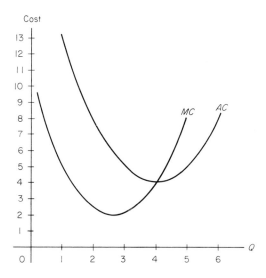

FIGURE 9-2   Relation Between Average Cost and Marginal Cost When Average Cost is a Minimum

appropriate value of Q:

$$\frac{d(AC)}{dQ} = -8 + 2Q = 0$$

$$2Q = 8$$

$$Q = 4$$

To satisfy the sufficient condition for the minimum, evaluate the second derivative:

$$\frac{d^2(AC)}{dQ^2} = 2$$

The second derivative is positive for all values of Q, since it is a positive constant. Therefore, when Q is 4, the average cost is at its minimum. To find the minimum average cost, substitute $Q = 4$ into the average cost function, and solve for the value of the average cost:

$$AC = 20 - 8(4) + 4^2 = 4$$

A familiar relationship in economic theory is that when the average cost is at its minimum, the marginal cost is equal to the average cost. This can be shown by the following procedure: Let

$$C = \text{total cost}$$

$$C' = \text{marginal cost}$$

$$Q = \text{quantity of output}$$

$$A = \text{average cost} = \frac{C}{Q}$$

When the average cost, A, is at its minimum, dA/dQ must be equal to zero:

$$\frac{dA}{dQ} = \frac{C'Q - C}{Q^2} = 0$$

For this fraction to be zero, its numerator must be equal to zero. Therefore,

$$C'Q = C$$

$$C' = \frac{C}{Q}$$

Marginal cost = Average cost

It will be useful to examine the cost function discussed earlier to see whether marginal cost is indeed equal to average cost when the average cost is at its minimum. Total cost is defined as quantity times average cost. Therefore, the total cost equation is

$$TC = Q(20 - 8Q + Q^2) = 20Q - 8Q^2 + Q^3$$

Marginal cost is the first derivative of the total cost function.

$$MC = \frac{d(TC)}{dQ} = 20 - 16Q + 3Q^2$$

Average cost is at its minimum value of 4 when quantity is 4 units of output. Substitute $Q = 4$ into the equation for marginal cost to determine if marginal cost is equal to the average cost of 4 when the quantity is 4 units.

$$MC = 20 - 16(4) + 3(4^2) = 20 - 64 + 48 = 68 - 64 = 4$$

Thus $AC = MC = 4$ when the average cost is at its minimum value.

Consider a total utility function of a quadratic form

$$U = 10Q - Q^2$$

Total utility will be at a maximum when the marginal utility, the first derivative of utility with respect to quantity, is zero. First find the first derivative, set it equal to zero, and then solve for the quantity:

$$\frac{dU}{dQ} = 10 - 2Q = 0$$

$$2Q = 10$$

$$Q = 5$$

To satisfy the sufficient condition of a maximum, find the second derivative:

$$\frac{d^2U}{dQ^2} = -2$$

Since the second derivative is negative, total utility is at a maximum when $Q = 5$.

THEORY OF THE FIRM

Profit is defined as the difference between total revenue and total cost. Total cost includes both explicit out-of-pocket costs and the imputed implicit costs of the owner's resources used by the firm. To maximize profit, the first derivative of this difference is set equal to zero. Symbolically,

$$TP = R - C$$

where TP is total profit, R is total revenue and C is total cost. TP, R, and C are functions of quantity.

Profit maximization requires as a first-order condition that the first derivative of this function be zero:

$$\frac{dTP}{dQ} = \frac{dR}{dQ} - \frac{dC}{dQ} = 0$$

dTP/dQ is marginal profit, defined as marginal revenue minus marginal cost. dR/dQ is marginal revenue, and dC/dQ is marginal cost. If

$$\frac{dR}{dQ} - \frac{dC}{dQ} = 0$$

then

$$\frac{dR}{dQ} = \frac{dC}{dQ}$$

For profit maximization, marginal revenue must be equal to marginal cost, and marginal profit must be zero.

The second-order condition of profit maximization is that the second derivative of the profit function must be negative. What this requires is that

$$\frac{d(MC)}{dQ} > \frac{d(MR)}{dQ}$$

Such an inequality would mean that

$$\frac{d^2TP}{dQ^2} = \frac{d^2R}{dQ^2} - \frac{d^2C}{dQ^2} < 0$$

This means that the second derivative of the profit function must be negative, for profit to be unambiguously defined as maximum. For the second derivative of the profit function to be negative, the slope of the marginal revenue function must be less than the slope of the marginal cost function at the point where the profit function reaches its maximum.

Consider the properties of a profit maximizing position for a firm operating under conditions of perfect competition. Economic theory holds that the demand curve facing a firm under perfect competition is horizontal, with a price elasticity of demand of infinity. This means that the firm can sell at a constant price all that it wishes to sell. Let the prevailing market price be 5. Then

$$P = 5$$

$$R = PQ = 5Q$$

$$\frac{dR}{dQ} = MR = 5$$

Assume that the firm's cost conditions are such that its average cost function is

$$AC = 20 - 8Q + Q^2$$

Then

$$TC = 20Q - 8Q^2 + Q^3$$

$$MC = 20 - 16Q + 3Q^2$$

Since TP, the amount of profit, is equal to total revenue minus total cost, the relationship can be expressed as

$$TP = 5Q - (20Q - 8Q^2 + Q^3)$$
$$= 5Q - 20Q + 8Q^2 - Q^3$$
$$= -15Q + 8Q^2 - Q^3$$

To find the value of Q at which profit will be maximized, find the first derivative of TP, set it equal to zero, and solve for Q.

$$\frac{dTP}{dQ} = -15 + 16Q - 3Q^2 = 0$$

Again using the quadratic formula, solve for the value or values of Q which will satisfy the condition

$$\frac{dTP}{dQ} = 0$$

There are two values of Q which will satisfy that condition: $Q = 1.2$ and $Q = 4.1$. To determine which of these quantities is the profit maximizing quantity, evaluate the second derivative:

$$\frac{d^2TP}{dQ^2} = 16 - 6Q$$

When $Q = 1.2$, the value of the second derivative is

$$16 - 6(1.2) = 8.8$$

When $Q = 1.2$, the second derivative is positive. This means that profit is at a minimum value in that region. Now, substituting $Q = 4.1$ into the second derivative gives

$$16 - 6(4.1) = -8.6$$

When $Q = 4.1$, the second derivative is negative. This means that profit is at a maximum value. When $Q = 4.1$, total revenue is

$$R = 5(4.1) = 20.5$$

Total cost is

$$C = 20(4.1) - 8(4.1)^2 + (4.1)^3 = 82 - 134.48 + 68.92 = 16.44$$

Total profit is then

$$TP = R - C = 20.5 - 16.44 = 4.06$$

The same profit-maximizing output can be found by setting marginal revenue equal to marginal cost, and solving for the quantity:

$$MR = 5$$

$$MC = 20 - 16Q + 3Q^2$$

$$MR = MC$$

$$5 = 20 - 16Q + 3Q^2$$

$$3Q^2 - 16Q + 15 = 0$$

Solving this equation by the quadratic formula gives for the values of Q,

$$Q = 1.2 \quad \text{or} \quad Q = 4.1$$

Again, reject $Q = 1.2$, because the value of the second derivative is positive. The solution $Q = 4.1$ is the desired result.

Monopoly Output as Half the Competitive Output

Consider the profit maximizing output of a firm operating as a monopolist. The demand curve facing a monopolist is downward sloping to the right. A greater quantity of output can be sold only if the firm is willing to reduce the price. Let the demand curve faced by the monopolist be a linear demand curve of the form

$$P = 10 - Q$$

Total revenue is price times quantity. Multiply both sides of the equation by Q to get the expression for total revenue:

$$R = PQ = 10Q - Q^2$$

Marginal revenue is the first derivative of this total revenue function:

$$\frac{dR}{dQ} = MR = 10 - 2Q$$

Now assume that the monopolist's average cost function is also linear, and of the form

$$AC = 2 + Q$$

Total cost is quantity times the average cost of production:

$$C = Q(AC) = 2Q + Q^2$$

Marginal cost is the derivative of the total cost function:

$$\frac{dC}{dQ} = 2 + 2Q$$

Total profit is defined as total revenue minus total cost:

$$TP = R - C = 10Q - Q^2 - (2Q + Q^2) = 8Q - 2Q^2$$

Profit maximization occurs where the marginal profit is equal to zero. Take the first derivative of the total profit expression, and set it equal to zero.

$$\frac{d(TP)}{dQ} = 8 - 4Q = 0$$

$$8 = 4Q$$

$$Q = 2$$

To satisfy the second-order condition of profit maximization, evaluate the second derivative:

$$\frac{d^2(TP)}{dQ^2} = -4$$

Since the second derivative is negative when the first derivative is equal to zero, the profit-maximizing output of the monopolist has been defined.

An alternative solution is to set marginal revenue equal to marginal cost, and solve for the appropriate value of Q:

$$10 - 2Q = 2 + 2Q$$
$$10 - 2 = 2Q + 2Q$$
$$8 = 4Q$$
$$Q = 2$$

When the profit-maximizing quantity of 2 units is produced, total revenue is equal to

$$R = 10Q - Q^2 = 10(2) - 2^2 = 20 - 4 = 16$$

Total cost corresponding to a quantity of 2 is

$$C = 2Q + Q^2 = 2(2) + 2^2 = 4 + 4 = 8$$

Total profit is therefore

$$TP = R - C = 16 - 8 = 8$$

If this monopolist, with these revenue and cost conditions, were suddenly subjected to competitive pressure and found it necessary to increase output and decrease price to a point where average cost would equal price, the output and pricing decision would have to be altered. Now the firm would have to find the quantity of output at which average cost would be equal to price. To find such an output, set $P = AC$.

$$10 - Q = 2 + Q$$
$$10 - 2 = Q + Q$$
$$8 = 2Q$$
$$Q = 4$$

The total revenue associated with an output quantity of 4 units is

$$R = 10Q - Q^2 = 10(4) - 4^2 = 40 - 16 = 24$$

The total cost of production of 4 units is

$$C = 2Q + Q^2 = 2(4) + 4^2 = 8 + 16 = 24$$

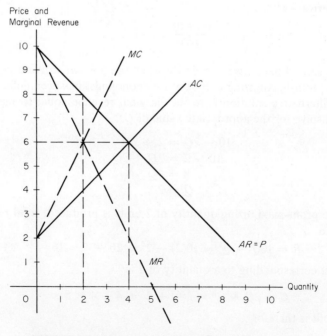

FIGURE 9-3   Monopoly and Competitive Outputs and Prices

The fact that price merely covers average cost and total revenue equals cost does not mean that the firm is not earning any profit. The economic definition of cost includes all explicit out-of-pocket costs plus all implicit costs accruing to the owners of the firm for the use of the owners' own productive resources. These are the normal earnings of these productive resources, or "normal" profit.

In this particular situation, with linear demand and cost curves, the competitive output of 4 is exactly twice the monopoly output of 2 units. These relationships are illustrated in Figure 9-3.

The graphic solution confirms the earlier mathematical solution. The monopoly output, defined by $MR = MC$, is 2 units, with a corresponding price of 8. The competitive output, defined by $AR = AC$, is 4 units, with a price of 6. The monopoly output, given linear revenue and cost functions, is one half the competitive output.

Sales Maximization

Professor William J. Baumol* suggests that business firms are not particularly interested in maximizing profits. They are interested in maximizing sales revenues. Often, sales revenues are maximized subject to the constraint of an acceptable minimum profit to satisfy the stockholders. As long as this minimum profit is earned, businessmen are not interested in additional profits per se. They are primarily interested in maximizing the sales revenue.

Baumol bases his hypothesis on his experience of consulting with business firms of many types. He finds that sales maximization rather than profit maximization becomes the goal of the firm because as sales revenues increase, many secondary problems tend to be solved. The firm finds it easier to acquire more capital because lenders and potential stockholders tend to look at the reports on sales as an aid to their lending decisions. When sales are booming, more workers are hired; workers' morale is high.

If sales revenue maximization is the goal rather than profit maximization, the behavior of the firm will be considerably different.

Assume that a sales maximizing firm has a demand function

$$P = 40 - Q$$

The sales revenue is the total revenue,

$$R = PQ = 40Q - Q^2$$

---

* William J. Baumol, *Business Behavior, Value and Growth*. New York: Macmillan, 1959. Rev. ed. (paperback), Harcourt, 1967.

Let the total cost function of the firm be

$$C = Q^2 + 12Q + 5$$

If the firm were a profit maximizer, its output would be set where

$$\frac{dR}{dQ} = \frac{dC}{dQ}$$

In the present case, the marginal revenue is

$$\frac{dR}{dQ} = 40 - 2Q = MR$$

Marginal cost is

$$\frac{dC}{dQ} = 2Q + 12 = MC$$

Setting these equal to each other and solving yields

$$40 - 2Q = 2Q + 12$$
$$40 - 12 = 4Q$$
$$Q = 7$$

At the profit maximizing output of $Q = 7$, the firm's cost and revenue situations are

$$P = 40 - Q = 40 - 7 = 33$$
$$R = PQ = 40Q - Q^2 = 280 - 49 = 231$$
$$C = Q^2 + 12Q + 5 = 7^2 + 12(7) + 5 = 49 + 84 + 5 = 138$$
$$TP = R - C = 231 - 138 = 93$$

If the firm were in pursuit of maximum sales revenue without any profit constraint, it would merely try to produce an output at which marginal revenue would be zero. The unconstrained sales maximization solution would show the following output, revenue, and cost situations:

$$\frac{dR}{dQ} = 40 - 2Q = 0$$

$$40 = 2Q$$

$$Q = 20$$

$$R = PQ = 40Q - Q^2 = 40(20) - 20^2 = 800 - 400 = 400$$

$$C = Q^2 + 12Q + 5 = 20^2 + (12)(20) + 5 = 400 + 240 + 5 = 645$$

$$TP = R - C = 400 - 645 = -245$$

The unconstrained sales-maximizing firm incurs a loss of 245 in this situation.

Now assume that the firm is interested in sales-revenue maximization, subject to a profit constraint of 50. A minimum profit of 50 must be earned in order to satisfy the owners of the business. Subject to this constraint, what will be the amount of output of the firm which seeks to maximize sales revenue? To solve for this condition, set the profit equation equal to the minimum profit constraint and solve for the value or values of Q which satisfy the constraint:

$$TP = 40Q - Q^2 - Q^2 - 12Q - 5 = 50$$

$$-2Q^2 + 28Q - 55 = 0$$

Solve for Q again by the use of the quadratic formula; the roots of the equation are

$$Q = 2.37 \quad \text{or} \quad Q = 11.6$$

Substitution of these values of Q into the demand, total-revenue, total-cost, and profit equations gives the following results:

$$Q = 2.37$$

$$P = 40 - Q = 40 - 2.37 = 37.63$$

$$R = PQ = (37.63)(2.37) = 89.18$$

$$C = Q^2 + 12Q + 5 = 2.37^2 + (12)(2.37) + 5$$

$$= 5.62 + 28.44 + 5 = 39.06$$

$$TP = R - C = 89.18 - 39.06 = 50.12$$

Thus an output of 2.37 meets the profit constraint. The amount of profit earned is 50.12, or about 50. It remains to be determined whether this output is the sales maximizing output subject to the profit constraint. Such a determination involves a comparison of the sales revenues corresponding to this output with the sales revenues corresponding to the output of 11.6, which also is a solution of the original constraint equation:

$$Q = 11.6$$

$$P = 40 - Q = 40 - 11.6 = 28.4$$

$$R = PQ = (28.4)(11.6) = 329.44$$

$$C = Q^2 + 12Q + 5 = 11.6^2 + (12)(11.6) + 5$$

$$= 278.76$$

$$TP = R - C = 329.44 - 278.76 = 50.68$$

Again, the output quantity of 11.6 meets the profit constraint.

The firm will choose to produce the quantity of 11.6 rather than the quantity of 2.37, because at the larger quantity sales revenue is greater.

POINT OF INFLECTION

Consider a function $y = f(x)$ which generates a curve such as that shown in Figure 9-4(a); it is similar to the general case of a total various cost curve. The curve $f(x)$ is a monotonically increasing function. It has neither a minimum nor a maximum value. But the curve has a region of concavity downward for values of x less than x_0. At x_0, the curve changes from

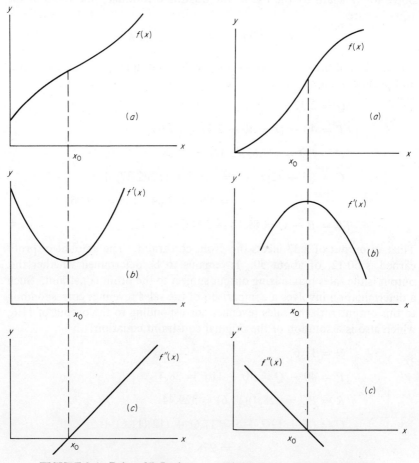

FIGURE 9-4   Point of Inflection   FIGURE 9-5   Point of Inflection

concave downward to convex downward, and begins to increase at an increasing rate. Figure 9-4(b) shows $f'(x)$ which measures the rate of change of $f(x)$. The curve $f'(x)$ decreases up to x_0, and reaches a minimum value at x_0. At x_0, $f'(x)$ is still a positive value, meaning that even though the rate of increase of $f(x)$ has reached its minimum, it is still positively sloped, and increasing. After x_0, $f'(x)$ increases, indicating that the curve $f(x)$ is increasing at an increasing rate. The curve $f(x)$ changes from a decreasing rate of increase to an increasing rate of increase at x_0.

Figure 9-4(c) shows the second derivative of $f(x)$. At values of x less than x_0, when $f'(x)$ is decreasing, $f''(x)$ assumes negative values. At x_0, when $f'(x)$ is at its minimum, $f''(x)$ assumes a value of zero. For x greater than x_0, $f''(x)$ is positive.

The point on the function $f(x)$ corresponding to $x = x_0$ is called a *point of inflection*. For a point of inflection to exist, therefore, the first derivative must assume a stationary value, and the second derivative must be equal to zero.

As a second example of an inflectional point, consider the curve shown in Figure 9-5(a). This curve initially increases at an increasing rate, and then increases at a decreasing rate. The initial portion of the curve is convex below, and the latter portion is concave below.

The curve $f(x)$ is similar in shape to the total product curve often used in production theory. Again the point of inflection occurs when $x = x_0$. This is the point at which $f(x)$ changes from convexity to concavity below; this is also the point at which $f'(x)$ is at a maximum [Figure 9-5(b)] and $f''(x)$ is zero [Figure 9-5(c)].

A numerical example of a point of inflection may be helpful. Let the function be

$$y = 6x - 3x^2 + 0.5x^3$$

$$y' = 6 - 6x + 1.5x^2$$

$$y'' = -6 + 3x = 0$$

$$3x = 6$$

$$x = 2$$

The point of inflection occurs when $x = 2$. Substituting $x = 2$ into the original equation indicates that the value of y at which inflection occurs is

$$y = 6(2) - 3(2^2) + 0.5(2^3) = 12 - 12 + 4 = 4$$

To summarize this discussion of the maximum, minimum, and inflectional points of a function: the sufficient condition for a maximum is that $f''(x)$ be negative; for a minimum, that $f''(x)$ be positive; and for a point of inflection, that $f''(x)$ be zero.

FUNCTIONS OF SEVERAL VARIABLES

On a farm of a given size, the amount of output of corn depends on the amount of labor units employed and the amount of capital involved in all types of equipment, buildings, fertilizers, and so on. If it is assumed that a capital investment of $250,000 has been made on the farm, output of corn can be gradually increased as the number of labor units applied is increased. But there is some maximum amount of output which can be coaxed out of a farm of a fixed size with a finite and fixed amount of capital investment.

In a similar way, a large farm family may propose to use the labor services within the household to produce a crop. The amount of farm labor available is then fixed at some quantity. To make this amount of farm labor as efficient as possible, the farmer might successively add various amounts of capital to the farm operation, in the form of a tractor, a fertilizer spreader, and so on. As the amount of capital increases, output increases gradually. But a maximum amount of output exists beyond which the harvest of the farm cannot be pushed unless the farm size and the number of workers are increased.

Farm output of corn can be thought to be dependent upon the amount of capital investment and the number of units of farm labor used. This functional relationship is designated symbolically by

$$Q = f(C, L)$$

where Q is the quantity of output, C is the amount of capital, and L is the number of labor units. Given a fixed amount of capital C_0, the maximum output of corn with varying amounts of labor will be achieved when

$$\frac{\partial Q}{\partial L} = 0 \quad \text{and} \quad \frac{\partial^2 Q}{\partial L^2} < 0$$

With a fixed amount of labor L_0, the maximum quantity of output of corn which can be produced with varying amounts of capital will be reached when

$$\frac{\partial Q}{\partial C} = 0 \quad \text{and} \quad \frac{\partial^2 Q}{\partial C^2} < 0$$

Further, it can be shown that the quantity of output can be maximized with both capital and labor varying when the following conditions are met:

1. $\dfrac{\partial Q}{\partial L} = 0 \qquad \dfrac{\partial Q}{\partial C} = 0$

2. $\dfrac{\partial^2 Q}{\partial L^2} < 0 \qquad \dfrac{\partial^2 Q}{\partial C^2} < 0$

3. $\dfrac{\partial^2 Q}{\partial L^2} \cdot \dfrac{\partial^2 Q}{\partial C^2} > \left(\dfrac{\partial^2 Q}{\partial L\, \partial C} \right)^2$

Consider the following example. Suppose the production function of corn is

$$Q = 20L + 30C - 2L^2 - 3C^2$$

Find the first partial derivatives of Q with respect to L and C and set each first partial derivative equal to zero:

$$\frac{\partial Q}{\partial L} = 20 - 4L = 0$$

$$\frac{\partial Q}{\partial C} = 30 - 6C = 0$$

Solve for the values of L and C at which the first partial derivatives are zero:

$$20 - 4L = 0 \qquad 20 = 4L \qquad L = 5$$

$$30 - 6C = 0 \qquad 30 = 6C \qquad C = 5$$

Evaluate the signs of the second partial derivatives:

$$\frac{\partial^2 Q}{\partial L^2} = -4 \qquad \frac{\partial^2 Q}{\partial C^2} = -6$$

Both partial derivatives are negative, indicating that maximum values are involved.

The first partial derivative with respect to labor is an expression free of C; and the first partial derivative with respect to capital is free of L. Thus the second-order mixed partial derivatives are zero. Condition 3 for a maximum is automatically met, since

$$\frac{\partial^2 Q}{\partial L^2} \cdot \frac{\partial^2 Q}{\partial C^2} = (-4)(-6) = 24 > 0$$

Determine the amount of maximum output of corn by substituting $L = 5$ and $C = 5$ into the original production function:

$$Q = 20(5) + 30(5) - 2(5^2) - 3(5^2)$$

$$= 100 + 150 - 50 - 75$$

$$= 125$$

PRICE DISCRIMINATION BY A MONOPOLIST

Price discrimination is the practice of charging different prices for the same product in different markets. A monopolist can practice price discrimination if the elasticity of demand is different in each of the submarkets. If the monopolist equates his aggregate marginal revenue function, which is the sum of marginal revenues of the submarkets, to his marginal cost function, then the rule of profit maximization is invoked. This will also give the total output which will be distributed among the submarkets. The monopolist will then equate the marginal revenues of each submarket with the aggregate marginal revenue at the point of profit maximization, i.e., at $MC = MR$, then

$$MR = MR_1 = MR_2 = \cdots = MR_i$$

Using this rule, the monopolist will determine the price in each submarket from the submarket's demand curve.

For simplicity, assume that the monopolist can divide his market into two submarkets, and that he will supply market 1 with quantity Q_1 and market 2 with quantity Q_2. Also assume that the monopolist has the general total revenue and total cost functions as follows:

$$TR = TR(Q) = TR(Q_1 + Q_2) = TR_1(Q_1) + TR_2(Q_2)$$

$$C = C(Q) = C(Q_1 + Q_2)$$

where TR_1 and TR_2 represent the total revenue in the first and second markets respectively. The profit function π is

$$\pi = TR - C = TR_1(Q_1) + TR_2(Q_2) - C(Q_1 + Q_2)$$

Now use the rule of profit maximization:

$$\frac{d\pi}{dQ} = \frac{d(TR)}{dQ} - \frac{dC}{dQ} = 0$$

$$\frac{d(TR)}{dQ} = \frac{dC}{dQ}$$

or $MR = MC$. The above is for the aggregate functions. Now find the profit maximization equations for the individual functions.

$$\frac{\partial \pi}{\partial Q_1} = \frac{\partial TR_1(Q_1)}{\partial Q_1} + \frac{\partial TR_2(Q_2)}{\partial Q_1} - \frac{\partial C(Q_1 + Q_2)}{\partial Q_1} = 0$$

$$\frac{\partial \pi}{\partial Q_1} = \frac{\partial TR_1(Q_1)}{\partial Q_1} - \frac{\partial C(Q)}{\partial Q_1} \frac{\partial Q}{\partial Q_1} = \frac{\partial TR_1(Q_1)}{\partial Q_1} - \frac{\partial C(Q)}{\partial Q_1} = MR_1 - MC = 0$$

$$\frac{\partial \pi}{\partial Q_2} = \frac{\partial TR_1(Q_1)}{\partial Q_2} + \frac{\partial TR_2(Q_2)}{\partial Q_2} - \frac{\partial C(Q)}{\partial Q_2} \frac{\partial Q}{\partial Q_2} = 0$$

$$\frac{\partial \pi}{\partial Q_2} = \frac{\partial TR_2(Q_2)}{\partial Q_2} - \frac{\partial C(Q)}{\partial Q_2} = MR_2 - MC = 0$$

Thus

$$MC = MR = MR_1 = MR_2$$

the marginal revenues of the submarkets are equated to the aggregate marginal revenue.

To be sure that this is a profit maximization, the second-order conditions must be checked:

$$\frac{\partial^2 \pi}{\partial Q_1^{\,2}} = \frac{\partial MR_1}{\partial Q_1} - \frac{\partial MC}{\partial Q_1} \quad \text{and} \quad \frac{\partial^2 \pi}{\partial Q_2^{\,2}} = \frac{\partial MR_2}{\partial Q_2} - \frac{\partial MC}{\partial Q_2}$$

$$\frac{\partial^2 \pi}{\partial Q_1 \, \partial Q_2} = \left(\frac{\partial^2 C(Q)}{\partial Q_1 \, \partial Q_2} = \frac{\partial^2 C(Q)}{\partial Q_2 \, \partial Q_1} \right) = \frac{\partial^2 \pi}{\partial Q_2 \, \partial Q_1}$$

Thus

$$\frac{\partial MC}{\partial Q_1} = \frac{\partial MC}{\partial Q_2}$$

This is written as MC'. Rewrite as follows:

$$\frac{\partial MR_1}{\partial Q_1} = MR_1'$$

$$\frac{\partial MR_2}{\partial Q_2} = MR_2'$$

Now the following conditions must be satisfied:

$$\begin{vmatrix} \dfrac{\partial^2 \pi}{\partial Q_1^{\,2}} & \dfrac{\partial^2 \pi}{\partial Q_2 \, \partial Q_1} \\[2ex] \dfrac{\partial^2 \pi}{\partial Q_1 \, \partial Q_2} & \dfrac{\partial^2 \pi}{\partial Q_2^{\,2}} \end{vmatrix} > 0$$

and

$$\frac{\partial^2 \pi}{\partial Q_1^{\,2}} < 0 \qquad \frac{\partial^2 \pi}{\partial Q_2^{\,2}} < 0$$

$$\frac{\partial^2 \pi}{\partial Q_1^{\,2}} = MR_1' - MC' < 0 \qquad \text{or} \qquad MR_1' < MC'$$

$$\frac{\partial^2 \pi}{\partial Q_2^{\,2}} = MR_2' - MC' < 0 \qquad \text{or} \qquad MR_2' < MC'$$

This was proved to be true in an earlier discussion.

$$\begin{vmatrix} MR'_1 - MC' & -MC' \\ -MC' & MR'_2 - MC' \end{vmatrix}$$

$$= (MR'_1 - MC')(MR'_2 - MC') - (-MC')(-MC') > 0$$
$$= MR'_1 MR'_2 - MC'(MR'_1 + MR'_2) > 0$$

Thus the second-order conditions hold.

Another implication of price discrimination is of interest. Suppose that there are two submarkets and that market 1 has the higher elasticity of demand. Note that

$$MR = P\left(1 - \frac{1}{E}\right)$$

Since marginal revenues must be equal,

$$MR_1 = MR_2$$

$$P_1\left(1 - \frac{1}{E_1}\right) = P_2\left(1 - \frac{1}{E_2}\right)$$

$$E_1 > E_2$$

but

$$\frac{1}{E_1} < \frac{1}{E_2}$$

$$-\frac{1}{E_1} > -\frac{1}{E_2}$$

$$\left(1 - \frac{1}{E_1}\right) > \left(1 - \frac{1}{E_2}\right)$$

Thus equality can only occur if $P_2 > P_1$. This implies that the more elastic market has the lower price, or that the market with smallest elasticity is charged the highest price.

Here is a numerical example of a monopoly that has two submarkets with differing elasticities of demand. Suppose the firm has the following demand and cost functions:

$$P_1 = 24 - 2Q_1 \qquad P_2 = 30 - 3Q_2 \qquad C = 4 + 2Q^2$$

so that

$$TR_1 = P_1 Q_1 = 24Q_1 - 2Q_1^2$$
$$TR_2 = P_2 Q_2 = 30Q_2 - 3Q_2^2$$

and

$$MR_1 = 24 - 4Q_1 \qquad MR_2 = 30 - 6Q_2 \qquad MC = 4Q$$

at $MC = MR_1$

$$24 - 4Q_1 = 4Q_1 \qquad \text{or} \qquad Q_1 = 3$$

at $MC = MR_2$

$$30 - 6Q_2 = 4Q_2 \qquad \text{or} \qquad Q_2 = 3$$

Thus

$$Q = Q_1 + Q_2 = 6 \qquad \text{and} \qquad MR_1 = MR_2 = 12$$

at $Q_1 = 3$

$$P_1 = 18$$

and at $Q_2 = 3$

$$P_2 = 21$$

For the point elasticities

$$E = \frac{P}{Q}\frac{dQ}{dP}$$

$$E_1 = |(^{18}\!/_3)(-\tfrac{1}{2})| = 3$$

and

$$E_2 = |(^{21}\!/_3)(-\tfrac{1}{3})| = {}^{21}\!/_9 = 2\,\tfrac{1}{3}$$

or $E_1 > E_2$ if and only if $P_2 > P_1$. Note that the second-order conditions of profit maximization hold.

CONSTRAINED MAXIMUM, LAGRANGE MULTIPLIER

Theoretical maximum values are often not particularly relevant in real life, because of limited resources. Thus even if output could be pushed to some maximum given enough labor and capital, such a maximum lacks operational significance because the number of units of labor available to hire may be limited and the firm may have access to only a limited amount of capital. These constraints are placed on the farm or business by its production budget. In such an event, it is not really the absolute maximum but the attainable maximum subject to the constraint established by the budget that is of interest.

The following example will illustrate the problem of finding a constrained maximum subject to an external condition. The production function of corn is given by a new relationship:

$$Q = 40L - L^2 + 60C - C^2$$

Assume that the price of labor is 2 and the price of capital is 2. Assume further that the production budget of the farm is 60. Find the maximum amount of corn which could be produced with these prices for labor and capital and the available production budget.

A new concept must be introduced before the solution of this problem is attempted. The budget equation given by condition 2 of the problem above is

$$2L + 2C = 60$$

If the entire budget of 60 is to be used up in the period's production, the equation would be

$$2L + 2C - 60 = 0$$

The process of incorporating this constraint into the production function and solving for maximum Q in effect introduces the budget constraint into the production function. To do this, use a grafting procedure employing a LaGrange multiplier of λ with the budget equation.

The production function with the budget constraint added is now

$$Q = 40L - L^2 + 60C - C^2 + \lambda(2L + 2C - 60)$$

$$= 40L - L^2 + 60C - C^2 + 2\lambda L + 2\lambda C - 60\lambda$$

Take partial derivatives of Q with respect to L, C, and λ, and set each partial derivative equal to zero:

$$\frac{\partial Q}{\partial L} = 40 - 2L + 2\lambda = 0 \tag{1}$$

$$\frac{\partial Q}{\partial C} = 60 - 2C + 2\lambda = 0 \tag{2}$$

$$\frac{\partial Q}{\partial \lambda} = 2L + 2C - 60 = 0 \tag{3}$$

Solve these three simultaneous equations for the three unknowns L, C, and λ. Subtract equation (1) from equation (2):

$$20 - 2C + 2L = 0 \tag{4}$$

Add equations (3) and (4):

$$4L - 40 = 0$$

$$4L = 40$$

$$L = 10$$

Substitute $L = 10$ into equation (3):

$$2(10) + 2C = 60$$

$$2C = 40$$

$$C = 20$$

Substitute $C = 20$ into equation (2):

$$60 - 2(20) + 2\lambda = 0$$

$$20 = -2\lambda$$

$$\lambda = -10$$

Economic theory states that the equilibrium employment of two resources, given their prices, is given by the condition

$$\frac{MPP_a}{P_a} = \frac{MPP_b}{P_b}$$

where MPP_a is the marginal physical productivity of resource a, defined as the first partial derivative of output with respect to resource a. MPP_b is the marginal physical productivity of b. P_a and P_b are the prices of resource a and resource b respectively.

To determine whether the employment of 10 units of labor and 20 units of capital meets this condition of equilibrium, find the values of the marginal physical productivities of the two factors and divide each by its own price:

$$MPP_L = \frac{\partial Q}{\partial L} = 40 - 2L = 40 - 2(10) = 20$$

$$MPP_C = \frac{\partial Q}{\partial C} = 60 - 2C = 60 - 2(20) = 20$$

$$\tfrac{20}{2} + \tfrac{20}{2}$$

$$10 = 10$$

Thus this employment of labor and capital meets the economic condition of equilibrium.

Test to see whether the budget constraint is met.

$$2L + 2C = 60$$

$$2(10) + 2(20) = 20 + 40 = 60$$

The budget is exactly exhausted.

This problem can also be solved by the method used in Chapter 5, when the utility maximizing allocation of a budget expenditure between two goods was considered. To use that technique, proceed as follows: Fulfill the equilibrium condition of

$$\frac{MPP_L}{P_L} = \frac{MPP_C}{P_C}$$

by setting

$$\frac{\frac{\partial Q}{\partial L}}{P_L} = \frac{\frac{\partial Q}{\partial C}}{P_C}$$

Doing this gives

$$\frac{40 - 2L}{2} = \frac{60 - 2C}{2}$$

$$40 - 2L = 60 - 2C \tag{1}$$

Introduce the budget equation.

$$2L + 2C = 60 \tag{2}$$

Solve (1) and (2) simultaneously.

$$20 - 2C + 2L = 0 \tag{3}$$

$$-60 + 2C + 2L = 0 \tag{4}$$

Subtracting (4) from (3) gives

$$80 - 4C = 0$$
$$80 = 4C$$
$$C = 20$$

Substituting $C = 20$ into (2) yields

$$2L + 2(20) = 60$$
$$2L = 20$$
$$L = 10$$

The results are identical to those obtained earlier.

Now the total amount of corn production when the constrained maximum is achieved can be determined. To do this, substitute $L = 10$ and $C = 20$ into the original production function and solve for Q:

$$Q = 40L - L^2 + 60C - C^2$$
$$= (40)(10) - (10^2) + (60)(20) - (20^2)$$
$$= 400 - 100 + 1200 - 400$$
$$= 1100$$

This constrained maximum may now be compared with the unconstrained maximum output. For the unconstrained maximum, take the partial derivatives, set them equal to zero and solve for the values of L and C. Then substituting these values of L and C into the production function, find the maximum Q:

$$\frac{\partial Q}{\partial L} = 40 - 2L = 0$$

$$40 = 2L$$

$$L = 20$$

$$\frac{\partial Q}{\partial C} = 60 - 2C = 0$$

$$60 = 2C$$

$$C = 30$$

$$Q = (40)(20) - (20^2) + (60)(30) - (30^2)$$

$$= 800 - 400 + 1800 - 900$$

$$= 1300$$

The unconstrained maximum of 1300 exceeds the constrained maximum of 1100 by 200. The sacrifice of 200 units of output is necessitated by the budget constraint.

The utility functions of two goods, A and B, were considered in Chapter 5. The utility functions were

$$U_A = 36Q_A - 2Q_A^2$$

$$U_B = 20Q_B - Q_B^2$$

The budget was

$$4Q_A + 2Q_B = 20$$

The utility maximizing quantities of A and B can be found by using the LaGrange multiplier. The total utility derived from the consumption of various quantities of both A and B is the sum of $U_A + U_B$:

$$U = U_A + U_B = 36Q_A - 2Q_A^2 + 20Q_B - Q_B^2$$

Introducing the LaGrange multiplier with the consumer budget constraint changes the function to

$$U = 36Q_A - 2Q_A^2 + 20Q_B - Q_B^2 + \lambda(4Q_A + 2Q_B - 20)$$

$$= 36Q_A - 2Q_A^2 + 20Q_B - Q_B^2 + 4\lambda Q_A + 2\lambda Q_B - 20\lambda$$

Find the partial derivatives of U with respect to Q_A, Q_B, and λ, and set each equal to zero.

$$\frac{\partial U}{\partial Q_A} = 36 - 4Q_A + 4\lambda = 0 \tag{1}$$

$$\frac{\partial U}{\partial Q_B} = 20 - 2Q_B + 2\lambda = 0 \tag{2}$$

$$\frac{\partial U}{\partial \lambda} = 4Q_A + 2Q_B - 20 = 0 \tag{3}$$

Solving simultaneously, find $Q_A = 3$ and $Q_B = 4$. These solutions agree with the solutions found earlier in Chapter 5.

MINIMA

In a function $z = f(x, y)$, the conditions necessary for a minimum value to obtain are

1. $$\frac{\partial z}{\partial x} = 0 \qquad \frac{\partial z}{\partial y} = 0$$

2. $$\frac{\partial^2 z}{\partial x^2} > 0 \qquad \frac{\partial^2 z}{\partial y^2} > 0$$

3. $$\frac{\partial^2 z}{\partial x^2} \cdot \frac{\partial^2 z}{\partial y^2} > \left(\frac{\partial^2 z}{\partial x \, \partial y}\right)^2$$

The following example will illustrate the identification of a minimum for a function of two variables:

$$z = f(x, y) = 20 + 3x^2 - 4x + y^2 - y$$

First find the first derivatives and set them equal to zero:

$$f_x = 6x - 4 = 0 \qquad x = \tfrac{2}{3}$$
$$f_y = 2y - 1 = 0 \qquad y = \tfrac{1}{2}$$

To evaluate whether this is a maximum or a minimum, find the values of the second derivatives:

$$f_{xx} = 6 \qquad f_{yy} = 2$$

Since both second partial derivatives are positive, this is a minimum. Finally, test for condition 3 for a minimum:

$$f_{yx} = 0 \qquad f_{xy} = 0$$

Therefore $(f_{xx})(f_{yy}) > (f_{yx})(f_{xy})$ and condition 3 is fulfilled.

MAXIMA OR MINIMA INVOLVING MORE THAN TWO VARIABLES

Maximum

Given a function $R = f(x_1, x_2, x_3)$, the conditions for a maximum are the following:

1. The first partial derivative of the function with respect to each of the independent variables must be equal to zero, which is to say

$$f_{x_1} = f_{x_2} = f_{x_3} = 0$$

2. In the case of three independent variables, three determinants of the variables' second partial derivatives may be formed, and these determinants must alternate in value in such a way that the determinants of odd order are negative, and the determinants of even order are positive. In this case the determinants in question and their signs must be $f_{x_1 x_1} < 0$

$$\begin{vmatrix} f_{x_1 x_1} & f_{x_1 x_2} \\ f_{x_2 x_1} & f_{x_2 x_2} \end{vmatrix} > 0$$

$$\begin{vmatrix} f_{x_1 x_1} & f_{x_1 x_2} & f_{x_1 x_3} \\ f_{x_2 x_1} & f_{x_2 x_2} & f_{x_2 x_3} \\ f_{x_3 x_1} & f_{x_3 x_2} & f_{x_3 x_3} \end{vmatrix} < 0$$

A numerical example will illustrate. A firm manufactures three products x_1, x_2, and x_3, and their sales contribution to the total revenue (R) of the firm is given by the following function:

$$R = 5x_1 + 4x_2 + x_2 x_3 - x_1^2 - x_2^2 - x_3^2$$

The firm is interested in determining the quantities of the three products which when sold will maximize the revenue R. The first condition of maximization is that the first partial derivative of the function with respect to each independent variable must be zero, i.e.,

$$\frac{\partial R}{\partial x_1} = 5 - 2x_1 = 0$$

$$\frac{\partial R}{\partial x_2} = 4 + x_3 - 2x_2 = 0$$

$$\frac{\partial R}{\partial x_3} = x_2 - 2x_3 = 0$$

Solving these simultaneous equations for the values of x_1, x_2, and x_3, gives

$$x_1 = 2.5 \qquad x_2 = \tfrac{8}{3} \qquad x_3 = \tfrac{4}{3}$$

To satisfy the second-order condition for a maximum, the three determinants of the various second partial derivatives must be evaluated. The second-order partial derivatives needed are the following. They can be substituted into their proper positions in the determinants shown above to determine the nature of the signs of the determinants of the various orders.

$$f_{x_1 x_1} = -2 \qquad f_{x_2 x_2} = -2 \qquad f_{x_3 x_3} = -2$$

$$f_{x_1 x_2} = 0 \qquad f_{x_1 x_3} = 0 \qquad f_{x_3 x_2} = 1$$

$$f_{x_2 x_1} = 0 \qquad f_{x_2 x_3} = 1 \qquad f_{x_3 x_1} = 0$$

Forming the required determinants using the various second partial derivatives just found gives

$$-2 < 0$$

$$\begin{vmatrix} -2 & 0 \\ 0 & -2 \end{vmatrix} = 4 > 0$$

$$\begin{vmatrix} -2 & 0 & 0 \\ 0 & -2 & 1 \\ 0 & 1 & -2 \end{vmatrix} = -6 < 0$$

This system of finding maximum values may be applied to cases involving as many variables as may be needed in a given problem.

A note of caution is in order at this point. If the above example had yielded determinants whose signs did not follow the pattern specified, and they were not all positive, then neither a maximum nor a minimum would have been established.

Minimum

The minimum of a function of more than two independent variables, for example $C = f(u, v, w)$, must satisfy the following conditions:

1. The first partial derivative of the function with respect to each of the independent variables must be zero, that is

$$\frac{\partial C}{\partial u} = 0 \qquad \frac{\partial C}{\partial v} = 0 \qquad \frac{\partial C}{\partial w} = 0$$

2. At the values of u, v, and w where the first condition is satisfied, all the following determinants must be positive, that is

$$f_{uu} > 0$$

$$\begin{vmatrix} f_{uu} & f_{uv} \\ f_{vu} & f_{vv} \end{vmatrix} > 0$$

$$\begin{vmatrix} f_{uu} & f_{uv} & f_{uw} \\ f_{vu} & f_{vv} & f_{vw} \\ f_{wu} & f_{wv} & f_{ww} \end{vmatrix} > 0$$

As an economic example, consider the firm whose total cost of production (C) is a function of three factors of production, u, v, and w. The firm is interested in minimizing the cost of production and wishes to find the values of u, v, and w at which this cost may be minimized:

$$C = 2u^2 + uv + 4v^2 + uw + vw + 3w^2 + 10$$

First find the first partial derivatives of the function with respect to all three variables, set them equal to zero, and find the values of u, v, and w which will satisfy all three equations:

$$\frac{\partial C}{\partial u} = 4u + v + w = 0$$

$$\frac{\partial C}{\partial v} = u + 8v + w = 0$$

$$\frac{\partial C}{\partial w} = u + v + 6w = 0$$

These are homogeneous equations of degree 1 and the three equations are independent. The only values of u, v, and w which will satisfy the first condition are

$$u = v = w = 0 \quad \text{and} \quad C = 10$$

Secondly, examine the signs of the determinants to decide whether this value of the independent variables will insure a minimum of the function. The second partial derivatives which will be needed to evaluate the signs of the determinants are

$$\begin{array}{ll} f_{uu} = 4 & f_{vw} = 1 \\ f_{uw} = 1 & f_{wu} = 1 \\ f_{wv} = 1 & f_{vv} = 8 \\ f_{vu} = f_{uv} = 1 & f_{ww} = 6 \end{array}$$

Hence if a minimum exists, the second-order conditions may be determined:

$$f_{uu} = 4 > 0$$

$$\begin{vmatrix} 4 & 1 \\ 1 & 8 \end{vmatrix} = 31 > 0$$

$$\begin{vmatrix} 4 & 1 & 1 \\ 1 & 8 & 1 \\ 1 & 1 & 6 \end{vmatrix} = 176 > 0$$

A STUDY OF SEVERAL DUOPOLY MODELS

A Generalization of the Cournot Model

Suppose that there are two firms, A and B, that will operate in the market. Their only costs are initial fixed costs. Thus marginal cost will be zero. Assume also that demand and marginal revenue are linear functions. For simplicity, assume that the output (the distance from the origin to the point where the demand curve cuts the quantity axis) is 1 unit of value. It will also be necessary to assume a similar relationship for the price axis.

Suppose that A is the only seller in the market. He will maximize his profit by equating marginal revenue to the zero marginal cost. His output and price will each be one half of the total possible, taking the total possible as the point where the demand curve intersects the axis in each case. Only the quantity axis will be discussed here, but a similar relationship can be constructed for the price axis.

Now B enters the market. He observes that half of the demand function is left. B will attempt to maximize his profit, so his output will be one-half of the remaining possible one-half, or one-fourth. Cournot made the vital assumption here that each firm expects his rival *never* to change his output even though he observes the changes.

A expects B's output to continue at one-fourth so that three-fourths will remain for A. But with linear demand and marginal revenue, A will maximize profit by producing at one-half of the remaining three-fourths or three-eighths. B observes that five-eighths of the market remains to him, but he will maximize profit by producing five-sixteenths.

This process will continue until each produces one-third of the possible output, so that their total output is two-thirds of the possible output. Table 9-1 summarizes this process.

TABLE 9-1

Market that Remains for A	Output of A	Market that Remains for B	Output of B
1	$\frac{1}{2}$	$\frac{1}{2}$	$\frac{1}{4}$
$\frac{3}{4}$	$\frac{3}{8}$	$\frac{5}{8}$	$\frac{5}{16}$
$\frac{11}{16}$	$\frac{11}{32}$	$\frac{21}{32}$	$\frac{21}{64}$
$\frac{43}{64}$	$\frac{43}{128}$	$\frac{85}{128}$	$\frac{85}{256}$
.	.	.	.
.	.	.	.
.	.	.	.
$\frac{2}{3}$	$\frac{1}{3}$	$\frac{2}{3}$	$\frac{1}{3}$

The outputs of A and B can also be found by summing geometric series:

$$\text{Output of } A = (\tfrac{1}{2} - \tfrac{1}{8} - \tfrac{1}{32} - \tfrac{1}{128} - \cdots) = \tfrac{1}{3}$$
$$\text{Output of } B = (\tfrac{1}{4} + \tfrac{1}{16} + \tfrac{1}{64} + \cdots) = \tfrac{1}{3}$$

By a rearrangement of terms (a topic of infinite series), the outputs of A and B can be expressed as

$$\text{Output of } A = \tfrac{1}{2} - \tfrac{1}{2}(\tfrac{1}{2})^2 - \tfrac{1}{2}(\tfrac{1}{2})^4 - \tfrac{1}{2}(\tfrac{1}{2})^6 - \cdots = \tfrac{1}{3}$$
$$\text{Output of } B = (\tfrac{1}{2})^2 + (\tfrac{1}{2})^4 + (\tfrac{1}{2})^6 + \cdots = \tfrac{1}{3}$$

(Note: The Cournot equilibrium will be discussed later in the reaction models.)

Consider the duopolists to be at a Cournot equilibrium. Assume also that each duopolist has found his profit function in terms of his and his rival's outputs.

$$\pi_A = 20Q_1 - 3Q_1^2 - 3Q_2 \qquad\qquad \pi_B = 16Q_2 - 2Q_2^2 - 5Q_1$$

$$\frac{\partial \pi_A}{\partial Q_1} = 20 - 6Q_1 = 0 \qquad\qquad \frac{\partial \pi_B}{\partial Q_2} = 16 - 4Q_2 = 0$$

$$Q_1 = 3\tfrac{1}{3} \qquad\qquad Q_2 = 4$$

$$\pi_A = 20(\tfrac{10}{3}) - 3(\tfrac{10}{3})^2 - 3(4) \qquad\qquad \pi_B = 16(4) - 2(4)^2 - 5(\tfrac{10}{3})$$

$$= 21.333 \qquad\qquad = 15.333$$

$$\pi_A + \pi_B = 36.67$$

It will be interesting to compare the Cournot equilibrium with the joint maximization model, i.e., the case in which the two firms will combine their profit functions into an aggregate profit function by collusion.

$$\pi = \pi_A + \pi_B = 15Q_1 + 13Q_2 - 3Q_1^2 - 2Q_2^2$$

$$\frac{\partial \pi}{\partial Q_1} = 15 - 6Q_1 = 0$$

so that

$$Q_1 = 2\tfrac{1}{2}$$

$$\frac{\partial \pi}{\partial Q_2} = 13 - 4Q_2 = 0$$

so that

$$Q_2 = 3\tfrac{1}{4}$$

$$\pi = 15(\tfrac{5}{2}) + 13(\tfrac{13}{4}) - 3(\tfrac{5}{2})^2 - 2(\tfrac{13}{4})^2 = 39.875$$

$$\pi_A = 20(\tfrac{5}{2}) - 3(\tfrac{5}{2})^2 - 3(\tfrac{13}{4}) = 21.5$$

$$\pi_B = 16(\tfrac{13}{4}) - 2(\tfrac{13}{4})^2 - 5(\tfrac{5}{2}) = 18.375$$

As a result of the collusion both the total profit and the individual profits have risen.

Hotelling's Stable Duopoly Model†

Suppose that there are two firms A and B. Each firm has a market to which only that firm can distribute its product, i.e., A has the "sheltered market" a and B has the "sheltered market" b. Located between A and B, there are x and y buyers to whom A and B will sell respectively. Assume that the buyers are spread in a linear form whose length is L, i.e.,

$$(a + x) + (y + b) = L$$

The prices set by A and B must be such that buyers from either of the sheltered markets will not find it cheaper to go to the rival's market. For a particular pair of prices, then, the buyers between A and B will be divided if the delivered prices are equal. Thus if P_A, P_B are the respective prices of A and B, and C is the cost of transportation,

$$P_A + Cx = P_B + Cy$$

† See also the excellent discussion in Ferguson's *Microeconomic Theory*, Irwin, 1966, pp. 273–275.

To find the numbers of buyers x and y, solve the two equations simultaneously so that

$$x = \frac{1}{2}\left(L - a - b + \frac{P_B - P_A}{C}\right)$$

$$y = \frac{1}{2}\left(L - a - b + \frac{P_A - P_B}{C}\right)$$

Profit is then price multiplied by the number of buyers:

$$\pi_A = P_A(a + x) = \frac{1}{2}(L + a - b)P_A - \frac{P_A^2}{2C} + \frac{P_A P_B}{2C}$$

$$\pi_B = P_B(b + y) = \frac{1}{2}(L - a + b)P_B - \frac{P_B^2}{2C} + \frac{P_A P_B}{2C}$$

Each firm believes that his competitor will not change price. Thus each will attempt to maximize profit:

$$\frac{\partial \pi_A}{\partial P_A} = \frac{1}{2}(L + a - b) - \frac{P_A}{C} + \frac{P_B}{2C} = 0$$

$$\frac{\partial \pi_B}{\partial P_B} = \frac{1}{2}(L - a + b) - \frac{P_B}{C} + \frac{P_A}{2C} = 0$$

These equations can be solved simultaneously to find the prices, P_A and P_B:

$$P_A = C\left(L + \frac{a - b}{3}\right)$$

$$P_B = C\left(L - \frac{a - b}{3}\right)$$

In order to find the quantities Q_A and Q_B, substitute P_A and P_B into the equations for x and y so that

$$Q_A = a + x = \frac{1}{2}\left(L + \frac{a - b}{3}\right)$$

$$Q_B = b + y = \frac{1}{2}\left(L - \frac{a - b}{3}\right)$$

Thus the price and quantity at equilibrium can be found.

Consider the following example:

$$a = 100 \qquad b = 400 \qquad L = 1200 \qquad C = 0.01$$

$$100 + x + y + 400 = 1200$$

$$x + y = 700$$

$$P_A + 0.01x = P_B + 0.01y$$

$$P_A = 0.01\left(1200 + \frac{100 - 400}{3}\right) = 0.01(1200 - 100) = \$11.00$$

$$P_B = 0.01\left(1200 - \frac{100 - 400}{3}\right) = 0.01(1200 + 100) = \$13.00$$

$$x = \frac{1}{2}\left(1200 - 100 - 400 + \frac{13 - 11}{0.01}\right) = \frac{1}{2}(700 + 200) = 450$$

$$y = \frac{1}{2}\left(1200 - 100 - 400 + \frac{11 - 13}{0.01}\right) = \frac{1}{2}(700 - 200) = 250$$

$$Q_A = a + x = 100 + 450 = 550 = \frac{1}{2}\left(L + \frac{a - b}{3}\right) = \frac{1}{2}(1200 - 100)$$

$$Q_B = b + y = 400 + 250 = 650 = \frac{1}{2}\left(L - \frac{a - b}{3}\right) = \frac{1}{2}(1200 + 100)$$

$$\pi_A = P_A(a + x) = P_A Q_A = (11)(550) = \$6050$$

$$\pi_B = P_B(b + y) = P_B Q_B = (13)(650) = \$8450$$

Notice that the factor of cost was not considered in this problem. The reason is that the seller must have a marginal cost of zero.

Some Duopoly Reaction Models, Including Frisch's Conjectural Variation

Suppose that the total market demand for a product is given by the function $p = f(Q)$, and that both duopolists sell at the same price. The duopolists can be designated I and II. Assume that duopolist I produces Q_1 at the total cost of $TC_1 = F_1(Q_1)$. Similarly, designate the output of duopolist II as Q_2 and his total cost function as $TC_2 = F_2(Q_2)$. Since there are only these two producers, the total output Q is the sum of their outputs:

$$Q = Q_1 + Q_2$$

The market demand function may be written as

$$p = f(Q) = f(Q_1 + Q_2)$$

The quantity that each duopolist will contribute to the total output will depend upon his reaction to the action taken by his rival. In short, the problem is to develop a model which will provide a systematic method for predicting the patterns of changes in Q_1 and Q_2.

First consider some possibilities about the total cost functions of the duopolists. The simplest case would be to assume that they have the same cost functions, except possibly for the total fixed cost. The duopolists have the same marginal cost functions so that

$$MC_1 = MC_2 = MC$$

where MC is the marginal cost of the common total cost function. This is to say

$$\frac{dF_1(Q_1)}{dQ_1} = \frac{dF_2(Q_2)}{dQ_2} = \frac{dF(Q)}{dQ}$$

where $F(Q)$ is the common total cost function.

Each duopolist will try to equate his marginal revenue with the common marginal cost. Keep in mind that

$$Q = Q_1 + Q_2$$

and that the duopolists face the common demand curve

$$p = f(Q) = f(Q_1 + Q_2)$$

Duopolist I's total revenue is given by

$$pQ_1 = f(Q)Q_1$$

Duopolist II's total revenue is

$$pQ_2 = f(Q)Q_2$$

The marginal revenue of duopolist I is

$$\frac{d[f(Q)Q_1]}{dQ_1} = f(Q) + Q_1 \frac{df(Q)}{dQ_1}$$

and the marginal revenue of duopolist II is

$$\frac{d[f(Q)Q_2]}{dQ_2} = f(Q) + Q_2 \frac{df(Q)}{dQ_2}$$

The marginal revenues of the duopolists equated to the marginal cost function is

$$f(Q) + Q_1 \frac{df(Q)}{dQ_1} = \frac{dF(Q)}{dQ} = f(Q) + Q_2 \frac{df(Q)}{dQ_2}$$

$$MR_1 = MC = MR_2$$

Then set $MR_1 = MR_2$, or

$$f(Q) + Q_1 \frac{df(Q)}{dQ_1} = f(Q) + Q_2 \frac{df(Q)}{dQ_2}$$

If $f(Q)$ is subtracted from both sides of the equation $f(Q)$,

$$Q_1 \frac{df(Q)}{dQ_1} = Q_2 \frac{df(Q)}{dQ_2}$$

This may be rearranged to

$$\frac{Q_1}{Q_2} = \frac{dQ_1}{dQ_2}$$

This in turn yields $Q_1 = Q_2$.† Since

$$Q = Q_1 + Q_2$$

the result is

$$Q_1 = Q_2 = \frac{1}{2}Q$$

Therefore as a general proposition it can be said that

$$f(Q) + \frac{1}{2}Q \frac{df(Q)}{dQ} = \frac{dF(\frac{1}{2}Q)}{dQ}$$

Now consider the case in which one of the duopolists changes his output. He expects the other duopolist to react to this change. If enough

---

† Using material from Chapter 10 on integrals, this may be proved by integrating

$$\frac{Q_1}{Q_2} = \frac{dQ_1}{dQ_2}$$

which may be written as

$$\frac{dQ_1}{Q_1} = \frac{dQ_2}{Q_2}$$

Then

$$\int \frac{dQ_1}{Q_1} = \int \frac{dQ_2}{Q_2}$$

$\ln Q_1 + C = \ln Q_2 + C$

$$\ln Q_1 = \ln Q_2$$

$Q_1 = Q_2$.

data about the reaction patterns of the duopolists were available, it would be possible to construct the reaction curve of duopolist I to changes in the output of duopolist II, and similarly the reaction curve of duopolist II to variations in the output of duopolist I. Each of these reaction curves in the $Q_1 Q_2$ plane would be negatively sloped.

At point A, where C_1 and C_2 intersect, the reaction of duopolist I is just what duopolist II expects, and the decision by duopolist II to produce $\bar{Q}_2$ leads duopolist I to produce $\bar{Q}_1$. The decision by duopolist I to produce $\bar{Q}_1$ leads duopolist II to produce $\bar{Q}_2$, and neither firm will have reason to change output.

From the discussion so far it is apparent that the reaction curve C_1 of duopolist I has the equation

$$Q_1 = g(Q_2)$$

and the reaction curve C_2 of duopolist II is represented by

$$Q_2 = h(Q_1)$$

If duopolist II were to change his output by a given amount, he could find his rival duopolist's rate of change as

$$\frac{dQ_1}{dQ_2} = \frac{dg(Q_2)}{dQ_2}$$

Conversely, any change in output by I would bring about the expected rate of change by II:

$$\frac{dQ_2}{dQ_1} = \frac{dh(Q_1)}{dQ_1}$$

These derivatives are the so-called "conjectural variations."

Assuming that each duopolist is a profit maximizer and keeping in mind that the demand curve is

$$p = f(Q) = f(Q_1 + Q_2)$$

the marginal revenue for duopolist I is

$$MR_1 = \frac{d(TR_1)}{dQ_1} = \frac{d(pQ_1)}{dQ_1} = \frac{d[Q_1 f(Q)]}{dQ_1}$$

$$= f(Q) + Q_1 \frac{df(Q)}{dQ} \cdot \frac{d(Q_1 + Q_2)}{dQ_1}$$

$$= f(Q) + Q_1 \frac{df(Q)}{dQ} \left(\frac{dQ_1}{dQ_1} + \frac{dQ_2}{dQ_1} \right)$$

$$= f(Q) + Q_1 \frac{df(Q)}{dQ} \left(1 + \frac{dQ_2}{dQ_1} \right)$$

To maximize profit, duopolist I will equate his marginal revenue to his marginal cost, or

$$f(Q) + Q_1 \frac{df(Q)}{dQ}\left(1 + \frac{dQ_2}{dQ_1}\right) = \frac{d(TC_1)}{dQ_1} \qquad (1)$$

The reaction curve C_1 of duopolist I may be derived by solving this profit-maximizing function for dQ_2/dQ_1. Similarly, the reaction curve C_2 of duopolist II may be derived from

$$f(Q) + Q_2 \frac{df(Q)}{dQ}\left(1 + \frac{dQ_1}{dQ_2}\right) = \frac{d(TC_2)}{dQ_2} \qquad (2)$$

At the point of equilibrium A, the intersection of C_1 and C_2, neither of the duopolists will change his output; therefore

$$\frac{dQ_2}{dQ_1} = \frac{dQ_1}{dQ_2} = 0$$

At the point of equilibrium then, equation (1) reduces to

$$f(Q) + Q_1 \frac{df(Q)}{dQ} = \frac{d(TC_1)}{dQ_1} \qquad (3)$$

and equation (2) becomes

$$f(Q) + Q_2 \frac{df(Q)}{dQ} = \frac{d(TC_2)}{dQ_2} \qquad (4)$$

Now suppose that duopolist I assumes that any change he may wish to make from the equilibrium point A (for whatever reason) will bring about no change in the output produced by duopolist II. However, duopolist II correctly judges the effect of any change on his part on the output decision of duopolist I. The effect of a parametric shift in the reaction curve of duopolist II upon the output quantities of both duopolists can be examined. Before proceeding, assume the following:

1. $0 > \dfrac{dQ_1}{dQ_2} > -1$

2. $\dfrac{df(Q)}{dQ} < 0$

Then it is clear that

$$f(Q) + Q_2 \frac{df(Q)}{dQ} > Q_2 \frac{df(Q)}{dQ}\left(1 + \frac{dQ_1}{dQ_2}\right) + f(Q)$$

The new reaction curve C_2' of duopolist II is given by

$$f(Q) + Q_2 \frac{df(Q)}{dQ} \left(1 + \frac{dQ_1}{dQ_2}\right) = \frac{d(TC_2)}{dQ_2} \tag{5}$$

Comparing equation (5) with equation (4) shows that the right-hand members of (4) and (5) are identical, but the left-hand members are different, and the curve shifts. This shift results in an increase in output by duopolist II and a decrease in output by duopolist I.

Numerical Examples of Conjectural Variation

Suppose the duopolists of the foregoing discussion are at a point of equilibrium, and the problem is to find the reaction curve and output of each. Assume that the duopolists have identical total cost functions. Since the duopolists are at equilibrium, it will be assumed that neither will take any action, i.e., the conjectural variation will be zero at the point of equilibrium. With the identical cost functions, each produces one-half of the total output.

Let market demand be given by

$$P = 84 - Q = f(Q)$$

and let total cost be

$$TC_1 = TC_2 = TC = Q^2 + 4Q + 4$$

Note that for Q in the market demand equation above

$$Q = Q_1 + Q_2$$

To find the reaction curve C_1 of duopolist I, use:

$$\frac{d(TR_1)}{dQ_1} = MR_1 = f(Q) + Q_1 \frac{df(Q)}{dQ} = \frac{d(TC_1)}{dQ_1} = MC_1$$

$$84 - Q + Q_1(-1) = 2Q_1 + 4$$
$$84 - (Q_1 + Q_2) - Q_1 = 2Q_1 + 4$$
$$80 - Q_2 = 4Q_1$$
$$20 - \tfrac{1}{4}Q_2 = Q_1$$

is the reaction curve of duopolist I.

Similarly, the reaction curve C_2 of duopolist *II* can be found by using the following:

$$\frac{d(TR_2)}{dQ_2} = MR_2 = f(Q) + Q_2\frac{df(Q)}{dQ} = \frac{d(TC_2)}{dQ_2} = MC_2$$

$$84 - Q + Q_2(-1) = 2Q_2 + 4$$
$$80 - (Q_1 + Q_2) - Q_2 = 2Q_2$$
$$20 - \tfrac{1}{4}Q_1 = Q_2$$

This is the reaction curve C_2 of duopolist *II*.

The equilibrium position of the reaction curves (lines) is the point where they intersect:

$$20 - \tfrac{1}{4}Q_1 = Q_2$$
$$20 - \tfrac{1}{4}(20 - \tfrac{1}{4}Q_2) = Q_2$$
$$15 + \tfrac{1}{16}Q_2 = Q_2$$
$$15 = \tfrac{15}{16}Q_2$$
$$16 = Q_2 = Q_1$$

This is the point of equilibrium.

$$Q_1 + Q_2 = 32 = Q \quad\text{and}\quad P = 52$$

Compare this situation with monopoly output, assuming a profit-maximizing monopolist:

$$MR = 84 - 2Q = 2Q + 4 = MC$$
$$80 = 4Q$$
$$20 = Q$$
$$P = 64$$

Thus the duopolists produce more, charge a smaller price, and hence receive less profit.

Now consider an example where a reaction does occur. Suppose duopolist *I* assumes that duopolist *II* will not change his output, i.e., actually, duopolist *I* wishes to remain at a point of equilibrium as in the previous example. However, duopolist *II* is able to find the effect of changes in output by duopolist *I* upon his own output. Thus duopolist *II* reacts. We know that duopolist *I* wants to remain on his reaction curve C_1:

$$Q_1 = 20 - \tfrac{1}{4}Q_2$$

For duopolist *II* to react, he must know his conjectural variation

$$\frac{dQ_1}{dQ_2} = -\frac{1}{4}$$

Dupolist *II* determines his reaction curve from the following:

$$f(Q) + Q_2 \frac{df(Q)}{dQ} \left(1 + \frac{dQ_1}{dQ_2}\right) = \frac{d(TC_2)}{dQ_2}$$

$$84 - Q + (Q_2)(-1)(1 - \tfrac{1}{4}) = 2Q_2 + 4$$

$$80 - Q_1 - Q_2 - \tfrac{3}{4}Q_2 = 2Q_2$$

$$80 - Q_1 = 2Q_2 + \tfrac{7}{4}Q_2 = \tfrac{15}{4}Q_2$$

$$\tfrac{320}{15} - \tfrac{4}{15}Q_1 = Q_2$$

This is the new reaction curve of duopolist *II*.

To find the new point of equilibrium, solve the equations of the reaction curves:

$$\tfrac{320}{15} - \tfrac{4}{15}Q_1 = Q_2$$

$$\tfrac{320}{15} - \tfrac{4}{15}(20 - \tfrac{1}{4}Q_2) = Q_2$$

$$320 - 80 + Q_2 = 15Q_2$$

$$240 = 14Q_2$$

$$Q_2 = 17\tfrac{1}{7}$$

$$Q_1 = 20 - \tfrac{1}{4}(17\tfrac{1}{7}) = 15\tfrac{5}{7}$$

$$Q_1 + Q_2 = 32\tfrac{6}{7}$$

$$P = 51\tfrac{1}{7}$$

Thus duopolist *II* has increased his output while the output of duopolist *I* has decreased. Also, the total output has increased and price has decreased. Comparing profits, at the first equilibrium position,

$$\pi_I = \pi_{II} = 508$$

and at the second

$$\pi_I = 489.88 \qquad \pi_{II} = 510.29$$

Thus duopolist *II* increased his profits while duopolist *I*'s profits decreased.

MAXIMIZATION OF A TAX ON OUTPUT

Suppose a monopolist is maximizing profit and has the following demand and total cost functions, respectively:

$$P = D - EQ$$

$$TC = AQ^2 + BQ + C$$

where A, B, C, D, and E are all positive. Suppose the government places a tax on the output so that the revenue generated by the tax will be maximized. Let R be the revenue from the tax, t the tax per unit of output, and Q the output of the monopolist. Then revenue from the tax will be $R = tQ$.

Presumably the monopolist will add the tax to his cost function and try to pass the tax on to the consumer. It will become apparent that the imposition of the tax will cause the monopolist to raise his price and restrict output. After the imposition of the tax, the total-cost function is

$$TC = AQ^2 + (B + t)Q + C$$

and the total revenue function is

$$TR = PQ = DQ - EQ^2$$

Since the monopolist is a profit maximizer, he equates MC with MR.

$$MC = \frac{d(TC)}{dQ} = 2AQ + (B + t)$$

$$MR = \frac{d(TR)}{dQ} = D - 2EQ$$

$$2AQ + (B + t) = D - 2EQ$$

$$2AQ + 2EQ = D - (B + t)$$

$$2Q(A + E) = D - (B + t)$$

$$Q = \frac{D - (B + t)}{2(A + E)}$$

This is the quantity the monopolist produces after the tax is imposed, and the price he charges is

$$P = D - EQ = D - E\left[\frac{D - (B + t)}{2(A + E)}\right] = \frac{2AD + E(D + B + t)}{2(A + E)}$$

The tax revenue will be

$$R = tQ = t\frac{D - (B + t)}{2(A + E)}$$

$$= \frac{tD - Bt - t^2}{2(A + E)}$$

To maximize revenue, set

$$\frac{dR}{dt} = 0$$

then

$$\frac{dR}{dt} = \frac{D - B - 2t}{2(A + E)} = 0$$

$$D - B - 2t = 0$$

$$D - B = 2t$$

$$\tfrac{1}{2}(D - B) = t$$

If this tax rate is to provide maximum revenue, the second-order condition

$$\frac{d^2R}{dt^2} < 0$$

must hold.

$$\frac{d^2R}{dt^2} = \frac{-2}{2(A + E)} = \frac{-1}{A + E} < 0$$

Thus the government will maximize its revenue if the tax rate per unit of output is

$$t = \tfrac{1}{2}(D - B)$$

The tax will have an effect on price and output. The monopolist's output *before* the tax, can be found by equating *MC* with *MR*.

$$MC = MR$$

$$2AQ + B = D - 2EQ$$

$$2AQ + 2EQ = D - B$$

$$Q = \frac{D - B}{2(A + E)}$$

Comparing the two quantities of output will show that

$$\frac{D - B}{2(A + E)} > \frac{D - B - t}{2(A + E)}$$

(This inequality can be simplified to show that $0 > -t$, which is true since $t > 0$.) Thus imposing the tax reduces the output of the monopolist.

The price, on the other hand, is raised. Before the tax

$$Q = \frac{D - B}{2(A + E)}$$

so that price

$$P = D - EQ = D - E\left[\frac{D - B}{2(A + E)}\right] = \frac{2AD + E(D + B)}{2(A + E)}$$

Comparing the prices yields

$$\frac{2AD + E(D + B + t)}{2(A + E)} > \frac{2AD + E(D + B)}{2(A + E)}$$

(This inequality can be simplified to show that $Et > 0$, which is true by the original statement of the problem.) Thus the price is raised after the tax is levied. The actual differences in price and quantity are

$$\Delta Q = \frac{D - B}{2(A + E)} - \frac{D - (B + t)}{2(A + E)} = \frac{t}{2(A + E)}$$

$$\Delta P = \frac{2AD + E(D + B)}{2(A + E)} - \frac{2AD + E(D + B + t)}{2(A + E)} = -\frac{tE}{2(A + E)}$$

Thus the increase in price is less than one half the tax rate and the decrease in quantity is less than one half the tax rate.

Now consider the following numerical example:

$$P = 18 - Q$$

$$TC = Q^2 + 2Q + 2$$

Before the tax, the monopolist will operate at $MC = MR$.

$$2Q + 2 = 18 - 2Q$$
$$4Q = 16$$
$$Q = 4$$
$$P = 18 - Q = 18 - 4 = 14$$

Suppose the government levies a tax of

$$t = \tfrac{1}{2}(D - B) = \tfrac{1}{2}(18 - 2) = \tfrac{1}{2}(16) = 8$$

Now the monopolist's cost function will be

$$TC = Q^2 + (8 + 2)Q + 2$$

Again, maximizing profit yields

$$MC = MR$$
$$2Q + 10 = 18 - 2Q$$
$$4Q = 8$$
$$Q = 2 < 4$$

and price will be

$$P = 18 - 2 = 18 - 2 = 16 > 14$$

This shows that quantity is reduced and price is raised. The actual change in price and quantity is found to be

$$\Delta P = -\frac{tE}{2(A+E)} = -\frac{(8)(1)}{(2)(1+1)} = -\frac{8}{4} = -2$$

$$\Delta Q = \frac{t}{2(A+E)} = \frac{8}{2(2)} = \frac{8}{4} = 2$$

or

$$\Delta P = 14 - 16 = -2$$

$$\Delta Q = 4 - 2 = 2$$

PROBLEMS

1. Find the maxima and minima for the following functions.

(a) $y = x^2 + 14x + 48$

(b) $y = \frac{1}{3}x^3 - x$

(c) $y = \dfrac{1}{x-4}$

(d) $y = x + x^{3/4}$

(e) $y = ae^{-b^2 x^2}$

(f) $y = x^2 e^{-x}$

(g) $y = (x-2)^3 + 7$

(h) $y = \frac{1}{3}x^3 - \frac{3}{2}x^2 - 10x + 12$

(i) $y = x + \dfrac{1}{x}$

(j) $y = \frac{1}{4}x^4 + x^3 + \frac{3}{2}x^2 + x + 6$

2. A function $f(x)$ is said to be increasing at $x = x_0$ if for a sufficiently small h,
$$f(x_0 - h) < f(x_0) < f(x_0 + h)$$
If $f'(x_0) > 0$, then use the definition of the derivative to prove that $f(x)$ is increasing at $x = x_0$.

3. Find any function with a maximum and find how the sign of the derivative changes in the neighborhood of the maximum. How does the sign of the derivative change in the neighborhood of a minimum?

4. If $y = f(x)$ is differentiable on $a \le x \le b$, and $f(x)$ has a relative maximum or minimum at $x = x_0$ for $a < x_0 < b$, prove, by using the definition of the derivative, that $f'(x_0) = 0$. [Hint: Find $f'(x_0)$ bounded $0 \le f'(x_0) \le 0$.]

5. Find the maxima or minima of the function

$$y = (K_1 - x)^2 + (K_2 - x)^2 + \cdots + (K\hat{n} - x)^2$$

6. If

$$f(x) = ax^2 + 2bx + c$$

with $a > 0$, find the maxima and minima. What type of stationary point does the curve have for $f(x) \geq 0$ if and only if $b^2 - ac \geq 0$? Illustrate with a numerical example.

7. (Rolle's theorem) If $f(x)$ is continuous on $a \leq x \leq b$ and $f'(x)$ exists on $a < x < b$ and $f(a) = f(b) = 0$, prove that there exists at least one point $x = x_0$ on $a < x < b$ such that $f'(x_0) = 0$.

8. If perfect competition exists, show that maximum profit exists where $P = MR = MC$.

9. Given the following average cost functions, prove that marginal cost intersects at the minimum of the average cost:

(a) $AC = \frac{1}{4}x + 35 + \dfrac{25}{x}$

(b) $AC = x^3 - 4x^2 + 16$

(c) $AC = x + \dfrac{1}{x}$

10. Find the maxima of the following utility functions:

(a) $U = 4Q - Q^2$ (b) $U = 20Q - 10Q^2$

11. If perfect competition exists, find maximum total revenue, cost, and profit, given price and average cost:

(a) $P = 10$ $AC = x^2 + \dfrac{3}{2}x - 8 + \dfrac{9}{x}$

(b) $P = 15$ $AC = \dfrac{1}{3}x^2 - 2x - 5 + \dfrac{99}{x}$

(c) $P = 2$ $AC = \dfrac{x^2}{3} + \dfrac{1}{2}x - 4 + \dfrac{10}{3x}$

12. Show that monopoly output is half competitive output for the following, and graph:

(a) $P = 9 - Q$ $AC = 1 + Q$
(b) $P = 5 - \frac{1}{2}Q$ $AC = 1 + \frac{1}{5}Q$
(c) $P = 10 - 2Q$ $AC = 3 + \frac{3}{2}Q$

13. Find the quantity for sales maximization for the given profit constraint, and check:

(a) $P = 20 - Q$ $C = Q^2$ $\pi = 10$

(b) $P = 16 - Q$ $C = Q^2 + 2Q + 4$ $\pi = 6$

(c) $P = 20 - 2Q$ $C = 2Q^2 - 4Q - 4$ $\pi = 24$

14. Find the inflection points for the following:

(a) $y = \frac{1}{3}x^3 + \frac{1}{2}x^2 - 6x + 8$ (d) $y = x^2 + 6x - 13$

(b) $y = \frac{1}{3}x^3 + x + 1$ (e) $y = x^2 e^x$

(c) $y = (x + 4)^4 + 9x + 2$

15. Graph y, dy/dx, d^2y/dx^2, d^3y/dx^3, and d^4y/dx^4 for the following functions. What are the relationships between y and d^3y/dx^3 with respect to changes in the curve?

(a) $y = (x - 2)^3 + 1$

(b) $y = x^3 - 2x^2 + x - 1$

(c) $y = \frac{1}{4}x^4 - \frac{3}{2}x^2$

(d) $y = 3x^4 - 10x^3 - 12x^2 + 12x - 7$

16. If a function

$$y = ax^3 + bx^2 + cx + d$$

has two stationary points, i.e., a maximum and minimum, prove that the inflection point is their bisector.

17. A function whose equation is

$$y = ax^3 + bx^2 + cx + d$$

has a maximum at $(1, -4)$ and an inflection point at $(2, -6)$. Find the coefficients a, b, c, d.

18. Find the maxima and minima of the following functions:

(a) $Z = x^3 + y^3 - 3x - 3y + 12$

(b) $Z = x^2 + y^2 - 2x - 4y + 17$

(c) $Z = x^2 - xy + y^2 + 4x + 4y + 10$

(d) $Z = x^2 + 3x^2y - 6x - 3y + 19$

(e) $Z = x^2 + y^2 - 2x - 4y + 7$

(f) $Z = x^3 + 3xy^2 + 15x^2 + 3y^2 + 2$

(g) $Z = x^3 + 3xy^2 - 15x^2 - 3y^2 + 6$

(h) $Z = x^3 + 3xy + y^3$

(i) $Z = x + y + xy - x^2 - y^2$

(j) $Z = x^2 + 4xy + 3y^2$

19. Find the critical points of the following functions:

   (a) $W = 3x^2 + 2y^2 + z^2 - 6x + 4y - 2z + 7$
   (b) $W = x^2 + y^2 + z^2 - 2xy + 4xz - 6yz - 2x + 8y + 10z + 12$

20. A critical point that is neither a maximum nor a minimum is a saddle point. The conditions for a saddle point are satisfied if

$$f_{xx}f_{yy} - f_{xy}^2 < 0$$

Check the following for maxima, minima, and saddle points:

   (a) $z = x^3 + y^3 - 12x - 12y + 16$
   (b) $z = x^3 + 3xy^2 + 15x^2 + 3y^2 + 8$
   (c) $z = x^2 + xy - 2x - 2y - 2$
   (d) $z = x^2 + y^2 - 4x - 4y + 12$

21. If

$$f_{xx}f_{yy} = f_{xy}^2$$

what conclusions can be drawn?

22. If $U = f(x, y)$ is a utility function and

$$M = xP_x + yP_y$$

is the budget constraint, use the LaGrange multiplier to find the maximum utility.

23. If $Q = f(C, L)$ is the production function and $C = iK + wL$ is the total cost function, use the LaGrange multiplier method to find the maximum output.

24. If a function $F(x, y, z)$ is subject to the constraint

$$F(x, y, z) = 0$$

prove that a necessary condition for $F(x, y, z)$ to have an extreme value is that

$$F_xG_y - F_yG_x = 0$$

25. If

$$F(x, y, z) = 0 \qquad G(x, y, z) = 0 \qquad \phi = F + \lambda G \qquad \phi_x = 0$$

and $\phi_y = 0$ are given, prove that

$$F_xG_y - F_yG_x = 0$$

where λ is a constant.

26. Solve the following by the method of LaGrange multipliers:

(a) $Z = x^2 + y^2 + 2x + 2y + 3$ subject to $x + y = 2$
(b) $Z = 30 + 20x + 10y + y^2 + x^2$ subject to $3x + y = 4$
(c) minimum for $W = x^2 + y^2 + z^2$ subject to $2z + 2x - y - 16$
$$= 0$$
(d) maximum for $W = xyz$ subject to $x + y + z - 18 = 0$

27. Given the production function

$$f(L, C, R) = L^2C^2R^3$$

and the budget constraint

$$L + C + R = 7$$

use two methods to find the maximum output.

28. Find the critical points of the production function:

$$f(L, C, R, W) = L^aC^bR^cW^d \quad \text{if} \quad L + C + R + W = A$$

for $a, b, c, d, A > 0$.

29. Interpret geometrically and find the minimum of

$$f(x, y, z) = x^2 + y^2 + z^2$$

subject to the constraint $ax + by + cz = d$.

30. Find the maximum volume of a rectangle that is enclosed in a sphere of radius r.

31. Find the maximum volume of a rectangular parallelepiped that can be enclosed in the ellipsoid

$$\frac{x^2}{a^2} + \frac{y^2}{b^2} + \frac{z^2}{c^2} = 1$$

10

ELEMENTS OF
INTEGRAL CALCULUS

The inverse of the subtraction operation is addition; the opposite of division is multiplication. Taking the square root of a number nullifies the effect of raising that number to its second power. In a similar way, integration is the inverse operation of differentiation.

Integral calculus is concerned with the problem of finding the function $f(x)$ from its derivative $f'(x)$. If, therefore,

$$f'(x) = g(x)$$

integration of $g(x)$ will yield $f(x)$.

In integral calculus, it is customary to use differentials. Therefore, integration is the process of finding $f(x)$ from

$$df(x) = f'(x)\,dx = g(x)\,dx$$

When this relationship is integrated,

$$\int f'(x)\,dx = f(x)$$

SOME TECHNIQUES OF INTEGRATION

Integral calculus is a vast subject. There are many rules to govern the process of integrating the many forms of mathematical expressions. Only a few particularly useful laws of integral calculus can be discussed here.

1. The integral of the sum or difference of two or more differentials is equal to the sum or difference of the integrals of the differentials taken individually. That is to say

$$\int (du + dv - dw) = \int du + \int dv - \int dw$$

where u, v, and w are functions of a single variable, such as x. For example, consider the derivative

$$\frac{dy}{dx} = 6x + 2 - 3x^2$$

Multiplying both members of the equation by dx gives the differential expression

$$dy = (6x + 2 - 3x^2)\, dx = 6x\, dx + 2\, dx - 3x^2\, dx$$

Integrating gives

$$\int dy = \int (6x + 2 - 3x^2)\, dx = \int 6x\, dx + \int 2\, dx - \int 3x^2\, dx$$

2. A constant factor may be placed either before or after the integral sign.

$$\int a\, du = a \int du$$

For example,

$$\int dy = \int 6x\, dx + \int 2\, dx - \int 3x^2\, dx = 6 \int x\, dx + 2 \int dx - 3 \int x^2\, dx$$

3. The integral of a differential expression of x is equal to x plus a constant term.

$$\int dx = x + c$$

In the differential expression of x below, the integral is

$$6 \int dx = 6x + c$$

4. Remembering that integration is the inverse operation of differentiation, and since

$$d(x^{n+1}) = (n + 1)x^n\, dx$$

it is apparent that

$$\int x^n\, dx = \frac{x^{n+1}}{n + 1} + c$$

The example used in 1 and 2 above may be integrated by using 4: Find

$$\int (6x + 2 - 3x^2)\, dx$$

Solution:

$$\int dy = 6 \int x\, dx + 2 \int dx - 3 \int x^2\, dx + c$$

$$y = \frac{6x^2}{2} + 2x - \frac{3x^3}{3} + c = 3x^2 + 2x - x^3 + c$$

To prove that the resulting function is the integral of the given differential expression, the integral expression may be differentiated. If the resulting expression is identical to the differential originally given, the correct integration has been performed:

$$\frac{dy}{dx} = 6x + 2 - 3x^2$$

$$dy = (6x + 2 - 3x^2)\, dx$$

Example: Marginal revenue is the first derivative of total revenue. The process of calculating the total revenue from marginal revenue involves the integration of a given marginal revenue expression. Suppose marginal revenue is given by the function

$$MR = R' = 10 - 2Q$$

Expressing the *MR* function in differentials gives

$$MR\, dQ = R'\, dQ = (10 - 2Q)\, dQ = 10\, dQ - 2Q\, dQ$$

Integrating yields

$$\int R'\, dQ = \int 10\, dQ - \int 2Q\, dQ$$

$$= 10Q - \frac{2Q^2}{2} + c = 10Q - Q^2 + c$$

Proof:

$$d(10Q - Q^2 + c) = (10 - 2Q)\, dQ$$

Example: Marginal cost is the first derivative of total cost. Total cost can be obtained from a given marginal cost function by integration. Suppose the marginal cost function is

$$MC = \frac{dC}{dQ} = 50 - 20Q + 3Q^2$$

Then, total cost is the integral of *MC*.

$$TC = \int MC\, dQ = \int 50\, dQ - \int 20Q\, dQ + \int 3Q^2\, dQ$$

$$= 50Q - \frac{20Q^2}{2} + \frac{3Q^3}{3} + k$$

$$= 50Q - 10Q^2 + Q^3 + k$$

Proof:

$$MC = \frac{d(TC)}{dQ} = 50 - 20Q + 3Q^2$$

$$MC\,dQ = d(TC) = (50 - 20Q + 3Q^2)\,dQ$$

Example: Find

$$\int x^{0.5}\,dx$$

Solution:

$$\int x^{0.5}\,dx = \frac{x^{1.5}}{1.5} + c = \frac{1}{1.5}x^{1.5} + c$$

Proof:

$$d\left(\frac{1}{1.5}x^{1.5} + c\right) = (x^{0.5})dx$$

Example: Find

$$\int \frac{1}{x^3}\,dx$$

Solution:

$$\int \frac{1}{x^3}\,dx = \int x^{-3}\,dx = \frac{x^{-2}}{-2} + c$$

$$= -\tfrac{1}{2}x^{-2} + c$$

Proof:

$$d(-\tfrac{1}{2}x^{-2} + c) = x^{-3}\,dx = \frac{1}{x^3}\,dx$$

Example: Find

$$\int (2x^3 + 5x^2 - 3x)\,dx$$

Solution:

$$\int (2x^3 + 5x^2 - 3x)\,dx = 2\int x^3\,dx + 5\int x^2\,dx - 3\int x\,dx + c$$

$$= \frac{2x^4}{4} + \frac{5x^3}{3} - \frac{3x^2}{2} + c = \frac{x^4}{2} + \frac{5}{3}x^3 - \frac{3}{2}x^2 + c$$

Proof:

$$d\left(\frac{x^4}{2} + \frac{5}{3}x^3 - \frac{3}{2}x^2 + c\right) = (2x^3 + 5x^2 - 3x)\,dx$$

Example: Find

$$\int 42x^5\,dx$$

Solution:

$$\int 42x^5 \, dx = \frac{42x^6}{6} + c = 7x^6 + c$$

Proof:

$$d(7x^6 + c) = 42x^5 \, dx$$

In Chapter 4, in the discussion of the rule for finding the derivative of a composite function, it was stated that if

$$y = [f(x)]^{n+1}$$

$$\frac{dy}{dx} = (n + 1)f'(x)[f(x)]^n$$

or in differential terms

$$dy = \{(n + 1)f'(x)[f(x)]^n\} \, dx$$

For example, if

$$y = (2x^2 + x)^2$$

then the derivative of the function is

$$\frac{dy}{dx} = 2(4x + 1)(2x^2 + x)$$

$$dy = [2(4x + 1)(2x^2 + x)] \, dx$$

The fifth rule for integration, then, is

5. $$\int f'(x)[f(x)^n] \, dx = \frac{[f(x)]^{n+1}}{n + 1} + c$$

In the example just cited, if only the differential expression were available, the integral would be found by using 5. Find

$$\int [2(4x + 1)(2x^2 + x)] \, dx$$

Solution:

$$\int [2(4x + 1)(2x^2 + x)] \, dx = \frac{2(2x^2 + x)^2}{2} + c = (2x^2 + x)^2$$

The proof has already been shown.

Example: Find

$$\int (3x^2 + 4x)(x^3 + 2x^2 + 7)^3 \, dx$$

Solution:

$$\int (3x^2 + 4x)(x^3 + 2x^2 + 7)^3 \, dx = \frac{(x^3 + 2x^2 + 7)^4}{4} + c$$

Proof:

$$\frac{d}{dx}\left[\frac{(x^3 + 2x^2 + 7)^4}{4} + c \right] = \frac{d}{dx} \left[\tfrac{1}{4}(x^3 + 2x^2 + 7)^4 + c \right]$$

$$= (3x^2 + 4x)(x^3 + 2x^2 + 7)^3$$

Example: Find

$$\int (3x^2 + 2)(x^3 + 2x + 5) \, dx$$

Solution:

$$\int (3x^2 + 2)(x^3 + 2x + 5) \, dx = \tfrac{1}{2}(x^3 + 2x + 5)^2 + c$$

Proof:

$$\frac{d}{dx} \left[\tfrac{1}{2}(x^3 + 2x + 5)^2 \right] = (3x^2 + 2)(x^3 + 2x + 5)$$

In each of the examples illustrating 5, the differential expression to be integrated consists of two multiplicative terms, one of which is the derivative of the other. Whenever such an expression is encountered, the integral may be worked out by using 5.

In differentiating a logarithmic expression of x, the following rule was developed:

$$\frac{d}{dx} \ln x = \frac{1}{x}$$

with the corresponding differential

$$d \ln x = \frac{1}{x} dx$$

The rule for integrating such a differential expression is

6. $$\int \frac{1}{x} dx = \ln x + c$$

Example: Find

$$\int \frac{2}{x} dx$$

Solution:

$$\int \frac{2}{x} dx = 2 \int \frac{1}{x} dx = 2 \ln x + c$$

Proof:

$$\frac{d}{dx}(2 \ln x + c) = \frac{2}{x}$$

$$d(2 \ln x + c) = \frac{2}{x} dx$$

Example: Find

$$\int \frac{1}{6x} dx$$

Solution:

$$\int \frac{1}{6x} dx = \frac{1}{6} \int \frac{1}{x} dx = \frac{1}{6} \ln x + c$$

Proof:

$$\frac{d}{dx}\left(\frac{1}{6} \ln x + c\right) = \frac{1}{6x}$$

$$d\left(\frac{1}{6} \ln x + c\right) = \frac{1}{6x} dx$$

The derivative of the logarithm of a function, u, such as

$$y = \ln u = \ln (4x^2 + 2x - 5)$$

is

$$\frac{dy}{dx} = \frac{1}{u} du = \frac{8x + 2}{4x^2 + 2x - 5}$$

in which the numerator is the derivative of the denominator. This fact leads to the seventh rule of integration, which says that if the expression to be integrated is a ratio whose numerator is the derivative of the denominator, then the integral of the expression is the natural logarithm of the denominator plus a constant:

7.
$$\int \frac{f'(x)}{f(x)} dx = \ln f(x) + c$$

Example: Find

$$\int \frac{3x^2 + 2}{x^3 + 2x + 5} dx$$

Solution: Since the numerator is the derivative of the denominator, 7 may be applied directly.

$$\int \frac{3x^2 + 2}{x^3 + 2x + 5} dx = \ln (x^3 + 2x + 5) + c$$

Proof:

$$d[\ln(x^3 + 2x + 5)] + dc = \frac{3x^2 + 2}{x^3 + 2x + 5} dx$$

Example: Find

$$\int \frac{x}{x^2 + 1} dx$$

Solution: Let $v = x^2 + 1$. Then $dv = 2x$. Multiply both the numerator and the denominator by 2, thus making the numerator the derivative of the denominator.

$$\int \frac{x}{x^2 + 1} dx = \frac{1}{2} \int \frac{2x}{x^2 + 1} dx = \frac{1}{2} \ln (x^2 + 1) + c$$

Proof:

$$d\left[\frac{1}{2} \ln (x^2 + 1)\right] + dc = \frac{2x}{2(x^2 + 1)} dx = \frac{x}{x^2 + 1} dx$$

Example: Find

$$\int \frac{x + 4}{3x^2 + 24x} dx$$

Solution: Let $v = 3x^2 + 24x$. Then $dv = 6x + 24$. Multiply both the numerator and the denominator by 6, thus making the numerator the derivative of the denominator.

$$\int \frac{x + 4}{3x^2 + 24x} dx = \frac{1}{6} \int \frac{6x + 24}{3x^2 + 24x} dx = \frac{1}{6} \ln (3x^2 + 24x) + c$$

Proof:

$$d[\frac{1}{6} \ln (3x^2 + 24x)] + dc = \frac{6x + 24}{6(3x^2 + 24x)} dx$$

$$= \frac{6(x + 4)}{6(3x^2 + 24x)} dx$$

$$= \frac{x + 4}{3x^2 + 24x} dx$$

The examples below involve the integration of various fractional expressions by the application of the theory of rational fractions. This is essentially the method of reducing a given proper fraction into its corresponding partial fractions. The techniques of finding partial fractions are explained in Chapter 2. You are urged to review that section before studying the following examples.

Example: First examine an improper fraction and its integral. Find

$$\int \frac{x+3}{x+5} \, dx$$

Solution: Since the degree of the numerator is equal to the degree of the denominator, this fraction can be reduced to a combination of integral and fractional expressions by dividing the numerator by the denominator. While reducing the fraction and while finding partial fractions, the integral sign and the *dx* expression are omitted. Dividing gives

$$\frac{x+3}{x+5} = 1 - \frac{2}{x+5}$$

This expression is now readily integrable:

$$\int \frac{x+3}{x+5} \, dx = \int \left(1 - \frac{2}{x+5}\right) dx$$

$$= \int dx - 2 \int \frac{dx}{x+5}$$

$$= x - 2 \ln(x+5) + c$$

Proof:

$$d[x - 2 \ln(x+5) + c] = \left(1 - \frac{2}{x+5} + dc\right) dx$$

$$= \left(1 - \frac{2}{x+5}\right) dx$$

The expression

$$1 - \frac{2}{x+5}$$

may be converted into the original fraction by substituting $(x+5)/(x+5)$ for 1. Then

$$\frac{x+5}{x+5} - \frac{2}{x+5} = \frac{x+3}{x+5}$$

Thus

$$\int \left(1 - \frac{2}{x+5}\right) dx = \int \frac{x+3}{x+5} \, dx$$

which is the original expression.

Example: In this case the denominator is composed of factors of the first degree with none repeating. Find

$$\int \frac{3x+4}{x^3 + x^2 - 6x} \, dx$$

Solution: The denominator may be decomposed into its linear factors such that

$$\frac{3x + 4}{x^3 + x^2 - 6x} = \frac{3x + 4}{x(x - 2)(x + 3)}$$

Hence the following identity can be established:

$$\frac{3x + 4}{x(x - 2)(x + 3)} = \frac{A}{x} + \frac{B}{x - 2} + \frac{C}{x + 3} \tag{1}$$

Clearing (1) of fractions gives

$$3x + 4 = A(x - 2)(x + 3) + B(x)(x + 3) + C(x)(x - 2)$$
$$3x + 4 = (A + B + C)x^2 + (A + 3B - 2C)x - 6A \tag{2}$$

Since this equation is an identity, the coefficients of the like powers of x in the two members of the equation can be equated to obtain the three simultaneous equations

$$\left.\begin{array}{r} A + B + C = 0 \\ A + 3B - 2C = 3 \\ -6A = 4 \end{array}\right\} \tag{3}$$

The solution of (3) yields

$$A = -\tfrac{2}{3} \qquad B = 1 \qquad C = -\tfrac{1}{3}$$

Substituting these values of A, B, and C into equation (1),

$$\frac{3x + 4}{x^3 + x^2 - 6x} = -\frac{2}{3x} + \frac{1}{x - 2} - \frac{1}{3(x + 3)}$$

Therefore,

$$\int \frac{3x + 4}{x^3 + x^2 - 6x}\, dx = -\frac{2}{3} \int \frac{dx}{x} + \int \frac{1}{x - 2}\, dx - \frac{1}{3} \int \frac{dx}{x + 3}$$
$$= -\tfrac{2}{3} \ln x + \ln (x - 2) - \tfrac{1}{3} \ln (x + 3) + c$$

Proof:

$$d[-\tfrac{2}{3} \ln x + \ln (x - 2) - \tfrac{1}{3} \ln (x + 3) + c]$$
$$= \left[-\frac{2}{3x} + \frac{1}{x - 2} - \frac{1}{3(x + 3)}\right] dx$$

Simplification of this expression will yield the original differential expression.

Example: In this case the denominator is composed of factors of the first degree with some repeating. Find

$$\int \frac{(x^2 + 1)\, dx}{x(x + 1)^2}$$

The partial fractions are

$$\frac{x^2 + 1}{x(x + 1)^2} = \frac{A}{x} + \frac{B}{(x + 1)^2} + \frac{C}{x + 1} \tag{1}$$

Clearing (1) of fractions gives

$$x^2 + 1 = A(x + 1)^2 + Bx + C(x)(x + 1)$$

$$x^2 + 1 = (A + C)x^2 + (2A + B + C)x + A \tag{2}$$

Equating the coefficients of the like powers of x leads to the three simultaneous equations

$$\left. \begin{array}{l} A \qquad + C = 1 \\ 2A + B + C = 0 \\ A \qquad\qquad = 1 \end{array} \right\} \tag{3}$$

Solving (3) yields

$$A = 1 \qquad B = -2 \qquad C = 0$$

Substitute these values into equation (1).

$$\frac{x^2 + 1}{x(x + 1)^2} = \frac{1}{x} - \frac{2}{(x + 1)^2}$$

Therefore,

$$\int \frac{(x^2 + 1)\,dx}{x(x + 1)^2} = \int \left[\frac{1}{x} - \frac{2}{(x + 1)^2} \right] dx$$

$$= \ln x + \frac{2}{x + 1} + c$$

Proof:

$$d \left(\ln x + \frac{2}{x + 1} + c \right) = \left(\frac{1}{x} - \frac{2}{(x + 1)^2} \right) dx$$

Example: The denominator is composed of factors of the second degree with none repeating. Find

$$\int \frac{4\,dx}{x^3 + 4x} = \int \frac{4\,dx}{x(x^2 + 4)}$$

Solution: Assume that

$$\frac{4}{x(x^2 + 4)} = \frac{A}{x} + \frac{Bx + C}{x^2 + 4}$$

Clearing of fractions gives

$$4 = (A + B)x^2 + Cx + 4A$$

Equating the coefficients of the like-powered terms of x yields

$$A + B = 0 \qquad C = 0 \qquad 4A = 4$$

From these simultaneous equations,

$$A = 1 \qquad B = -1 \qquad C = 0$$

Substituting gives

$$\frac{4}{x(x^2 + 4)} = \frac{1}{x} - \frac{x}{x^2 + 4}$$

Therefore,

$$\int \frac{4\,dx}{x(x^2 + 4)} = \int \left(\frac{1}{x} - \frac{x}{x^2 + 4} \right) dx$$
$$= \ln x - \tfrac{1}{2} \ln (x^2 + 4) + c$$

Proof:

$$d[\ln x - \tfrac{1}{2} \ln (x^2 + 4) + c] = \left[\frac{1}{x} - \frac{x}{x^2 + 4} \right] dx$$

The derivative of the natural exponential function $y = e^x$ is

$$\frac{dy}{dx} = e^x$$

or in differential form,

$$dy = e^x\,dx$$

Thus the rule can be stated as

8. $\displaystyle \int e^x\,dx = e^x + c$

Example: Find

$$\int 6e^x\,dx$$

Solution:

$$\int 6e^x\,dx = 6e^x + c$$

Proof:

$$d[6e^x + c] = 6e^x\,dx$$

Example: Find

$$\int \tfrac{2}{3} e^x\,dx$$

Solution:

$$\int \tfrac{2}{3}e^x \, dx = \tfrac{2}{3}e^x + c$$

Proof:

$$d[\tfrac{2}{3}e^x + c] = \tfrac{2}{3}e^x \, dx$$

Example: Find

$$\int ae^x \, dx$$

Solution:

$$\int ae^x \, dx = a \int e^x \, dx = ae^x + c$$

Proof:

$$d[ae^x + c] = ae^x \, dx$$

If the differential expression to be integrated is of the form $dy = e^{ax} \, dx$ the integral is

9. $\int e^{ax} \, dx = \dfrac{e^{ax}}{a} + c$

Example: Find

$$\int e^{5x} \, dx$$

Solution:

$$\int e^{5x} \, dx = \dfrac{e^{5x}}{5} + c$$

Proof:

$$d\left[\dfrac{e^{5x}}{5} + c\right] = d[\tfrac{1}{5}e^{5x} + c]$$
$$= e^{5x} \, dx$$

Example: Find

$$\int e^{7x} \, dx$$

Solution:

$$\int e^{7x} \, dx = \dfrac{e^{7x}}{7} + c$$

Proof:

$$d\left[\dfrac{e^{7x}}{7} + c\right] = e^{7x} \, dx$$

Example: Find

$$\int e^{(p+q)x} \, dx$$

Solution:

$$\int e^{(p+q)x}\, dx = \frac{e^{(p+q)x}}{p+q} + c$$

Proof:

$$d\left[\frac{e^{(p+q)x}}{p+q} + c\right] = e^{(p+q)x}\, dx$$

The derivative of a natural exponential function of the form $y = e^{f(x)}$ is

$$\frac{dy}{dx} = f'(x)e^{f(x)}$$

$$dy = f'(x)e^{f(x)}\, dx$$

The rule is

10. $\int f'(x)e^{f(x)}\, dx = e^{f(x)} + c$

Example: Find

$$\int (6x + 2)e^{(3x^2+2x+5)}\, dx$$

Solution: Since

$$6x + 2 = \frac{d}{dx}(3x^2 + 2x + 5)$$

apply 10 and write

$$\int (6x + 2)e^{(3x^2+2x+5)}\, dx = e^{(3x^2+2x+5)} + c$$

Proof:

$$d[e^{(3x^2+2x+5)} + c] = (6x + 2)e^{(3x^2+2x+5)}\, dx$$

Example: Find

$$\int \cos x e^{\sin x}\, dx$$

Solution:

$$\cos x = \frac{d}{dx}\sin x$$

$$\int \cos x e^{\sin x}\, dx = e^{\sin x} + c$$

Proof:

$$d[e^{\sin x} + c] = \cos x e^{\sin x}\, dx$$

Example: Find

$$\int 2x \cos x^2 e^{\sin x^2}\, dx$$

Solution: Here

$$\frac{d}{dx}\sin x^2 = 2x \cos x^2$$

$$\int 2x \cos x^2 e^{\sin x^2}\, dx = e^{\sin x^2} + c$$

Proof:

$$d[e^{\sin x^2} + c] = 2x \cos x^2 e^{\sin x^2}\, dx$$

INTEGRATION OF TRIGONOMETRIC FORMS

This section contains a brief discussion of the integration of functions such as

$$y = \int \sin x\, dx$$

$$y = \int \sec^2 x \tan x\, dx$$

Since many calculus texts and fairly complete tables of integrals are accessible, the material given below is brief. It is intended to serve primarily as an introduction to this type of function. All formulae given will be in the form

$$y = f(u)$$

where $u = g(x)$ in order to imply the broadest possible application.

1. Consider the form

$$y = \int \sin u\, du$$

Solution:

$$\int \sin u\, du = -\cos u$$

Example: Let

$$y = \int \sin^3 x \cos x\, dx$$

Solution: Let $u = \sin x$. Then

$$du = \cos x\, dx$$

and

$$\int u^3\, du = \tfrac{1}{4}u^4 + c = \tfrac{1}{4}\sin^4 x + c$$

Example:

$$y = \int \tan x \cos x \, dx$$

Solution:

$$\int \tan x \cos dx = \int \frac{\sin x}{\cos x} \cos x \, dx = \int \sin x \, dx = -\cos x + c$$

2. Consider the form

$$y = \int \cos x \, dx$$

Solution:

$$\int \cos x \, dx = \sin x + c$$

Example:

$$y = \int (\sin x - \sin^3 x + \cos x) \, dx$$

Solution:

$$\int (\sin x - \sin^3 x + \cos x) \, dx = \int [\sin x(1 - \sin^2 x) + \cos x) \, dx$$

$$= \int (\cos^2 x \sin x + \cos x) \, dx$$

$$= \int \cos^2 x \sin x \, dx + \int \cos x \, dx$$

Let

$$u = \cos x$$

$$du = -\sin x \, dx$$

and

$$\int -u^2 \, du + \sin x + c = -\tfrac{1}{3}u^3 + \sin x + c$$

$$= -\tfrac{1}{3} \cos^3 x + \sin x + c$$

Example:

$$y = \int (\sin x - \cos x) \, dx$$

Solution:

$$\int (\sin x - \cos x) \, dx = \int \sin x \, dx - \int \cos x \, dx$$

$$= -\cos x - \sin x + c$$

3. Consider the form

$$y = \int \tan u \, du$$

Solution:

$$\int \tan u \, du = \int \frac{\sin u}{\cos u} \, du$$

Let

$$v = \cos u$$
$$dv = -\sin u \, du$$

Substituting gives

$$-\int \frac{dv}{v} = -\ln v + c = \ln \frac{1}{v} + c = \ln \frac{1}{\cos u} + c = \ln \sec u + c$$

Example:

$$y = \int (\cos^2 x \sin x - \tan x) \, dx$$

Solution:

$$\int (\cos^2 x \sin x - \tan x) \, dx = \int \cos^2 x \sin x \, dx - \int \tan x \, dx$$

Let

$$u = \cos x$$
$$du = -\sin x \, dx$$

Substituting gives

$$-\int u^2 \, du - \ln \sec x + c = -\tfrac{1}{3}u^3 + \ln \frac{1}{\sec x} + c$$
$$= -\tfrac{1}{3} \cos^3 x + \ln \cos x + c$$

Example:

$$y = \int (\sec^4 x - \sec^2 x + 1) \, dx$$

Solution:

$$\int (\sec^4 x - \sec^2 x + 1) \, dx = \int [(1 + \tan^2 x) \sec^2 x - \sec^2 x + 1] \, dx$$

$$= \int (\sec^2 x + \tan^2 x \sec^2 x - \sec^2 x + 1) \, dx$$

$$= \int (\tan^2 x \sec^2 x + 1) \, dx$$

Let

$$u = \tan x$$
$$du = \sec^2 x \, dx$$
$$\int (u^2 \, du + 1) \, dx = \tfrac{1}{3}u^3 + x + c$$
$$= \tfrac{1}{3} \tan^3 x + x + c$$

4. Consider the form

$$y = \int \cot u \, du$$

Solution:

$$\int \cot u \, du = \int \frac{\cos u}{\sin u} \, du$$

Let

$$v = \sin u$$

$$dv = \cos u \, du$$

$$\int \frac{dv}{v} = \ln v + c = \ln \sin u + c$$

Example:

$$y = \int \frac{1 - \sin^2 x}{\sin x \cos x} \, dx$$

Solution:

$$\int \frac{1 - \sin^2 x}{\sin x \cos x} = \int \frac{\cos^2 x}{\sin x \cos x} \, dx$$

$$= \int \frac{\cos x}{\sin x} \, dx$$

$$= \int \cot x \, dx$$

$$= \ln \sin x + c$$

Example:

$$y = \int \cot^2 \theta \csc^2 \theta \, d\theta$$

Solution:

$$\int \cot^2 \theta \csc^2 \theta \, d\theta$$

Let

$$u = \cot \theta$$

$$du = -\csc^2 \theta \, d\theta$$

Substituting gives

$$-\int u^2 \, du = -\tfrac{1}{3}u^3 + c = -\tfrac{1}{3}\cot^3 \theta + c$$

5. Consider the form

$$y = \int \sec u \, du$$

Solution:

$$\int \sec u \; du = \int \sec u \; \frac{\tan u + \sec u}{\tan u + \sec u} du$$

$$= \int \frac{\sec u(\tan u + \sec u)}{\tan u + \sec u} du$$

$$= \int \frac{\sec u \tan u + \sec^2 u}{\tan u + \sec u} du$$

Let

$$v = \tan u + \sec u$$

$$dv = (\sec u \tan u + \sec^2 u) \; du$$

Substituting gives

$$\int \frac{dv}{v} = \log v + c$$

$$= \ln (\tan u + \sec u) + c$$

Example:

$$y = \int (\sec^2 x \tan x + 1) \sec x \; dx$$

Solution:

$$\int (\sec^2 x \tan x + 1) \sec x \; dx = \int (\sec^3 x \tan x + \sec x) \; dx$$

$$= \int \sec^3 x \tan x \; dx + \int \sec x \; dx$$

Let

$$u = \sec x$$

$$du = \sec x \tan x \; dx$$

Substituting gives

$$\int u^2 \; du + \ln (\tan x + \sec x) + c = \tfrac{1}{3} u^3 + \ln (\tan x + \sec x) + c$$

$$= \tfrac{1}{3} \sec^3 x + \ln (\tan x + \sec x) + c$$

Example:

$$y = \int \frac{\cos^2 x}{\cos x - \sin x \cos x} dx$$

Solution:

$$\int \frac{\cos^2 x}{\cos x - \sin x \cos x}\,dx = \int \frac{1 - \sin^2 x}{\cos x(1 - \sin x)}\,dx$$

$$= \int \frac{(1 - \sin x)(1 + \sin x)}{\cos x(1 - \sin x)}\,dx$$

$$= \int \frac{1 + \sin x}{\cos x}\,dx$$

$$= \int \frac{1}{\cos x}\,dx + \int \frac{\sin x}{\cos x}\,dx$$

$$= \int \sec x\,dx + \int \tan x\,dx$$

$$= \ln(\tan x + \sec x) + \ln \sec x + c$$

6. Finally, consider the form

$$y = \int \csc u\,du$$

Solution:

$$\int \csc u\,du = \int \frac{\csc u(\csc u + \cot u)}{(\csc u + \cot u)}\,du$$

Let

$$v = \csc u + \cot u$$

Then

$$dv = -\csc u(\csc u + \cot u)\,du$$

Substituting yields

$$-\int \frac{dv}{v} = -\ln v + c = -\ln(\csc u + \cot u) + c$$

Example:

$$y = \int \sec x \cot x\,dx$$

Solution:

$$\int \sec x \cot x\,dx = \int \frac{1}{\cos x}\frac{\cos x}{\sin x}\,dx$$

$$= \int \frac{1}{\sin x}\,dx$$

$$= \int \csc x\,dx$$

$$= -\ln(\cot x + \csc x) + c$$

Example:

$$y = \int \csc x \, (\cot^3 x \sec^2 x + 1) \, dx$$

Solution:

$$\int \csc x \, (\cot^3 x \sec^2 x + 1) \, dx = \int \cot^3 x \sec^2 x \csc x \, dx + \int \csc x \, dx$$

$$= \int \cot^2 x \sec^2 x \cot x \csc x \, dx + \int \csc x \, dx$$

$$= \int \frac{\cos^2 x}{\sin^2 x} \frac{1}{\cos^2 x} \cot x \csc x \, dx$$
$$- \ln(\cot x + \csc x)$$

$$= \int \frac{1}{\sin^2 x} \cot x \csc x \, dx$$
$$- \ln(\cot x + \csc x) + c$$

$$= \int \csc^2 x \cot x \csc x \, dx$$
$$- \ln(\cot x + \csc x) + c$$

Let

$$u = \csc x$$
$$du = -\cot x \csc x \, dx$$

Substitute

$$-\int u^2 \, du - \ln(\cot x + \csc x) + c = -\tfrac{1}{3} u^3 - \ln(\cot x + \csc x) + c$$

$$= -\tfrac{1}{3} \csc^3 x - \ln(\cot x + \csc x) + c$$

By now, you will have observed that a great deal of finesse is involved in obtaining the integrals of trigonometric functions. Although skill in handling this type of function can be mastered, a convenient table of integral forms is a definite asset for working with functions requiring the integration of trigonometric forms. As a matter of fact, such tables are of great use in handling all types of integration, not just trigonometric forms.

CONSTANT OF INTEGRATION

When the marginal cost function was integrated to get the total cost function, the integral expression contained a term c. Likewise, in the integrals of the various other $f'(x)$ and $f'(Q)$ expressions, there was a constant term c or k.

To understand the need for introducing a constant term in the indefinite integral of a differential expression, consider the process of differentiation. Recall that the derivative of a constant is equal to zero,

$$\frac{d}{dx} c = 0$$

Thus for example, in differentiating

$$y = x^2 + 10$$

$$y' = 2x$$

the constant term 10 would disappear. In order to find the original function from the derivative, it must be known that one or more constant terms may have been lost in the process of integration. Therefore, an arbitrary constant term must be introduced in the integral expression to represent the algebraic sum of the constants in the original $f(x)$ which may have been lost during differentiation. For example, the integral of $y' = 2x$ is the expression

$$\int y' \, dx = \int 2x \, dx = \frac{2x^2}{2} + c$$

The question now is, "Is there a method for finding the precise magnitude of the constant of integration?" For example, can a specific magnitude be given to the term c in the integral expression above? The constant of integration can be found in every case, if the value of the integral at some one value of the variable is known.

In the total revenue function considered earlier, suppose it is known that when the quantity sold is zero, the amount of total revenue is zero. The necessary constant of integration can then be found. Solutions for the constants of integration for a few selected problems are given below.

1. Find the total revenue function whose marginal revenue is

$$MR = 10 - 2Q$$

when it is known that total revenue is zero when $Q = 0$.
Solution:

$$M \int R \, dQ = \int 10 \, dQ - \int 2Q \, dQ = 10Q - Q^2 + c$$

$$10Q - Q^2 = 0 \qquad \text{when} \qquad Q = 0$$

Substituting $Q = 0$ into the integral expression, and setting that equal to zero, solve for the value of c:

$$10(0) - 2(0^2) + c = 0$$
$$c = 0$$

The complete form of the integral expression now becomes

$$TR = 10Q - Q^2 + 0$$
$$= 10Q - Q^2$$

2. Find the total cost function whose marginal cost function is

$$MC = 50 - 20Q + 3Q^2$$

It is known that total cost is 100 when $Q = 0$.
Solution:

$$TC = \int MC \, dQ = 50 \int dQ - 20 \int Q \, dQ + 3 \int Q^2 \, dQ$$
$$= 50Q - 10Q^2 + Q^3 + k$$

Set $TC = 100$ when $Q = 0$.

$$50(0) - 10(0^2) + 0^3 + k = 100$$
$$k = 100$$

Total cost is, therefore, given by

$$TC = 50Q - 10Q^2 + Q^3 + 100$$

In this example, the constant of integration, $k = 100$, can be interpreted as the total fixed cost, which has a constant magnitude at all values of output Q, including $Q = 0$.

3. A third economic example of the determination of the constant of integration is the aggregate consumption function, where

$$MPC = \frac{dC}{dY} = 0.6$$

Assume that C has a value of 220 when $Y = 200$.
Solution:

$$C = \int MPC \, dY = 0.6 \int dY = 0.6Y + k$$

Since C, the amount of consumption, is 220 when $Y = 200$, the following equation can be solved for k:

$$0.6(200) + k = 220$$
$$120 + k = 220$$
$$k = 220 - 120 = 100$$

The complete form of the consumption function is, therefore,

$$C = 100 + 0.6\,Y$$

This consumption function was also discussed earlier in the text.

THE DEFINITE INTEGRAL

The definite integral of a function defines the area under the curve generated by the function. The definite integral plays a very important role in economic theory. For example, the definite integral of the marginal cost function gives the total cost. The definite integral of the marginal revenue function is the total revenue. The definite integral of the marginal propensity function is the amount of consumption.

The first step in considering the definite integral is to define the differential of the area under a curve.

Differential of the Area Under a Curve

A continuous function

$$y = f(x)$$

is the equation of the curve AB in Figure 10-1. The ordinate CD is a fixed

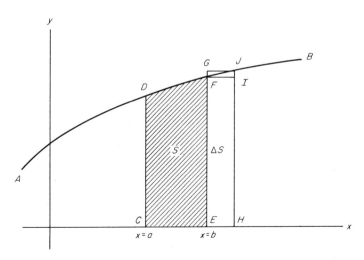

FIGURE 10-1   Differential of an Area Under a Curve

line. The line *EF* is the variable ordinate. The area *CDEF* is designated by x. Then as x takes on an increment Δx, the area under the curve increases by Δs, where $\Delta s = EFJH$. When the rectangles *EFIH* and *EGJH* are examined, it is apparent from the diagram that

$$EFIH < \Delta s < EGJH$$

or

$$EF\,(\Delta x) < \Delta s < HJ\,(\Delta x)$$

Dividing each term of this inequality by Δx gives

$$EF < \frac{\Delta s}{\Delta x} < HJ$$

Now as Δx approaches zero as a limit, the ordinate *HJ* approaches *EG*, and

$$\frac{ds}{dx} = y = EG$$

Expressing this relationship as a differential gives

$$ds = y\,dx$$

The differential of the area under a curve between two ordinates and above the x-axis is equal to the product of the variable ordinate (in this case *EG*) and the differential of x.

The Definite Integral

From the definition of the differential of the area under a curve, it follows that

$$y = f(x)$$
$$ds = y\,dx$$
$$ds = f(x)\,dx$$

Integrating gives

$$s = \int f(x)\,dx$$

Let

$$\int f(x)\,dx = \phi(x) + c$$

Then the area under the curve is defined by the relation

$$s = \phi(x) + c$$

To determine the value of c, note that the area under the curve is zero when $x = a$. Thus

$$0 = \phi(a) + c \qquad \text{or} \qquad c = -\phi(a)$$

Substituting the value of c into the equation for the area gives

$$s = \phi(x) - \phi(a)$$

The shaded area under the curve in Figure 10-1 is defined for $x = b$, thus

$$CDFE = \phi(b) - \phi(a)$$

The calculation of the numerical value of the area under a curve is called *definite integration*. It is also called *integration between limits*. If a is taken as the lower and b as the upper limit, the definite integral is represented by the symbol

$$\int_a^b y\, dx \qquad \text{or} \qquad \int_a^b f(x)\, dx$$

In finding the definite integral, the constant of integration disappears. For example, if

$$\int f(x)\, dx = \phi(x) + c$$

then, by definition

$$\int_a^b f(x)\, dx = [\phi(b) + c] - [\phi(a) + c]$$
$$= \phi(b) + c - \phi(a) - c$$
$$= \phi(b) - \phi(a)$$

The calculation of the definite integral may be summarized in the following steps.

1. Find the indefinite integral of the given differential expression.
2. Substitute into the indefinite integral, first the upper limit of the variable, and then the lower limit. Subtract the latter value from the former.
3. The constant of integration will disappear in finding the definite integral.

Some examples of calculating the definite integral are as follows.

1. Find

$$\int_1^3 x^2\, dx$$

Solution:

$$\int_1^3 x^2\, dx = \left[\frac{x^3}{3}\right]_1^3 = \frac{3^3}{3} - \frac{1^3}{3} = \frac{27}{3} - \frac{1}{3} = \frac{26}{3} = 8\tfrac{2}{3}$$

2. Find $(10 - 2Q) \, dQ$.

Solution:

$$\int_0^3 (10 - 2Q) \, dQ = [10Q - Q^2]_0^3$$
$$= [10(3) - 3^2] - 0$$
$$= 30 - 9 = 21$$

Notice that $10 - 2Q$ is the expression for marginal revenue that was considered earlier. By integrating the marginal revenue function between $Q = 0$ and $Q = 3$, the value of total revenue corresponding to $Q = 3$ can be found. This integral is illustrated geometrically by Figure 10-2. At a sales quantity of 3 units, total revenue corresponds to the linear distance AB on the total revenue diagram, and that same total revenue is shown by the area $Ocba$ in the diagram of marginal revenue. The definite integral between $Q = 0$ and $Q = a$ in the marginal revenue diagram represents the total revenue of $AB = 21$.

3. Find

$$\int_0^4 (50 - 20Q + 3Q^2) \, dQ$$

Solution:

$$\int_0^4 (50 - 20Q + 3Q^2) \, dQ$$
$$= [50Q - 10Q^2 + Q^3]_0^4 = [50(4) - 10(4^2) + 4^3] - 0$$
$$= 200 - 160 + 64 = 104$$

The differential expression $50 - 20Q + 3Q^2$ is the marginal cost function that has appeared earlier. The definite integral of the marginal cost function between $Q = 0$ and $Q = 4$ is the total cost of producing 4 units, so the total cost of producing 4 units is 104. Figure 10-3 diagrams a total cost function and the corresponding marginal cost function. The total cost for producing 4 units is represented geometrically in the total cost diagram by the linear distance AB. This same total cost is represented by the definite integral of the marginal cost function between $Q = 0$ and $Q = 4$, which is represented in the lower diagram by the area under the curve, $Ocba$. Therefore

$$AB = Ocba = 104$$

4. Assume that the marginal propensity to consume is a constant equal to 0.8. Then

$$MPC = \frac{dC}{dY} = 0.8$$

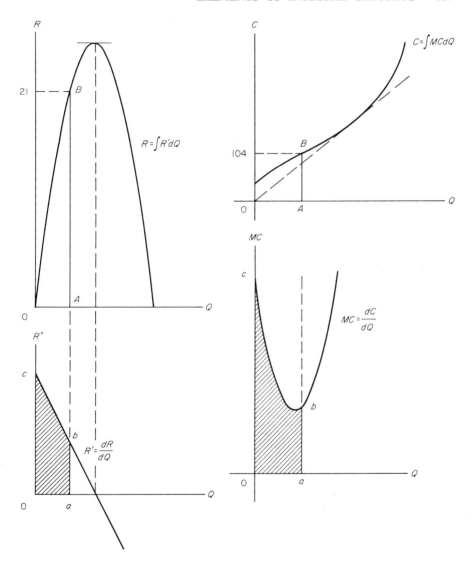

FIGURE 10-2   Total Revenue Curve and
Marginal Revenue Curve

FIGURE 10-3   Total Cost Curve and
Marginal Cost Curve

or, in differential terms,

$$dC = 0.8 \, dY$$

Figure 10-4 shows *MPC* graphically as a horizontal line at a height 0.8. The amount of consumption when disposable income is 300 is the definite

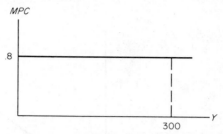

FIGURE 10-4   Marginal Propensity to Consume

integral of $dC = 0.8\ dY$ from $Y = 0$ to $Y = 300$. To find such a definite integral, show

$$\int_0^{300} 0.8\ dY = [0.8\,Y]_0^{300} = 0.8(300) - 0.8(0) = 240$$

Notice that this is the area of the rectangle $300 \times 0.8 = 240$. This discussion applies to a proportional consumption function which passes through origin.

5. Consider the function

$$y = 3x$$

The graph of this function is shown in Figure 10-5. The function forms a

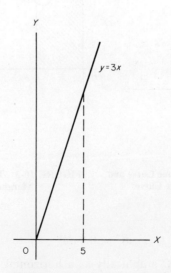

FIGURE 10-5   A Right Triangle

right triangle with the x-axis and the ordinate at $x = 5$. The area of the triangle equals one half of the altitude times the base, or 37.5. The definite integral of this function between $x = 0$ and $x = 5$ is

$$\int_0^5 3x \, dx = \left[\frac{3x^2}{2}\right]_0^5 = \left[\frac{3(5^2)}{2} - 0\right]$$
$$= {}^{75}\!/\!_2 = 37.5$$

6. When the curve of a function being integrated crosses the x-axis, it must be determined whether the desired result is the *absolute* value of the area under the curve or its *algebraic* value. For example, consider

$$y = \int_0^4 (x - 2) \, dx$$

This gives the area

$$y = \left[\frac{x^2}{2} - 2x\right]_0^4 = [8 - 8] - [0] = 0$$

Figure 10-6 shows the graph of this function, which indicates that the negative area OAB is exactly offset by BCD. If, therefore, the *sum* of the areas of the triangles is of interest, proceed as follows. First determine

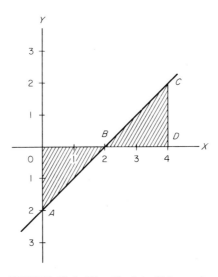

FIGURE 10-6   The Absolute Value and
the Algebraic Value of an Area Under a
Curve

that the curve crosses the x-axis when $x = 2$. Then the sum of the areas is

$$A = \int_0^2 (x - 2)\, dx + \int_2^4 (x - 2)\, dx$$

$$= \left[\frac{x^2}{2} - 2x\right]_0^2 + \left[\frac{x^2}{2} - 2x\right]_2^4$$

$$= [(\tfrac{4}{2} - 4) - 0] + [(\tfrac{16}{2} - 8) - (\tfrac{4}{2} - 4)]$$

$$= [-2] + [2]$$
$$\quad(OAB)\ (BCD)$$

Then the sum of the absolute values of the two areas is

$$A = 2 + 2 = 4$$

7. Find the area bounded by the parabola

$$R = 5x - x^2$$

and the x-axis (see Figure 10-7).

$$\int_0^5 R\, dx = \int_0^5 (5x - x^2)\, dx$$

$$= \left[\frac{5x^2}{2} - \frac{x^3}{3}\right]_0^5 = [\tfrac{125}{2} - \tfrac{125}{3}] - 0$$

$$= \tfrac{125}{6}$$

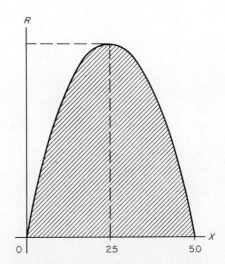

FIGURE 10-7 Area Under the Curve
Between $X = 0$ and $X = 5$

8. A consumer's demand curve indicates the maximum price the consumer would be willing to pay for each quantity of the good. Thus if the seller could devise a means by which the consumer could be made to pay his maximum price for each unit of the good, the area under the demand curve would represent the maximum amount of money the seller could extract from the buyer. Under normal circumstances, however, sellers do not practice this type of pricing. Instead, the price is set either by market forces of supply and demand or arbitrarily. When the price is set at $p = p_0$, the consumer buys that quantity which corresponds to his idea of the value of the good. In such an event the consumer is said to receive a consumer's surplus. Figure 10-8 shows the demand curve of the consumer, the price and the amount of consumer surplus. The area bounded by the demand curve, the axes and the ordinates at $x = x_0$ represents the maximum amount of money the consumer could be forced to pay for x_0 units of the good. He actually pays only $p_0 x_0$, so the shaded triangular area represents the consumer surplus. The consumer surplus is clearly the area under the demand curve minus the rectangle:

$$\int_0^{x_0} f(x)\, dx - p_0 x_0$$

where $f(x)$ is the demand function. If the demand curve is represented by the function

$$p = 10 - x \qquad p_0 = 4 \qquad x_0 = 6$$

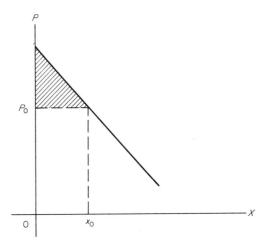

**FIGURE 10-8   Consumer Surplus As An Area Under
the Demand Curve**

the consumer surplus is

$$\int_0^6 (10 - x)\, dx - 24 = \left[10x - \frac{x^2}{2}\right]_0^6 - 24 = 60 - 18 - 24 = 18$$

If the demand function were a rectangular hyperbola

$$p = \frac{9}{x + 2}$$

and the supply curve were of the form

$$p = 2 + x$$

the equilibrium quantity x would be found by setting the supply price equal to the demand price

$$\frac{9}{x + 2} = 2 + x$$
$$9 = x^2 + 4x + 4$$
$$x^2 + 4x - 5 = 0$$
$$(x - 1)(x + 5) = 0$$
$$x = 1 \text{ or } x = -5$$

Since a negative quantity can be rejected, set $x_0 = 1$. Substituting either in the supply function or the demand function, $p_0 = 3$. Thus consumer surplus would be defined by the relation

$$\int_0^1 \frac{9}{x + 2}\, dx - 3 = [9 \ln (x + 2)]_0^1 - 3$$
$$= [9 \ln 3 - 9 \ln (2)] - 3$$
$$= 9.8874 - 6.2379 - 3 = 0.6495$$

9. *Domar's capital growth model:*[†] Since investment increases productive capacity and also creates income, is there some rate of growth of investment which will equate the rate of increase in productive capacity to the rate of increase in income? This is the question which Domar set out to answer. The symbols are:

I = annual rate of investment
Y = national income
P = productive capacity
v = the net value added by production brought about by new investment I

---

† Evsey Domar, "Expansion and Employment," *American Economic Review*, Vol. 37 (March, 1947), pp. 34–55.

$s = v/I =$ the ratio of the net value added to the new investment
$v = Is =$ the output of new investment
$\alpha =$ marginal propensity to save
$\sigma =$ potential social average productivity of investment.

This is the ratio of the time rate of increase in productive capacity to the rate of investment, or

$$\sigma = \frac{dP/dt}{I}$$

The rate of increase in productive capacity over time is

$$\frac{dP}{dt} = \sigma I(t)$$

The rate of increase in national income due to investment is, of course, the multiplier

$$\frac{dY}{dI} = \frac{1}{\alpha}$$

which in differential terms is

$$dY = \frac{1}{\alpha} dI$$

Differentiating with respect to time gives

$$\frac{dY}{dt} = \frac{1}{\alpha} \frac{dI}{dt}$$

Equilibrium is maintained through time if

$$\frac{dY}{dt} = \frac{dP}{dt}$$

which is to say

$$\sigma I = \frac{1}{\alpha} \frac{dI}{dt}$$

Multiplying through by $\alpha\, dt$ gives

$$\sigma\alpha\, dt I = dI$$

Dividing by I gives

$$\sigma\alpha\, dt = \frac{1}{I} dI$$

Taking the definite integral of both sides of the equation from $t = 0$ to $t = t$ yields

$$\int_0^t \sigma\alpha\, dt = \int_0^t \frac{1}{I(t)}\, dI(t)$$

$$[\sigma\alpha t]_0^t = [\ln I(t)]_0^t + c$$

To find c, let $t = 0$ as an initial condition.

$$0 = \ln I(0) - \ln I(0) + c$$

$$0 = c$$

$$\sigma\alpha t = \ln I(t) - \ln I(0)$$

$$\sigma\alpha t = \ln \frac{I(t)}{I(0)}$$

$$e^{\sigma\alpha t} = \frac{I(t)}{I(0)}$$

$$I(t) = I(0)e^{\sigma\alpha t}$$

To maintain full employment equilibrium, investment must grow at the rate of $\sigma\alpha$.

APPROXIMATE INTEGRATION

Most differential expressions encountered in elementary economic problems are forms that are easily integrable. Occasionally, however, a given differential expression may be either difficult or impossible to integrate. In such a case, some rules for finding an approximation to the definite integral may be applied. Two such rules are the *trapezoidal rule* and the *parabolic rule* (Simpson's rule).

Trapezoidal Rule

Given the expression

$$y = f(x)\, dx$$

which traces out the curve shown in Figure 10-9, the area under the curve, above the x-axis, and between the ordinates at $x = a$ and $x = b$ is

$$\int_a^b f(x)\, dx$$

Such an area may be approximated by adding together the trapezoids included within it. The procedure is as follows: Divide the distance $b - a$ into n equal parts each of length Δx. Thus

$$\Delta x = \frac{b - a}{n}$$

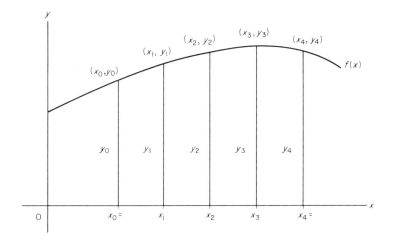

FIGURE 10-9   Illustrative Application of the Trapezoidal Rule

Let the abscissa values of the points of division be

$$x_0 = a$$
$$x_1 = a + \Delta x$$
$$x_2 = a + 2\,\Delta x,\, \ldots,\, x_n = a + n\,\Delta x = b$$

Find the ordinate values that correspond to these values of the abscissa. Let these ordinate values be

$$y_0 = f(x_0)$$
$$y_1 = f(x_1)$$
$$y_2 = f(x_2),\, \ldots,\, y_n = f(x_n)$$

Join

$$y_0 \text{ and } y_1 \qquad y_1 \text{ and } y_2, \ldots \qquad y_{n-1} \text{ and } y_n$$

thus forming n different trapezoids. The area of a trapezoid equals one half the sum of the two parallel sides multiplied by the altitude. Thus the areas of the various trapezoids are

$$\tfrac{1}{2}(y_0 + y_1)\,\Delta x = \text{area of trapezoid } 1$$
$$\tfrac{1}{2}(y_1 + y_2)\,\Delta x = \text{area of trapezoid } 2$$
$$\begin{array}{cccc} \cdot & \cdot & \cdot & \cdot \\ \cdot & \cdot & \cdot & \cdot \\ \cdot & \cdot & \cdot & \cdot \end{array}$$
$$\tfrac{1}{2}(y_{n-1} + y_n)\,\Delta x = \text{area of trapezoid } n$$

Adding together all of the trapezoidal areas gives the approximate value of the area under the curve.

$$\text{Area} = (\tfrac{1}{2}y_0 + y_1 + y_2 + \cdots + y_{n-1} + \tfrac{1}{2}y_n)\,\Delta x$$

Obviously, the greater the number of these trapezoidal areas is, the more closely the sum of their areas will approximate the area under the curve.

Example: Find

$$\int_0^{10} x^2\,dx$$

by the trapezoidal rule, dividing the distance from $x = 0$ to $x = 10$ into 10 equal parts.

Solution:

$$\Delta x = \frac{b-a}{n} = \frac{10-0}{10} = 1$$

Substituting

$$x = 0, 1, 2, \ldots, 10$$

into x^2 yields the values

$$y = 0, 1, 4, 9, 16, 25, 36, 49, 64, 81, 100$$

Thus the area is

$$A = (0 + 1 + 4 + 9 + 16 + 25 + 36 + 49 + 64 + 81 + {}^{100}\!/_2)1$$
$$= 335$$

Integrating gives

$$\int_0^{10} x^2\,dx = \left[\frac{x^3}{3}\right]_0^{10} = \left[\frac{10^3}{3}\right] - 0 = 333\tfrac{1}{3}$$

Here the approximation of the area under the curve is in error by about one half of 1 percent.

Example: Find

$$\int_0^4 \frac{dx}{4+x}$$

by the trapezoidal rule, letting $n = 4$.

Solution:

$$\Delta x = \frac{4-0}{4} = 1$$

When

$$y = \frac{1}{4+x}$$

the corresponding values of x and y are

$x:$	0	1	2	3	4
$y:$	0.25	0.2	0.167	0.143	0.125

Hence the area is

$$A = (0.125 + 0.2 + 0.167 + 0.143 + 0.063)1 = 0.698$$

Integrating gives

$$\int_0^4 \frac{dx}{4 + x} = [\ln(4 + x)]_0^4$$

$$= \ln 8 - \ln 4 = 2.0794 - 1.3863 = 0.6931$$

Simpson's Rule (Parabolic Rule)

Sometimes the calculation of the definite integral involves finding the area under a parabolic arc between two specified ordinates as limits. In some cases the function may be difficult or impossible to integrate. Simpson's rule is particularly appropriate to use as a means of calculating the approximate value of the area under such a curve.

The derivation of Simpson's rule can be illustrated by an example. Consider parabolic arc P_0P_2 in Figure 10-10. It is a part of a parabola whose axis is parallel to the OY axis. The point P_1 is chosen such that $AO = OB$. The ordinates of P_0, P_1, and P_2 are respectively y_0, y_1, and y_2.

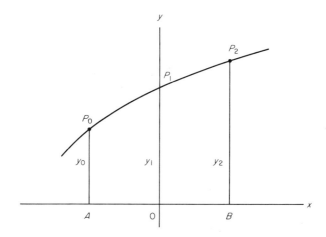

FIGURE 10-10   Illustrative Application of Simpson's Rule

According to Simpson's rule, the area bounded by the parabola, the x-axis and the ordinates P_0 and P_2 is

$$z = \tfrac{1}{3}h(y_0 + 4y_1 + y_2)$$

where h is the distance $AO = OB$. The reasoning is illustrated step by step as follows: Take the y-axis along the ordinate of P_1. Since the distance on the abscissa

$$AO = OB = h$$

then

$$AB = 2h$$

The equation of a parabola with the axis parallel to OY is (consult Chapter 3):

$$(x - h)^2 = 2p(y - k)$$

Solving for y yields an equation of the general form

$$y = ax^2 + 2bx + c \tag{1}$$

The required area

$$AP_0P_1P_2B = z$$

is the definite integral of (1) between the limits $x = -h$ and $x = h$.

$$z = \int_{-h}^{h} (ax^2 + 2bx + c)\, dx = \left[\frac{a}{3}x^3 + bx^2 + cx\right]_{-h}^{h}$$

$$= \left[\frac{a}{3}h^3 + bh^2 + ch\right] - \left[\frac{a}{3}(-h)^3 + b(-h)^2 + c(-h)\right]$$

$$= \tfrac{2}{3}ah^3 + 2ch$$

By first integrating between the limits $-h$ and 0, and then between the limits 0 and h, the same measure of the area can be derived.

$$z = \tfrac{2}{3}ah^3 + 2ch$$

Substituting the values $x = -h$, $x = 0$, and $x = h$ into (1) gives the following pairs of coordinates:

$$y_0 = ah^2 - 2bh + c = AP_0 \qquad \text{if } x = -h$$

$$y_1 = c = OP_1 \qquad \text{if } x = 0$$

$$y_2 = ah^2 + 2bh + c = BP_2 \qquad \text{if } x = h$$

Thus the area is

$$z = \tfrac{1}{3}h(y_0 + 4y_1 + y_2) = \tfrac{2}{3}ah^3 + 2ch$$

With this result in mind, consider an application of Simpson's rule for finding the approximate area under a curve.

When using the trapezoidal rule, the extremities of the ordinates corresponding to the various values of the abscissa can be connected to form a series of trapezoids. Summing the areas of the trapezoids gives an approximate value of the area under the curve. Simpson's rule relies upon essentially the same principle. The major difference between the trapezoidal and Simpson's rules is that in the latter, arcs of parabolas are fitted to three points along the curve. The sum of the areas under these parabolic arcs gives an approximation of the value of the area under the curve. Usually Simpson's rule will provide a closer approximation of the area under the curve than will the trapezoidal rule.

Figure 10-11 illustrates a case which requires an estimate of the area under the curve between the ordinates A_0B_0 and A_4B_4. The steps are as follows: Divide the interval between

$$x = a = OA_0$$

and

$$x = b = OA_4$$

into an *even* number (n) of parts, in this case into 4 equal parts. Each

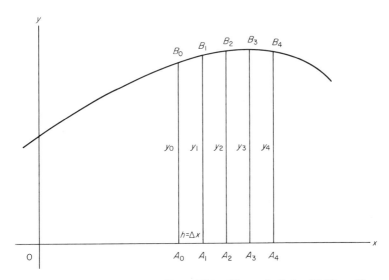

FIGURE 10-11   Area Under a Curve, Using Simpson's Rule with More Than
Two Parabolic Arcs

interval is equal to Δx, i.e.,

$$A_0 A_1 = \Delta x, \ A_1 A_2 = \Delta x$$
$$A_2 A_3 = \Delta x$$
$$A_3 A_4 = \Delta x$$

The ordinates at the points $A_0, \ldots, A_4$ are $y_0, \ y_1, \ y_2, \ y_3,$ and y_4. The extremities of these ordinates are $B_0, \ B_1, \ B_2, \ B_3,$ and B_4. Join $B_0, \ B_1,$ and B_2 to form a parabolic arc. Then join points $B_2, \ B_3,$ and B_4 into a second parabolic arc. The area under each of the parabolic arcs is the sum of two parabolic strips. For example, the area $A_0 B_0 B_1 A_1$ is made up of the parabolic strips $A_0 B_0 B_1 A_1$ and $A_1 B_1 B_2 A_2$. The area of each of these double parabolic strips is given by the relation

$$\text{Area } A_0 B_0 B_2 A_2 = \tfrac{1}{3} h(y_0 + 4y_1 + y_2)$$
$$\text{Area } A_2 B_2 B_4 A_4 = \tfrac{1}{3} h(y_2 + 4y_3 + y_4)$$

In this example $h = \Delta x$. Adding the areas of the two double parabolic strips results in an approximate value of the area under the curve between the ordinates $A_0 B_0$ and $A_4 B_4$:

$$\text{Area } A_0 B_0 B_4 A_4 = \tfrac{1}{3} \Delta x(y_0 + 4y_1 + 2y_2 + 4y_3 + y_4)$$

Obviously, if the arcs were divided into more strips, their sum would provide a more accurate approximation of the area under the curve.

Thus, if the area were divided into an even number (n) of strips, Simpson's rule would provide the relation

$$\text{Area} = \tfrac{1}{3} \Delta x(y_0 + 4y_1 + 2y_2 + 4y_3 + 2y_4 + \cdots + y_n)$$

Example: Find the area

$$\int_1^{11} x^2 \, dx$$

by Simpson's rule, taking $n = 10$. Compare with the area found by integration.

Solution:

$$\frac{b-a}{n} = \frac{11-1}{10} = 1 = \Delta x$$

The area to be found is under the curve $y = x^2$. Substitute $x = 1, \ldots, x = 11$ into the equation of the curve to find the values of the ordinates:

x:	1	2	3	4	5	6	7	8	9	10	11
y:	1	4	9	16	25	36	49	64	81	100	121

Thus, by Simpson's rule,

$$\text{Area} = \tfrac{1}{3}[1 + 4(4) + 2(9) + 4(16) + 2(25) + 4(36) + 2(49)$$
$$+ 4(64) + 2(81) + 4(100) + 121]$$
$$= \tfrac{1}{3}[1330] = 443\tfrac{1}{3}$$

Integrating gives

$$\int_1^{11} x^2 \, dx = \left[\frac{x^3}{3}\right]_1^{11} = \frac{11^3}{3} - \tfrac{1}{3} = 443\tfrac{2}{3} - \tfrac{1}{3} = 443\tfrac{1}{3}$$

The definite integral agrees with the approximation by Simpson's rule.

Example: Find the area

$$\int_0^6 (6x - x^2) \, dx$$

by Simpson's rule, taking $n = 6$, and by finding the definite integral. Solution:

$$\frac{b - a}{n} = \frac{6 - 0}{6} = 1 = \Delta x$$

The area under consideration is under the curve

$$y = 6x - x^2$$

Substituting various values of x into the equation gives

x:	0	1	2	3	4	5	6
y:	0	5	8	9	8	5	0

By Simpson's rule,

$$\text{Area} = \tfrac{1}{3}[0 + 4(5) + 2(8) + 4(9) + 2(8) + 4(5) + 0]$$
$$= \tfrac{1}{3}[108] = 36$$

The definite integral is

$$\int_0^6 (6x - x^2) \, dx = \left[3x^2 - \frac{x^3}{3}\right]_0^6 = [(108 - 72) - 0] = 36$$

The two methods give exactly identical answers.

PROBLEMS

1. Integrate the following:

(a) $\int (-9)\, dx$

(n) $\int \dfrac{5\, dx}{x^3}$

(b) $\int (2\, dx - 4u\, du + v^2\, dv)$

(o) $\int 4(x - 2)^{5/2}$

(c) $\int \dfrac{u^m}{m + 1}\, du$

(p) $\int (6 - x)^4\, dx$

(d) $\int (7 - x^2 + 4x^3)\, dx$

(q) $\int \dfrac{4\, dx}{3x}$

(e) $\int (x + 6)^2\, dx$

(r) $\int \dfrac{dx}{6x + 3}$

(f) $\int \left(\dfrac{x^8 - 2x^2 + 1}{x^2} \right) dx$

(s) $\int \dfrac{x^2\, dx}{x^3 + 4}$

(g) $\int (1 - x)\sqrt[4]{x}\, dx$

(t) $\int \dfrac{(3x^2 - 2x - 5)\, dx}{(4x^3 - 4x^2 - 20x + 13)}$

(h) $\int \left(x^{1/2} + x^{0.7} - \dfrac{1}{x^{0.3}} \right) dx$

(u) $\int \dfrac{dx}{e^x + 1}$

(i) $\int (x^3 + 4)^4 3x^2\, dx$

(v) $\int e^{-x}\, dx$

(j) $\int (x^4 + x^2 + 1)^3 (2x^3 + x)\, dx$

(w) $\int \dfrac{(x + 3)}{x + 2}\, dx$

(k) $\int (\sqrt{x^4 - 2})x^3\, dx$

(x) $\int \dfrac{(x + 2)\, dx}{x + 7}$

(l) $\int \dfrac{12x^2\, dx}{(x^3 - 6)^4}$

(y) $\int \dfrac{dx}{x^2 - 16}$

(m) $\int (x + 1)^2 x\, dx$

(z) $\int \dfrac{(x - 5)\, dx}{(x - 4)^2}$

2. Integrate the following:

(a) $\displaystyle\int \frac{(5x^2 + 36x - 27)\,dx}{x - 6x^3 + 9x^2}$

(h) $\displaystyle\int 3e\,dx$

(b) $\displaystyle\int \frac{(3x^3 + 8x^2 + 6x - 2)\,dx}{x^4 + 3x^3 + 4x^2 + 6x + 4}$

(i) $\displaystyle\int 4^{3x}\,dx$

(c) $\displaystyle\int \frac{2x^3\,dx}{(x^2 + 1)^2}$

(j) $\displaystyle\int \frac{dx}{2x - 1} - \int \frac{dx}{2x + 1}$

(d) $\displaystyle\int (e^x + 6)^4 e^x\,dx$

(k) $\displaystyle\int \frac{e^{4x}\,dx}{e^{4x} + 4}$

(e) $\displaystyle\int (12e^{x^2})2x\,dx$

(l) $\displaystyle\int 24e^{x^3}x^2\,dx$

(f) $\displaystyle\int e^{6x}\,dx$

(m) $\displaystyle\int \left(e^x + \frac{1}{e^x}\right)^2 dx$

(g) $\displaystyle\int x^e\,dx$

(n) $\displaystyle\int \frac{(e^x - 1)\,dx}{e^x + 1}$

3. Integrate the following trigonometric functions by using identities when necessary:

(a) $\displaystyle\int \sin \tfrac{2}{3}x\,dx$

(f) $\displaystyle\int \tan x\,dx$

(b) $\displaystyle\int \cos 6x\,dx$

(g) $\displaystyle\int \cot x\,dx$

(c) $\displaystyle\int x \cos 2x^2\,dx$

(h) $\displaystyle\int (\sin e^x)e^x\,dx$

(d) $\displaystyle\int \sin^6 x \cos x\,dx$

(i) $\displaystyle\int e^{2\sin 3x} \cos 3x\,dx$

(e) $\displaystyle\int \cos^5 x \sin x\,dx$

(j) $\displaystyle\int 2 \sin x \cos x\,dx$

4. Derive the following either by using trigonometric identities or by using the derivative and integrating:

(a) $\displaystyle\int \tan x\,dx = \ln |\sec x| + c$

(b) $\displaystyle\int \cot x\,dx = \ln |\sin x| + c$

(c) $\displaystyle\int \sec x \, dx = \ln |\sec x + \tan x| + c$

(d) $\displaystyle\int \csc x \, dx = \ln |\csc x - \cot x| + c$

(e) $\displaystyle\int \sec^2 x \, dx = \tan x + c$

(f) $\displaystyle\int \csc^2 x \, dx = -\cot x + c$

(g) $\displaystyle\int \sec x \tan x \, dx = \sec x + c$

(h) $\displaystyle\int \csc x \cot x \, dx = -\csc x + c$

5. If the product of two functions cannot be easily integrated, then integration by parts is used. Derive the formula from differentials.

$$\int u \, dv = uv - \int v \, du$$

Apply this to the following:

(a) $\displaystyle\int xe^x \, dx$ 　　　　　　　(c) $\displaystyle\int x^2 \cos x \, dx$

(b) $\displaystyle\int x \ln x \, dx$ 　　　　　　　(d) $\displaystyle\int x \sin x \, dx$

6. If the integrand is in the form

$$\sqrt[n]{ax + b}$$

apply the substitution

$$ax + b = z^n$$

Integrate the following:

(a) $\displaystyle\int \frac{dx}{x\sqrt{x + 1}}$ 　　　　　　　(c) $\displaystyle\int \frac{dx}{(x - 3)\sqrt{x + 1}}$

(b) $\displaystyle\int \frac{dx}{2x\sqrt{1 - x}}$

7. Find the value of the constant of integration, given the initial conditions:

(a) $\displaystyle\frac{dy}{dx} = \frac{-x}{y}$ 　　　$x = 4, \, y = 3$

(b) $\dfrac{dy}{dx} = 3x^2 + 2x + 1$ $x = 1, y = 3$

(c) $\dfrac{dy}{dx} = 2xy$ $x = 0, y = 2$

(d) $\dfrac{dy}{dx} = \dfrac{x}{y}$ $x = 5, y = 4$

(e) $\dfrac{dx}{dy} = -yx^2$ $x = 1, y = 2$

8. Using the theory of integration, develop the area under the curve for a continuous function $f(x)$ on the interval $a \le x \le b$ as the limit of an infinite number of rectangles.

9. Evaluate the integrals

$$\int_1^4 x\, dx; \qquad \int_4^1 x\, dx$$

$$\int_2^5 (x^2 - x + 1)\, dx$$

$$\int_5^2 (x^2 - x + 1)\, dx$$

What can be drawn from this?

10. Evaluate the integrals

$$\int_1^1 x\, dx; \qquad \int_4^4 (x^2 + x + 1)\, dx$$

What conclusions can be reached?

11. If c is a constant, show that

$$\int_a^b c\, dx = c(b - a)$$

What type of area will be the result? Verify with numerical examples.

12. Evaluate the integrals

$$\int_1^5 x^2\, dx; \qquad \int_1^3 x^2\, dx; \qquad \int_3^5 x^2\, dx$$

$$\int_2^4 (x - 1)\, dx; \qquad \int_4^6 (x - 1)\, dx$$

$$\int_2^6 (x - 1)\, dx$$

What observations can be drawn?

13. Graph the functions and evaluate the integrals

$$\int_0^3 (4x - x^2)\, dx \qquad \int_0^3 \frac{x^2}{4}\, dx$$

What conclusions can be drawn?

14. Find the area under the curve, given the bounded ranges, and illustrate graphically:

(a) $x = 8 + 2y - y^2$ bounded by y-axis; $y = 3$; $y = 1$
(b) $y = x^3$ bounded by x-axis, y-axis; $x = 4$
(c) $y = x^3$ bounded by $y = x$
(d) $y = x^2$ bounded by $y = 4$
(e) $y = x^3 - 6x^2 + 8x$ bounded by x-axis

15. If (a, b) and (c, d) are points on a curve $y = f(x)$, and $f'(x)$ is continuous on $a \leq x \leq c$, the length of the arc between the two points is

$$L = \int_a^c \sqrt{1 + \left(\frac{dy}{dx}\right)^2}\, dx$$

Find the arc length for the following:

(a) $y = x^{3/2}$ from $x = 0$ to $x = 4$
(b) $y = \frac{2}{3}x^{3/2} - 4$ from $x = 0$ to $x = 3$

16. Evaluate the following trigonometric integrals:

(a) $\int_0^{\pi} - \sin x\, dx$

(b) $\int_0^{\pi} \cos \frac{x}{2}\, dx$

(c) $\int_0^{\pi} 2 \cos \frac{x}{4}\, dx$

(d) $\int_{\pi/2}^{\pi} \cos^3 x \sin x\, dx$

(e) $\int_0^{\pi/4} \sin^2 x\, dx$

17. Find the economic function if given its derivative and the initial conditions.

(a) $MR = 20 - Q$ $Q = 20$; $TR = 200$
(b) $MR = 100 - 40Q + 3Q^2$ $Q = 1$; $TR = 80$
(c) $MC = 9Q^2 - 4Q + 6$ $Q = 1$; $TC = 7$
(d) $MPC = 0.8$ $Y = 100$; $C = 120$
(e) $MP_L = 20 + 2L + 2C$ $C = 0$; $L = 1$; $Q = 31$
$\quad MP_C = 2C - 30 + 2L$

18. Find the total profit if
$$MR = 50 - Q \qquad MC = \tfrac{1}{2}Q + 35$$
Let the fixed cost be 25, and assume perfect competition. Is profit a maximum?

19. Evaluate the following:

(a) $\displaystyle\int_4^{10} \frac{dx}{x+2}$

(f) $\displaystyle\int_1^4 \frac{3\,dx}{2x}$

(b) $\displaystyle\int_1^e \ln x\,dx$

(g) $\displaystyle\int_0^1 \sqrt{1-x}\,dx$

(c) $\displaystyle\int_1^4 \frac{dx}{\sqrt{4x}}$

(h) $\displaystyle\int_{-a}^a \sqrt{a^2-x^2}\,dx$

(d) $\displaystyle\int_0^2 (2-x)^2\,dx$

(i) $\displaystyle\int_{-2}^2 (x^2-4)\,dx$
$$= 2\int_0^2 (x^2-4)\,dx$$

(e) $\displaystyle\int_0^1 e^{x^2}x\,dx$

(j) $\displaystyle\int_0^\pi \cos x\,dx$

20. Find the consumer surplus for the following:

(a) $P = 12 - 2x \qquad P_0 = 4 \qquad x_0 = 4$

(b) $D:P = \dfrac{12}{x+3} \qquad S:P = \tfrac{1}{3}x + 1$

21. Apply the trapezoidal rule to the following, and check by integration:
(a) $y = x \qquad a = 0;\ b = 2;\ n = 4$
(b) $y = x^3 \qquad a = 0;\ b = 4;\ n = 4$
(c) $y = x^2 \qquad a = 0;\ b = 2;\ n = 2$

22. The error caused by using the trapezoidal rule can be computed by using the formula
$$E = \frac{(b-a)}{12}(\Delta x)^2 f''(c) \qquad \text{for} \qquad a < c < b$$
Find the error in problem 20(b) and (c).

23. Apply Simpson's rule:

(a) $\displaystyle\int_0^2 x^2\,dx \qquad n = 4 \qquad$ (check by integration)

(b) $\displaystyle\int_0^\pi \frac{\sin x}{x}\,dx \qquad n = 4$

24. Compute

$$\int_0^1 \frac{dx}{x^2 + 1}$$

by Simpson's rule and the trapezoidal rule with $n = 4$.

25. The prismoidal formula states that if $f(x)$ is a polynomial of degree 3 or less, then

$$\int_a^b f(x) = \frac{h}{3}\left[f(a) + 4f\left(\frac{a + b}{2}\right) + f(b)\right]$$

where h is $\frac{1}{2}$ the distance ab. Apply this formula to

$$\int_1^3 x^3 \, dx$$

and check.

26. The error in Simpson's rule can be checked by the formula

$$E = -\frac{(b - a)}{180}(\Delta x)^4 f^{(4)}(c) \qquad \text{for} \qquad a < c < b$$

Check the error in problem 23.

27. The average value of a function is given by the formula

$$\frac{1}{b - a}\int_a^b f(x) \, dx$$

Find the average value of the following:

(a) $cx + d$ on $a \leq x \leq b$
(b) $\sqrt{2x + 1}$ on $4 \leq x \leq 12$

28. If quantity Q changes at a rate that at any instant of time t is proportional to the amount of Q present at that instant, and if quantity Q has the value Q_0 at the time $t = 0$, find Q as a function of t, assuming that consumption is decreasing the quantity. [Hint: $dQ/dt = -KQ$.]

29. An iterated integral

$$\int_a^b \int_{g(x)}^{h(x)} f(x, y) \, dy \, dx$$

can be evaluated thus:

$$\int_a^b \left[\int_{g(x)}^{h(x)} f(x, y) \, dy\right] dx$$

Evaluate the following:

(a) $\displaystyle\int_0^1\int_1^2 dy\ dx$

(b) $\displaystyle\int_0^1\int_{x^2}^x xy^2\ dy\ dx$

30. Solve the following differential equations:

(a) $(y + e^{-x}\cos y)\dfrac{dy}{dx} = x + e^{-x}\sin y$

(b) $(y^3 + x)\dfrac{dy}{dx} = -x^2 - y$

31. The equation

$$M(x, y)\ dx + N(x, y)\ dy = 0$$

is homogeneous if $M(x, y)$ and $N(x, y)$ are homogeneous of the same degree. Use the substitution

$$y = vx \qquad dy = v\ dx + x\ dv$$

to solve the following:

(a) $2xy\dfrac{dy}{dx} = x^2 - y^2$

(b) $2xy\dfrac{dy}{dx} = x^2 + y^2$

11
DIFFERENCE EQUATIONS

The distinction between statics and dynamics is that static analysis is concerned solely with the values of the economic variables at a given moment in time. The pattern of variation of any variable as a function of time is not part of the concern of static analysis. In statics, time is abstracted out. Dynamic analysis, on the other hand, explicitly recognizes time as a variable exerting an influence upon the economic variables. The level of national income is a function of time. The rate of investment is expressed as a certain amount of investment per period of time. The stock of capital grows or diminishes with the passage of time. The amount of consumption per period of time during the current year may be a function of the disposable income of either the current year or some previous year, and it is not unreasonable to postulate the current year's consumption as a function of some expected income of a future year. The level of prices may also exhibit a definite pattern of change through time, and levels of employment and unemployment will be influenced by the particular juncture of time at which they are measured.

In dynamic analysis, economic variables are assumed to undergo change and mutually affect each other. As such interaction occurs among the economic variables, the level of economic activities will be determined. A systematic treatment of the influence of time upon the values of the economic variables is the hallmark of dynamic analysis. The Harrod and Domar models of growth are examples of dynamic analysis.

In dynamic analysis, time may be treated either as changing by discrete and finite amounts or as a continuous variable. If the alternative of treating time as a discrete variable changing by finite amounts is taken, a system of analysis using difference equations can be used. If time is treated as a continuous variable, the system of analysis would involve differential equations.

In this chapter, attention is focused on difference equations and their applications in economic analysis. The nature of difference equations and their solutions are developed carefully. Several economic models involving difference equations are explored. In Chapter 12, the topic of differential equations is discussed, along with economic applications of differential equations

DEFINITIONS

A difference equation may be defined as an equation specifying the relationship between a dependent variable y_t and one or more finite differences of the independent variables $y_{(t-1)}$, $y_{(t-2)}$, etc.

The relationship which shows the amount receivable in year t, $A_{(t)}$, from an investment of an amount of principal P at a rate of interest i may be shown as a linear homogeneous difference equation of the first order with constant coefficients. This difference equation will be of the form

$$A_{(t)} - rA_{(t-1)} = 0$$

The equation where r is used to represent $i + 1$ is called linear because it involves only the first-power terms such as $A_{(t)}$ and $rA_{(t-1)}$. It is homogeneous because there is no constant term. It is said to involve constant coefficients because r is a constant once a value is assigned to it. It is a first-order difference equation because $A_{(t)}$ depends on $A_{(t-1)}$ and no earlier period. For example $A_{(t-2)}$, $A_{(t-3)}$, or any earlier periods of this sort are not involved.

This difference equation can be derived by proceeding step by step. It is given that at $t = 0$,

$$A_{(0)} = P$$

With each succeeding year, the amount receivable will increase to r times the amount receivable the previous year. That is to say, the growth pattern will be

$$A_{(0)} = P$$
$$A_{(1)} = rA_{(0)} = rP$$
$$A_{(2)} = rA_{(1)} = r(rP) = r^2P$$
$$A_{(3)} = rA_{(2)} = r(r^2P) = r^3P$$

$$\cdot \qquad \cdot \qquad \cdot$$
$$\cdot \qquad \cdot \qquad \cdot$$
$$\cdot \qquad \cdot \qquad \cdot$$

$$A_{(t)} = rA_{(t-1)} = r(r^{t-1}P) = r^tP$$

The equation

$$A_{(t)} - rA_{(t-1)} = 0$$

or

$$A_{(t)} = rA_{(t-1)} = r^tP$$

is said to be the solution of the difference equation. The solution of a difference equation must satisfy both the difference equation and the initial condition. Suppose that the amount invested is 100, i.e., $P = 100$, and $i = 0.05$, so that $r = 1.05$. The solution is checked as follows:

$$A_{(0)} = 1.05^0(100) = 100$$

This is the initial condition.

$$A_{(1)} = 1.05(100) = 105$$
$$A_{(2)} = 1.05^2(100) = 110.25$$

$$
\begin{array}{ccc}
\cdot & \cdot & \cdot \\
\cdot & \cdot & \cdot \\
\cdot & \cdot & \cdot
\end{array}
$$

This is the requirement of the difference equation.

THE GROWTH RATE

Assume that a corporation establishes as its objective a 3 percent annual rate of growth of sales revenue S. Let $S_{(t)}$ be the sales revenue of the current year, $S_{(t-1)}$ be the sales revenue of the immediately preceding year, and r be the annual rate of growth. The annual rate of growth of sales revenue is

$$r = \frac{S_{(t)} - S_{(t-1)}}{S_{(t-1)}}$$

Since the firm wishes to maintain a growth rate of 3 percent per year, $r = 0.03$, and the necessary growth is of the form

$$0.03 = \frac{S_{(t)} - S_{(t-1)}}{S_{(t-1)}}$$

or

$$0.03S_{(t-1)} = S_{(t)} - S_{(t-1)}$$
$$S_{(t)} = 1.03S_{(t-1)}$$

Take the year when this growth objective is adopted as the base or initial year, and designate it by $t = 0$. Then the sales revenue of that year is $S_{(0)}$. If $S_{(0)} = 100{,}000$, then

$$S_{(0)} = 100{,}000$$
$$S_{(1)} = 1.03S_{(0)} = 1.03(100{,}000)$$
$$S_{(2)} = 1.03S_{(1)} = 1.03[(1.03)(100{,}000)] = 1.03^2(100{,}000)$$
$$S_{(3)} = 1.03S_{(2)} = 1.03[1.03^2(100{,}000)]$$
$$= 1.03^3(100{,}000)$$

$$
\begin{array}{ccccccc}
\cdot & \cdot & \cdot & \cdot & \cdot & \cdot & \cdot \\
\cdot & \cdot & \cdot & \cdot & \cdot & \cdot & \cdot \\
\cdot & \cdot & \cdot & \cdot & \cdot & \cdot & \cdot
\end{array}
$$

$$S_{(t)} = 1.03[1.03^{t-1}(100{,}000)] = 1.03^t(100{,}000)$$

The solution of this difference equation is

$$S_{(t)} = 1.03^t S_{(0)}$$

To test this solution for the initial condition and the requirement of the difference equation, set

$$S_{(0)} = 1.03^0 S_{(0)} = 1.03^0 (100,000) = 100,000$$

and

$$S_{(1)} = 1.03 S_{(0)} = 1.03(100,000) = 103,000$$

and so on. Thus the solution meets both the initial condition of the problem and the requirement of the difference equation.

THE HARROD GROWTH MODEL

This model was constructed to explain the growth of a national economy.† In it, Harrod assumes that ex-ante saving is equal to ex-post saving and is some fixed proportion s of the level of income of the current period $Y_{(t)}$. If S_t represents the saving of the period t,

$$S_{(t)} = s Y_{(t)}$$

The ex-ante investment of the current period $I_{(t)}$ is assumed to be a constant proportion a of the increase in production (or income) during the current period over the production in the previous period. Algebraically,

$$I_{(t)} = a[Y_{(t)} - Y_{(t-1)}]$$

For equilibrium to prevail, planned saving must be equal to planned investment. That is

$$s Y_{(t)} = a[Y_{(t)} - Y_{(t-1)}]$$

Dividing both sides of the equation by a,

$$\frac{s}{a} Y_{(t)} = Y_{(t)} - Y_{(t-1)}$$

If s, a, and $Y_{(t)}$ are all taken to be positive, income must grow from period $t - 1$ to period t, in order to realize both the savings and investment plans.

To solve this difference equation model to specify the necessary rate of growth for the maintenance of equilibrium, take

$$s Y_{(t)} = a[Y_{(t)} - Y_{(t-1)}]$$

† Roy Harrod, "An Essay in Dynamic Theory," *Economic Journal*, March 1939.

and write

$$s Y_{(t)} = a Y_{(t)} - a Y_{(t-1)}$$

or

$$a Y_{(t-1)} = a Y_{(t)} - s Y_{(t)}$$

from which

$$Y_{(t)} = \frac{a}{a - s} Y_{(t-1)}$$

Now let

$$v = \frac{a}{a - s} \quad \text{and} \quad Y_{(0)} = K$$

The solution of this difference equation will be

$$Y_t = v^t K$$

In the Harrod model, it is assumed that, under normal circumstances, $a > s$. This follows from the equilibrium condition of the model

$$a[Y_{(t)} - Y_{(t-1)}] = s Y_{(t)}$$

Solving for s gives

$$s = a \frac{Y_{(t)} - Y_{(t-1)}}{Y_{(t)}}$$

As long as

$$Y_{(t)} - Y_{(t-1)} < Y_{(t)}$$

whatever value a may assume, s will be a fraction of a. Since $a > s$, the relation

$$v = \frac{a}{a - s}$$

is positive; and if v is positive, three cases of the time path of $Y_{(t)}$ can be described.

The solution

$$Y_{(t)} = v^t K$$

is the rate of growth of income, assuming the initial value of K, which is required in order to maintain equilibrium in the level of income. This growth rate is necessary to ensure that the planned savings of the community will be matched by the planned investment of the entrepreneurs.

Time Path of a Solution

Assume that a difference equation whose solution is

$$Y_{(t)} = B^t K$$

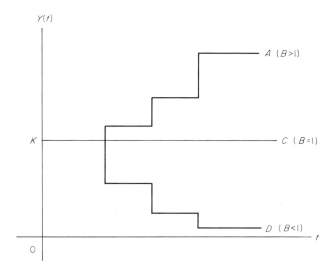

$Y(t)$

A $(B>1)$

K — C $(B=1)$

D $(B<1)$

t

O

**FIGURE 11-1   Three Alternative Time Paths of the Solution of a
Difference Equation**

is given, and that B and K are constants. First consider the situation when
$B > 0$. If B is greater than unity, $Y_{(t)}$ will grow indefinitely with increasing
values of t. The time path of $Y_{(t)}$ will be along the broken line KA in
Figure 11-1. If B is equal to unity, $B^t = 1$ for all values of t, and

$$Y_{(t)} = K$$

for all values of t. The time path of $Y_{(t)}$ will be the horizontal straight
line KC. If B is less than unity,

$$B > B^2 \qquad B^2 > B^3$$

and $Y_{(t)}$ will decrease in value, approaching zero as the limit. The time
path of $Y_{(t)}$ will be along the broken line KD.

The alternative situation arises when B is negative. If $B = -1$, B^t
will alternate in value between -1 and 1 and

$$Y_{(t)} = B^t K$$

will alternate in value between $-K$ and K as t alternates between odd and
even numbers. This effect is shown in Figure 11-2. If $B < -1$, B^t will
become progressively larger in absolute value, and will alternate in sign.
$Y_{(t)}$ will accordingly be negative in the first period, positive in the second,
and so on, as illustrated in Figure 11-3. If $0 > B > -1$, B^t will decrease
in absolute value and will alternate in sign. $Y_{(t)}$ will take on values of
decreasing magnitude and alternate sign, approaching zero. Figure 11-4
shows this effect.

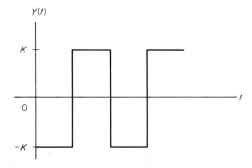

FIGURE 11-2   Time Path of $B^t K$ When $B = -1$

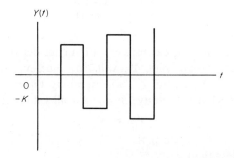

**FIGURE 11-3   Time Path of $B^t K$ When
$B < -1$**

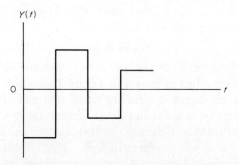

**FIGURE 11-4   Time Path of $B^t K$ When
$0 > B > -1$**

Time Path of the Harrod Model

In the Harrod growth model, s and a are both expected to be positive, and a is expected to be greater than s. Thus

$$v = \frac{a}{a - s}$$

is positive and greater than unity. The time path of

$$Y_{(t)} = v^t K$$

will be similar to KA in Figure 11-1.

Theorem: Given a difference equation of the form

$$y_{(t)} = Ay_{(t-1)} + B$$

whose solution is of the form

$$y_{(t)} = \begin{cases} A^t y_0 + B \dfrac{1 - A^t}{1 - A} & \text{if} \quad A \neq 1 \\ y_0 + Bt & \text{if} \quad A = 1 \end{cases}$$

and given a specified value for y_0, the time path of the sequence A^t is convergent for $-1 < A \leq 1$ with the following properties:

1. If $A = 0$, the sequence is constant with limit 0.
2. If $A = 1$, the sequence is constant with limit 1.
3. If $0 < A < 1$, the sequence is monotone decreasing with limit 0.
4. If $-1 < A < 0$, the sequence is damped oscillatory with limit 0.

Furthermore, the sequence diverges for $A = -1$ and for $|A| > 1$, with the properties:

1. If $A = -1$, the sequence oscillates finitely.
2. If $A < -1$, the sequence oscillates infinitely.
3. If $A > 1$, the sequence diverges to $+\infty$.

From this theorem conclusions can be drawn about the time path of $y_{(t)}$.

NONHOMOGENEOUS FIRST-ORDER LINEAR DIFFERENCE EQUATIONS

A difference equation of the form

$$af_{(t)} + bf_{(t-1)} = c$$

where a, b, and c are constants, is a nonhomogeneous linear difference equation with constant coefficients. It is nonhomogeneous because of the presence of the constant term c.

This equation may be written

$$f_{(t)} = \left(-\frac{b}{a}\right) f_{(t-1)} + \frac{c}{a}$$

Let the initial value be $f(0) = K$. By iteration,

$$f_{(1)} = \left(-\frac{b}{a}\right) f_{(0)} + \frac{c}{a} = \left(-\frac{b}{a}\right) K + \frac{c}{a}$$

$$f_{(2)} = \left(-\frac{b}{a}\right) f_{(1)} + \frac{c}{a}$$

$$= \left(-\frac{b}{a}\right)\left[\left(-\frac{b}{a}\right)K + \frac{c}{a}\right] + \frac{c}{a}$$

$$= \left(-\frac{b}{a}\right)^2 K + \left(-\frac{b}{a}\right)\frac{c}{a} + \frac{c}{a}$$

$$= \left(-\frac{b}{a}\right)^2 K + \frac{c}{a}\left[\left(-\frac{b}{a}\right) + 1\right]$$

$$= \left(-\frac{b}{a}\right)^2 K + \frac{c}{a}\left[\frac{\left(-\frac{b}{a}\right)^2 - 1}{\left(-\frac{b}{a}\right) - 1}\right]$$

$$\vdots \qquad \vdots \qquad \vdots$$

$$f_{(t)} = \left(-\frac{b}{a}\right)^t K + \frac{c}{a}\left[\frac{\left(-\frac{b}{a}\right)^t - 1}{\left(-\frac{b}{a}\right) - 1}\right]$$

A national income model with a time lag can serve to illustrate the use of a nonhomogeneous difference equation. Assume the following:

1. The amount of aggregate consumption expenditure during the current period is a function of the amount of disposable income for the period immediately preceding. The consumption function for period t is

$$C_{(t)} = f[Y_{(t-1)}] = a + bY_{(t-1)}$$

where a and b are constants. The constant b is the marginal propensity to consume.

2. For convenience, assume that the amount of net investment during the current period is fixed and is unaffected by the level of national income. It is a simple matter to revise the assumption with respect to the behavior of net investment. [This assumption will be revised later.] The investment function is

$$I_{(t)} = M$$

where M is a constant.

3. The level of income of the current period is the sum of the current-period consumption plus the current-period net investment.

$$Y_{(t)} = C_{(t)} + I_{(t)}$$

Substituting the values of $C_{(t)}$ and $I_{(t)}$ into this equation for the current-period national income gives

$$Y_{(t)} = a + bY_{(t-1)} + M$$

Let

$$a + M = N$$

which leads to

$$Y_t = bY_{(t-1)} + N$$

If the initial period's income is assumed to be $Y_{(0)} = Y_0$, the incomes of successive periods will be

$$Y_{(1)} = bY_{(0)} + N = bY_0 + N$$

$$Y_{(2)} = bY_{(1)} + N = b[bY_0 + N] + N$$

$$= b^2 Y_0 + bN + N$$

$$= b^2 Y_0 + N(1 + b)$$

$$= b^2 Y_0 + N\left(\frac{1 - b^2}{1 - b}\right)$$

$$\cdot \qquad \cdot \qquad \cdot$$
$$\cdot \qquad \cdot \qquad \cdot$$
$$\cdot \qquad \cdot \qquad \cdot$$

$$Y_{(t)} = b^t Y_0 + N\left(\frac{1 - b^t}{1 - b}\right)$$

Taking the limit of this expression as t approaches infinity gives

$$\lim_{t \to \infty} Y_{(t)} = N\left(\frac{1}{1-b}\right)$$

Recall that

$$N = a + M$$

where a is the constant term in the consumption function, M is the fixed amount of investment, and b is the marginal propensity to consume. Thus $Y_{(t)}$ tends toward the equilibrium level of income, i.e., the sum of the constants times the multiplier. The assignment of some numerical values to the constants a, b, and M will make it easier to examine the pattern of adjustment of Y. Let $a = 10$, $b = 0.8$, and $M = 10$. The consumption function and the investment function are

$$C_{(t)} = 10 + 0.8\,Y_{(t-1)}$$

$$I_{(t)} = 10$$

Given these functions, the equation for national income is

$$Y_{(t)} = 10 + 0.8\,Y_{(t-1)} + 10$$

The solution of this particular difference equation is

$$Y_{(t)} = 0.8^t Y_{(0)} + 20\left(\frac{1 - 0.8^t}{1 - 0.8}\right)$$

Set $Y_{(0)} = 80$:

$$Y_{(1)} = 0.8(80) + 20\left(\frac{1 - 0.8}{1 - 0.8}\right)$$

$$= 64 + 20 = 84$$

$$Y_{(2)} = 0.8^2(80) + 20\left(\frac{1 - 0.8^2}{1 - 0.8}\right)$$

$$= 51.2 + 36 = 87.2$$

$$\vdots \qquad \vdots \qquad \vdots$$

$$\vdots \qquad \vdots \qquad \vdots$$

$$Y_{(5)} = 0.8^5(80) + 20\left(\frac{1 - 0.8^5}{1 - 0.8}\right)$$

$$= 26.2144 + 67.232$$

$$= 93.4464$$

If the initial period's income were 80, $Y_{(t)}$ would continue to rise toward

100. Next set $Y_{(0)} = 120$. $Y_{(t)}$ in the subsequent periods will be

$$Y_{(1)} = 0.8(120) + 20\left(\frac{1 - 0.8}{1 - 0.8}\right)$$

$$= 96 + 20 = 116$$

$$Y_{(2)} = 0.8^2(120) + 20\left(\frac{1 - 0.8^2}{1 - 0.8}\right)$$

$$= 76.8 + 36 = 112.8$$

$$Y_{(5)} = 0.8^5(120) + 20\left(\frac{1 - 0.8^5}{1 - 0.8}\right)$$

$$= 39.3216 + 67.232 = 106.55$$

In this case, the initial period's income was set at 120, and subsequently $Y_{(t)}$ decreased toward 100. Now set $Y_{(0)} = 100$. Then

$$Y_{(1)} = 0.8(100) + 20\left(\frac{1 - 0.8}{1 - 0.8}\right)$$

$$= 80 + 20 = 100$$

$$Y_{(2)} = 0.8^2(100) + 20\left(\frac{1 - 0.8^2}{1 - 0.8}\right)$$

$$= 64 + 36 = 100$$

$$Y_{(5)} = 0.8^5(100) + 20\left(\frac{1 - 0.8^5}{1 - 0.8}\right)$$

$$= 32.768 + 67.232 = 100$$

In this case, $Y_{(t)}$ will remain equal to $Y_{(0)}$ in all subsequent periods. That is to say, Y will not change over time. This occurs when the initial period's income is the equilibrium income. To find the equilibrium income, take the income equation

$$Y_{(t)} = 20 + 0.8\,Y_{(t-1)}$$

and set

$$\overline{Y} = Y_{(t)} = Y_{(t-1)}$$

for at equilibrium the incomes for all periods will be equal. Then

$$\bar{Y} = 20 + 0.8\bar{Y}$$
$$\bar{Y} - 0.8\bar{Y} = 20$$
$$\bar{Y} = 100$$

For a second example, assume that the consumption function is the linear function that was used in the first example above.

$$C_{(t)} = a + bY_{(t-1)}$$

This example uses a Harrod type of investment function

$$I_{(t)} = g[Y_{(t)} - Y_{(t-1)}]$$

where g is a constant such that

$$0 < g < 1$$

The income of period t is defined in the same way as in the first example.

$$Y_{(t)} = C_{(t)} + I_{(t)}$$

Then

$$Y_{(t)} = a + bY_{(t-1)} + g[Y_{(t)} - Y_{(t-1)}]$$
$$= a + bY_{(t-1)} + gY_{(t)} - gY_{(t-1)}$$

Collecting terms and solving for $Y_{(t)}$ yields

$$Y_{(t)} = \frac{a}{1 - g} + \frac{b - g}{1 - g} Y_{(t-1)}$$

Let

$$\frac{a}{1 - g} = N \qquad \frac{b - g}{1 - g} = v \qquad Y_{(0)} = Y_0$$

The solution of the difference equation is

$$Y_{(t)} = v^t Y_0 + N\left(\frac{1 - v^t}{1 - v}\right)$$

Now assign the following numerical values to the constants:

$$a = 10 \qquad b = 0.8 \qquad g = 0.6$$

The consumption function, the investment function, and the national income function are

$$C_{(t)} = 10 + 0.8 Y_{(t-1)}$$
$$I_{(t)} = 0.6[Y_{(t)} - Y_{(t-1)}] = 0.6 Y_{(t)} - 0.6 Y_{(t-1)}$$
$$Y_{(t)} = 10 + 0.8 Y_{(t-1)} + 0.6 Y_{(t)} - 0.6 Y_{(t-1)}$$

or
$$Y_{(t)} = 0.5\,Y_{(t-1)} + 25$$
where
$$v = 0.5 \qquad N = 25$$

The solution of this particular difference equation is

$$Y_{(t)} = 0.5^t Y_{(0)} + 25\left(\frac{1 - 0.5^t}{1 - 0.5}\right)$$

In this case, if $Y_{(0)} = 50$, the incomes of subsequent periods will remain at 50. Thus $\bar{Y} = 50$. If $Y_{(0)} < 50$, incomes of subsequent periods will gradually increase and will approach 50 as a limit.

Both these examples serve to illustrate the time path of $Y_{(t)}$ with the various assumptions built into the behavioral equations of consumption, investment, and income.

THE COBWEB MODEL

A given commodity is bought and sold under conditions of pure competition so that forces of supply and demand determine the equilibrium price level. In such a market the demand schedule is $D = D(P)$ and the supply schedule is $S = S(P)$. Market equilibrium is achieved when the quantity supplied is equal to the quantity demanded, $D(P) = S(P)$. This equation will yield an equilibrium price level $\bar{P}$. Substitution of $\bar{P}$ into the demand equation and the supply equation will give the equilibrium quantity supplied and demanded:

$$\bar{Q} = D(\bar{P}) = S(\bar{P})$$

A dynamic model of price adjustment is constructed when a specific time lag is introduced into either the demand equation or the supply equation. Assume that a one-period lag exists in the supply function, while no lag applies to the demand function. The demand and supply functions now become

$$D_t = D(P_t) \qquad S_t = S(P_{t-1})$$

Quantity demanded in the period t depends upon the price prevailing in that period; quantity supplied during the current period t depends upon the price of the previous period, $t - 1$. Such a lag in production is often thought to apply particularly to agricultural output. Farmers plant for this year's harvest in the light of the prices they found last year. Once the crop has been harvested, it must be sold at whatever price will clear the market.

Let the supply and demand equations be

$$D_t = A + aP_t \atop S_t = B + bP_{t-1}} \tag{1}$$

At equilibrium, $D_t = S_t$, so that

$$A + aP_t = B + bP_{t-1} \tag{2}$$

Assuming that the equilibrium price $\bar{P}$ has been found,

$$\bar{P}_t = \bar{P}_{t-1} = \bar{P}_{t-2}$$

for all t. The equilibrium quantity supplied and the equilibrium quantity demanded are equal:

$$A + a\bar{P} = B + b\bar{P} \tag{3}$$

Let

$$p_t = P_t - \bar{P} \quad \text{and} \quad p_{t-1} = P_{t-1} - \bar{P}$$

so that p_t and p_{t-1} are the deviations of prevailing prices from the equilibrium price.

Subtracting (3) from (2) gives

$$aP_t - a\bar{P} = bP_{t-1} - b\bar{P}$$
$$a(P_t - \bar{P}) = b(P_{t-1} - \bar{P})$$

Substituting gives

$$ap_t = bp_{t-1}$$

Dividing by a gives

$$p_t = \frac{b}{a} p_{t-1}$$

The solution of this difference equation is

$$p_t = \left(\frac{b}{a}\right)^t p_0$$

which may be written in terms of the prices,

$$P_t - \bar{P} = \left(\frac{b}{a}\right)^t (P_0 - \bar{P})$$

or

$$P_t = \bar{P} + \left(\frac{b}{a}\right)^t (P_0 - \bar{P}) \tag{4}$$

Examine equation (4). If the initial price is equal to the equilibrium price, then

$$P_0 - \bar{P} = 0$$

and equation (4) reduces to $P_t = \bar{P}$. If the initial price differs from the equilibrium price, the time path of price movement will depend upon the ratio b/a. The number b is the slope of the supply curve, and is usually taken to be positive. The number a is the slope of the demand curve and is generally a negative number. Thus the ratio b/a is negative. The number $(b/a)^t$ will be alternately positive and negative as t is even and odd. Whether the price level will tend toward the equilibrium, move explosively away from equilibrium, or oscillate about the equilibrium will depend on the value of b/a. Consider the following three cases.

1. $(b/a) = -1$. In this case the supply curve and the demand curve have slopes which are numerically equal but opposite in sign, and equation (4) is of the form

$$P_t = \bar{P} + (-1)^t(P_0 - \bar{P})$$

If $P_0 = 12$ and $\bar{P} = 10$,

$$P_1 = 10 + (-1)(2) = 10 - 2 = 8$$
$$P_2 = 10 + (-1)^2(2) = 10 + 2 = 12$$
$$P_3 = 10 + (-1)^3(2) = 10 - 2 = 8$$
$$P_4 = 10 + (-1)^4(2) = 10 + 2 = 12$$

This situation is shown graphically in Figure 11-5.

2. $(b/a) < -1$. In this case the positive slope of the supply curve has a greater numerical value than the negative slope of the demand curve. The supply curve rises very rapidly, while the demand curve slopes gently to the right. In such an event, any deviation of the initial price from equilibrium

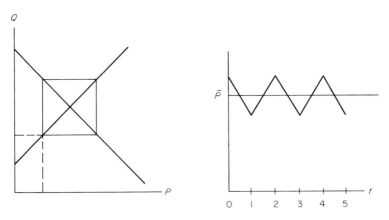

FIGURE 11-5   Time Path of a Cobweb Model When Demand and Supply Curves Have Identical Slopes

value will become magnified with the passage of time. Price in each succeeding period will move further away from equilibrium. This is an explosive cobweb.

To illustrate such a situation, let the supply curve be given by

$$S_t = 1 + P_{t-1}$$

and the demand curve by the equation

$$D_t = 10 - \frac{1}{2}P_t$$

The equilibrium price in this case is $\bar{P} = 6$. If the initial price is $P_0 = 5$, the time path of price movement is given by the difference equation

$$P_t = 6 + \left(\frac{1}{-0.5}\right)^t (5 - 6) = 6 + \left(\frac{1}{-0.5}\right)^t (-1)$$

The successive prices are

$$P_0 = 5$$
$$P_1 = 6 + (-2)(-1) = 8$$
$$P_2 = 6 + (-2)^2(-1) = 2$$
$$P_3 = 6 + (-2)^3(-1) = 14$$
$$P_4 = 6 + (-2)^4(-1) = -10$$

These price movements are shown in Figure 11-6.

3. $0 > (b/a) > -1$. The ratio of the slope of the supply curve to the slope of the demand curve is a negative fractional value. This means

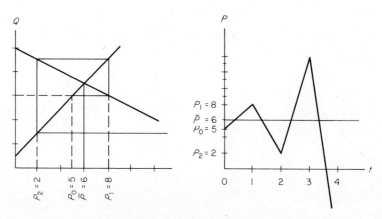

FIGURE 11-6   Time Path of a Cobweb Model When Supply Curve Has a
Greater Absolute Slope Than Demand Curve

that the demand curve has a negative slope whose absolute value is greater than the positive slope of the supply curve. The demand curve slopes steeply downward to the right, while the supply curve rises more gently upward. In this case, any deviation which might have existed between the price of the initial period and the equilibrium price will be reduced as time passes. Each succeeding period's price will be nearer the equilibrium price. The time path of price movement is one of damped oscillation, moving toward the equilibrium.

Let the supply equation be

$$S_t = 1 + 0.5P_{t-1}$$

and the demand equation

$$D_t = 10 - P_t$$

The equilibrium price is $\bar{P} = 6$. Let $P_0 = 8$. The time path of price movement is now given by the equation

$$P_t = 6 + (-0.5)^t(8 - 6) = 6 + (-0.5)^t(2)$$

The prices during the various periods are

$$P_0 = 8$$
$$P_1 = 6 + (-0.5)(2) = 6 - 1 = 5$$
$$P_2 = 6 + (-0.5)^2(2) = 6 + 0.5 = 6.5$$
$$P_3 = 6 + (-0.5)^3(2) = 6 - 0.25 = 5.75$$
$$P_4 = 6 + (-0.5)^4(2) = 6 + 0.125 = 6.125$$

Figure 11-7 illustrates this damping effect.

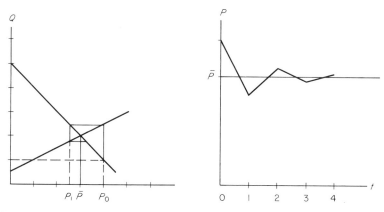

FIGURE 11-7 Time Path of a Cobweb Model When the Absolute Value of Slope of the Supply Curve is Less than that of the Demand Curve

SECOND-ORDER LINEAR DIFFERENCE EQUATIONS

In the situations discussed so far, the maximum amount of lag associated with any variable has been one period. What occurred in period t depended upon events in t or $t - 1$. Periods such as $t - 2$ and $t - 3$ were considered to have no impact upon the events of period t. A situation in which the maximum time lag is two periods, such as

$$Y_{(t)} = a Y_{(t-1)} + b Y_{(t-2)}$$

is called a *second-order difference equation*. The equations involving a maximum time lag of three periods are called *third-order difference equations*.

Consider an economy in which the entire national income of the given period is composed of proceeds from the sale of consumer goods and investment goods during that period:

$$Y_{(t)} = C_{(t)} + I_{(t)} \tag{1}$$

Consumption purchases of the period are assumed to be proportional to the income of the previous period. Thus the marginal propensity to consume is equal to the average propensity to consume. The consumption function may be stated as

$$C_{(t)} = c Y_{(t-1)} \tag{2}$$

where c is the marginal propensity to consume. The amount of investment occurring in period t is some fixed proportion of the increase in the national income between the two previous periods. This means that the investment decisions of entrepreneurs are based upon the acceleration principle. The investment function may assume the form

$$I_{(t)} = b[Y_{(t-1)} - Y_{(t-2)}] \tag{3}$$

Substituting (2) and (3) into (1), the national income equation takes the form

$$Y_{(t)} = c Y_{(t-1)} + b[Y_{(t-1)} - Y_{(t-2)}]$$

which is

$$Y_{(t)} = (c + b) Y_{(t-1)} - b Y_{(t-2)} \tag{4}$$

Equation (4) is a linear homogeneous second-order difference equation with constant coefficients. The procedure for solving this type of equation is as follows: In equation (4), make the substitution

$$c + b = -a$$

and write

$$Y_{(t)} = -a Y_{(t-1)} - b Y_{(t-2)} \tag{5}$$

In the previous section the solution of a homogeneous first-order difference equation was shown to be of the form

$$Y_{(t)} = r^t P$$

where r is a constant and P is the initial value of the first-order difference equation. Since it is reasonable to assume that the solution of the second-order difference equation may also take such a form,

$$Y_{(t)} = r^t$$

where the value of r will depend upon the coefficients a and b. Making this substitution in (5) results in

$$r^t = -ar^{t-1} - br^{t-2}$$

or

$$r^t + ar^{t-1} + br^{t-2} = 0$$

If each term is divided by r^{t-2}, the equation becomes

$$r^2 + ar + b = 0 \qquad (6)$$

Equation (6) is a quadratic equation in r whose solution by the quadratic formula gives the two roots

$$r_1 = \frac{-a + \sqrt{a^2 - 4b}}{2}$$

$$r_2 = \frac{-a - \sqrt{a^2 - 4b}}{2}$$

The suggested solutions of the difference equations are

$$Y_{(t)} = r_1^t P_1 \qquad \text{and} \qquad Y_{(t)} = r_2^t P_2$$

Furthermore

$$Y_{(t)} = r_1^t P_1 + r_2^t P_2$$

is also a solution, where P_1 and P_2 are arbitrary constants. To determine the values of P_1 and P_2, the values of any two periods, say the initial two periods, must be known. If

$$Y_{(0)} = M \qquad Y_{(1)} = N$$

then two simultaneous equations in P_1 and P_2 can be written,

$$Y_{(0)} = r_1^0 P_1 + r_2^0 P_2 = P_1 + P_2$$
$$Y_{(1)} = r_1 P_1 + r_2 P_2$$

where r_1 and r_2 are known numbers.

A numerical example will illustrate the procedure just outlined. Consider the following linear homogeneous second-order difference equation:

$$Y_{(t)} - 5Y_{(t-1)} + 6Y_{(t-2)} = 0 \left.\right\} \tag{1}$$
$$Y_{(0)} = 10 \qquad Y_{(1)} = 15 \left.\right\}$$

Let

$$Y_{(t)} = r^t$$

Substitute into the original difference equation (1):

$$r^t - 5r^{t-1} + 6r^{t-2} = 0$$

Divide each term by r^{t-2}, with the result that

$$r^2 - 5r + 6 = 0$$

Solve for r, and designate the solutions as r_1 and r_2:

$$r_1 = \frac{5 + \sqrt{25 - 24}}{2} = \frac{5 + 1}{2} = 3$$

$$r_2 = \frac{5 - \sqrt{25 - 24}}{2} = \frac{5 - 1}{2} = 2$$

The solution of the difference equation (1) is

$$Y_{(t)} = r_1{}^t P_1 + r_2{}^t P_2 = 3^t P_1 + 2^t P_2 \tag{2}$$

Substitute into the solution (2) the two initial conditions found in (1):

$$Y_{(0)} = 3^0 P_1 + 2^0 P_2 = 10$$
$$P_1 + P_2 = 10 \tag{3}$$
$$Y_{(1)} = 3^1 P_1 + 2^1 P_2 = 15$$
$$3P_1 + 2P_2 = 15 \tag{4}$$

Solving (3) and (4) simultaneously gives

$$P_1 = -5 \qquad P_2 = 15$$

The substitution of these values of P_1 and P_2 into equation (2) leads to the solution

$$Y_{(t)} = 3^t(-5) + 2^t(15)$$

Calculate several values of $Y_{(t)}$ to check the results:

$$Y_{(0)} = 3^0(-5) + 2^0(15) = -5 + 15 = 10$$
$$Y_{(1)} = 3^1(-5) + 2^1(15) = -15 + 30 = 15$$
$$Y_{(2)} = 3^2(-5) + 2^2(15) = -45 + 60 = 15$$
$$Y_{(3)} = 3^3(-5) + 2^3(15) = -135 + 120 = -15$$
$$Y_{(4)} = 3^4(-5) + 2^4(15) = -405 + 240 = -165$$

These results may be checked by substituting any pair of these calculated values into (1) to find the third $Y_{(t)}$.

Theorem: If the linear homogeneous difference equation is of the form

$$y_{(t)} + ay_{(t-1)} + by_{(t-2)} = 0$$

where a and b are constants and $b \neq 0$ and if r_1 and r_2 are the roots of the auxiliary equation

$$r^2 + ar + b = 0$$

then the solution of this difference equation is given by the following: If r_1 and r_2 are real and unequal, then

$$y_{(t)} = c_1 r_1{}^t + c_2 r_2{}^t$$

If r_1 and r_2 are real and equal, then

$$y_{(t)} = (c_1 + c_2 t) r_1{}^t$$

If r_1 and r_2 are complex conjugates with a general polar form:

$$r(\cos \theta \pm i \sin \theta)$$

then

$$y_{(t)} = Ar^t \cos (t\theta + B)$$

MULTIPLIER-ACCELERATOR MODEL

The discussion of second-order difference equations alluded to a national income model involving the multiplier and the accelerator. In this section, such a model will be constructed and solved to find the time path of national income. Assume that the amount of consumption during the current period is one-half of the national income of the preceding period, so that

$$C_{(t)} = 0.5 Y_{(t-1)} \tag{1}$$

The marginal propensity to consume and the average propensity to consume are equal to each other, and equal to 0.5 (the consumption function). The investment function is

$$I_{(t)} = 3[Y_{(t-1)} - Y_{(t-2)}] \tag{2}$$

Capital stock must grow at the rate of three times the increment of national income between any two consecutive periods. The number 3 is the *accelerator*. The *multiplier* is

$$\frac{1}{1-c} = \frac{1}{s} = \frac{1}{0.5} = 2$$

where c is marginal propensity to consume and s is marginal propensity to save. The national income function is

$$Y_{(t)} = C_{(t)} + I_{(t)} \tag{3}$$

The current period's national product (i.e., the current period's national income) is made up of consumption output and investment output. Let the incomes of the two initial periods be

$$Y_{(0)} = 8 \qquad Y_{(1)} = 10$$

Substituting (1) and (2) into (3) gives

$$Y_{(t)} = 0.5 Y_{(t-1)} + 3[Y_{(t-1)} - Y_{(t-2)}]$$

$$= 3.5 Y_{(t-1)} - 3 Y_{(t-2)} \tag{4}$$

Equation (4) is a second-order difference equation. Its solution will be found by the procedure outlined earlier. Set

$$Y_{(t)} = r^t$$

and substitute into (4), getting

$$r^t = 3.5 r^{t-1} - 3 r^{t-2} \tag{5}$$

Dividing each term in (5) by r^{t-2} gives

$$r^2 = 3.5r - 3$$

or

$$r^2 - 3.5r + 3 = 0 \tag{6}$$

Solving for r in (6) gives

$$r_1 = \frac{3.5 + \sqrt{3.5^2 - (4)(3)}}{2}$$

$$= \frac{3.5 + 0.5}{2} = \frac{4}{2} = 2$$

$$r_2 = \frac{3.5 - \sqrt{3.5^2 - (4)(3)}}{2}$$

$$= \frac{3.5 - 0.5}{2} = \frac{3}{2} = 1.5$$

The solution of the difference equation (4) is

$$Y_{(t)} = r_1^t P_1 + r_2^t P_2 = 2^t P_1 + 1.5^t P_2 \tag{7}$$

where P_1 and P_2 are constants to be determined.

To determine the values of P_1 and P_2, introduce $Y_{(0)}$ and $Y_{(1)}$ into equation (7):

$$Y_{(0)} = r_1{}^0 P_1 + r_2{}^0 P_2 = 2^0 P_1 + 1.5^0 P_2 = 8$$
$$P_1 + P_2 = 8 \tag{8}$$

$$Y_{(1)} = r_1{}^1 P_1 + r_2{}^1 P_2 = 2^1 P_1 + 1.5^1 P_2 = 10$$
$$2P_1 + 1.5P_2 = 10 \tag{9}$$

Solving (8) and (9) for P_1 and P_2 gives

$$P_1 = -4 \qquad P_2 = 12$$

Substitution of these values of P_1 and P_2 into equation (7) gives

$$Y_{(t)} = 2^t(-4) + 1.5^t(12) \tag{10}$$

Equation (10) represents the dynamic time path of the movement of national income. Equation (10) may be checked by calculating several values of $Y_{(t)}$ and comparing the results with the values given by (4).

NONHOMOGENEOUS SECOND-ORDER DIFFERENCE EQUATIONS

The discussion of first-order difference equations treated the homogeneous case, without a constant term, and the nonhomogeneous case with a constant term. So far this consideration of second-order difference equations has been confined to the homogeneous case. This section will deal with the nonhomogeneous case of the second-order difference equation.

In the national income model considered in the section on homogeneous second-order (linear) difference equations, government expenditures G are introduced. Assume that the government expenditures are independent of the level of national income, and are set at the level $G = 5$. Also assume that $C_{(t)} = 0.5 Y_{(t-1)}$ and that $I_{(t)} = 3[Y_{(t-1)} - Y_{(t-2)}]$. With these government expenditures added to $C_{(t)}$ and $I_{(t)}$, the national income equation becomes

$$Y_{(t)} = 3.5 Y_{(t-1)} - 3 Y_{(t-2)} + 5 \tag{1}$$

Equation (1) is a linear nonhomogeneous second-order difference equation.

In this case, assume the initial levels of national income are

$$\left. \begin{aligned} Y_{(0)} &= 20 \\ Y_{(1)} &= 30 \end{aligned} \right\} \tag{2}$$

To solve the difference equation (1) with the initial conditions (2), note that the difference equation (1) differs from the homogeneous equation that was solved earlier only by the presence of the constant. The difference between the homogeneous and the nonhomogeneous cases

$$Y_{(t)} = P_1 Y_{(t-1)} + P_2 Y_{(t-2)} \tag{3}$$

$$Y_{(t)} = P_1 Y_{(t-1)} + P_2 Y_{(t-2)} + G \tag{4}$$

is the presence in (4), the nonhomogeneous case, of the constant term G.

If an expression $r(t)$ could satisfy (3) as demonstrated earlier, and if $m(t)$ is an expression which satisfies (4), then it is easily proved that $r(t) + m(t)$ will also satisfy (4).

Now note that (3) is the homogeneous case of (4), the nonhomogeneous case, and that

$$Y_{(t)} = r^t$$

satisfies (3). It has been stated that there is some expression

$$Y_{(t)} = m(t)$$

which will satisfy (4). Substitution into (4) gives

$$m(t) = P_1 m(t) + P_2 m(t) + G$$

or

$$m(t) = \frac{G}{1 - P_1 - P_2}$$

Since $r(t) + m(t)$ will also satisfy the nonhomogeneous equation (4), as stated,

$$Y_{(t)} = r(t) + \frac{G}{1 - P_1 - P_2}$$

Again, the two constants P_1 and P_2 are to be determined, and two initial conditions are needed for their determination.

The procedure just outlined can be illustrated by an example of a national income model involving a nonhomogeneous second-order difference equation. The consumption function is

$$C_{(t)} = 0.5 Y_{(t-1)} \tag{1}$$

The investment function is

$$I_{(t)} = 3[Y_{(t-1)} - Y_{(t-2)}] \tag{2}$$

The government expenditure equation is

$$G = 10 \tag{3}$$

The national income equation is

$$Y_{(t)} = C_{(t)} + I_{(t)} + G \tag{4}$$

Substituting (1), (2), and (3) into (4), the national income equation becomes

$$Y_{(t)} = 3.5Y_{(t-1)} - 3Y_{(t-2)} + 10 \tag{5}$$

Let the initial conditions be

$$\left.\begin{array}{l} Y_{(0)} = 20 \\ Y_{(1)} = 30 \end{array}\right\} \tag{6}$$

Drop the constant term from (5), to get the "reduced equation," which is homogeneous:

$$Y_{(t)} = 3.5Y_{(t-1)} - 3Y_{(t-2)} \tag{7}$$

This reduced equation (7) has the solution

$$r^2 - 3.5r + 3r = 0 \qquad r_1 = 2 \qquad r_2 = 1.5$$

Thus

$$Y_{(t)} = P_1 2^t + P_2 1.5^t$$

Now find the expression $m(t)$ which satisfies (5), by substituting $m(t)$ for $Y_{(t)}$, $Y_{(t-1)}$, and $Y_{(t-2)}$:

$$m(t) = 3.5m(t) - 3m(t) + 10$$
$$m(t) - 3.5m(t) + 3m(t) = 10$$
$$0.5m(t) = 10$$
$$m(t) = 20$$

The general solution of (5) is

$$Y_{(t)} = r(t) + m(t) = P_1 2^t + P_2 1.5^t + 20 \tag{8}$$

To determine P_1 and P_2, substitute into the general solution (8) the initial conditions (6):

$$Y_{(0)} = P_1 2^0 + P_2 1.5^0 + 20 = 20$$

$$P_1 + P_2 = 0 \tag{9}$$

$$Y_{(1)} = P_1 2^1 + P_2 1.5^1 + 20 = 30$$

$$2P_1 + 1.5P_2 = 10 \tag{10}$$

The solution of (9) and (10) gives

$$P_1 = 20 \qquad P_2 = -20$$

The final solution is

$$Y_{(t)} = 20(2^t) + (-20)(1.5^t) + 20$$

PROBLEMS

1. If

$$\Delta y(x) = y(x + h) - y(x)$$
$$\Delta^2 y = \Delta(\Delta y), \ldots, \Delta^n y = \Delta(\Delta^{n-1} y)$$

   find $\Delta^2 y(x)$ and $\Delta^3 y(x)$.

2. If $y(x) = x^3$, find Δy, $\Delta^2 y$, $\Delta^3 y$, $\Delta^4 y$, and $\Delta^n y$.

3. If

$$C = \frac{a + bM}{1 - b}$$

   find ΔC and $\Delta C / \Delta M$.

4. If

$$\Delta Y_t = \Delta G_t + 6 \, \Delta D_t$$

   is a function where Y is national income, G is government expenditure, and D is government deficit over a period of time t, what conclusions can be drawn if

$$\Delta Y_t = 0$$

5. Compare $\Delta y(x)$ and dy/dx. Find $\Delta y(x)$ and dy/dx for the functions

$$y = x^2 \qquad y = x^3$$

6. Find the solution of the following:

   (a) $P_1 = aP_0$ if $P_0 = 1$; $a = 1.4$
   (b) $A_{(0)} = P$ at $t = 0$ if $P = 4$; $r = 2$
   (c) $A_{(0)} = P$ at $t = 0$ if $P = r^K$; $r = r$

7. If a corporation wishes to maintain a growth rate of 5% in sales revenue, find the solution if the initial period has sales of 200,000. What are the sales during the second period?

8. Develop Harrod's rate of growth of investment required to maintain full employment, given the consumption function

$$C_t = a + b Y_{t-1}$$

   and

$$I_{(0)} = I_0$$

   and

$$r I_t = Y_t - Y_{t-1} \qquad \text{for } r 0$$

   What does the sequence I_t do?

9. Find the income equilibrium if

$$C_t = 60 + 0.6 Y_{t-1}$$

$$I = 0.4(Y_t - Y_{t-1})$$

for $Y_{(0)} = 50$, $Y_{(0)} = 150$, $Y_{(0)} = 300$.

10. Determine the type of cobweb and graph the cobweb and the time path, given D_t and S_t:

(a) $D_t = 3 - 2p_t$ $S_t = p_{t-1} + 1$
(b) $D_t = 7 - p_t$ $S_t = p_{t-1} + 1$
(c) $D_t = 10 - p_t$ $S_t = 2p_{t-1} + 1$

11. Solve the following difference equations:

(a) $y_{t+1} - 3y_t = 0$
(b) $1 - 3y_{t-1} = y_t$ $y_0 = 6$
(c) $2y_t + y_{t-1} = 3$ $y_0 = 2$
(d) $y_t = 7 - 4y_{t-1}$ $y_0 = -4$
(e) $y_t - 13 = 4y_t$ $y_0 = 4$

12. Solve the difference equation

$$y_{k+1}^2 - 5y_{k+1}y_k + 6y_k = 0$$

by factoring to show that the two solutions are

$$y_k^{(1)} = y_0 2^k \qquad y_k^{(2)} = y_0 3^k$$

12
DIFFERENTIAL EQUATIONS

A differential equation involves at least one derivative of an unknown function. The purpose of this section is to study equations involving such derivatives in order to find those unknown functions.

The solution of differential equations forms an integral part of the process of scientific investigation. In most sciences, empirical data reveal a pattern of variation among the relevant variables as the variables influence each other. What is most readily revealed is the rate of change of one variable relative to another. To develop general laws which describe the phenomena giving rise to these variables, the functions from which the derivatives of the variables are derived must be found. This is essentially the process of solving differential equations.

ORDINARY AND PARTIAL DIFFERENTIAL EQUATIONS

An *ordinary* differential equation contains derivatives of functions involving only one independent variable. Thus the derivatives contained in an ordinary differential equation are, for example, of the form dy/dx. Equations such as

$$\frac{dy}{dx} = 2x + 5 \qquad \frac{dy}{dx} = \frac{1}{x}$$

are ordinary differential equations.

A *partial* differential equation involves partial derivatives of variables. The derivatives contained in a partial differential equation are derivatives of functions involving more than one independent variable. Examples of partial differential equations are

$$\frac{\partial z}{\partial x} = \frac{xz}{x^2 + y^2} \qquad \frac{\partial z}{\partial y} = \frac{yz}{x^2 + y^2}$$

This chapter will be concerned primarily with ordinary differential equations, and will have very little to say about partial differential equations.

THE ORDER AND DEGREE
OF A DIFFERENTIAL EQUATION

The order of a differential equation is given by the derivative of the highest order in the equation. For example, if the highest order derivative appearing in a differential equation is of first order, then the equation is a first-order differential equation. Equations such as

$$\frac{dy}{dx} = 2x \qquad \frac{dy}{dx} = -\frac{x}{y}$$

are examples of ordinary differential equations of the first order. At most, first derivatives are involved in both equations.

An equation such as

$$\frac{d^2y}{dx^2} + y = 0$$

is a differential equation of the second order because the derivative of highest order involved is a second derivative.

The largest exponent applied to the derivative of the highest order defines the degree of the differential equation. The equation

$$\left(\frac{d^2y}{dx^2}\right)^2 = \left(\frac{dy}{dx}\right)^3 + 2\frac{dy}{dx} + 1$$

which may be written more compactly as

$$y''^2 = y'^3 + 2y' + 1$$

is a differential equation of the second order and the second degree.

SOLVING A DIFFERENTIAL EQUATION

Given the ordinary differential equation

$$\frac{dy}{dx} = 2x \qquad (1)$$

integration will result in

$$y = x^2 + c \qquad (2)$$

Equation (2) is called a *general* or *complete solution* of (1). Some of the properties of the general solution represented by (2) are:

1. Equation (2) is free of any derivatives. No expression containing derivatives appears in the general solution.

2. Equation (2) satisfies the differential equation (1), for the first derivative of (2) is

$$\frac{dy}{dx} = 2x$$

3. Equation (2) contains the arbitrary constant c. A whole family of curves satisfying the differential equation (1) could be generated from (2) by assigning various values to c. Note that only one arbitrary constant c is involved in the general solution of the first-order differential equation (1). Given these properties, the definition of the general solution of a differential equation can be stated: *The general or complete solution of a differential equation is an equation free of derivatives, involving one or more of the variables, consistent with the differential equation, and containing a number of arbitrary constants equal to the order of the differential equation.*

If equation (2) is the general solution of the differential equation (1), then

$$y = x^2 + 5 \tag{3}$$

is called a *particular* solution of (1). It is called a particular solution in the sense that a specific value has been assigned to the arbitrary constant c, in this case $c = 5$. The determination of the specific value of the arbitrary constant depends on the knowledge of some initial condition. Suppose the function sought is such that its derivative is

$$\frac{dy}{dx} = 2x$$

and that the function passes through the point $(2, 9)$. Then

$$y = x^2 + c$$
$$9 = 2^2 + c$$
$$c = 5$$

The general solution is

$$y = x^2 + c$$

and the particular solution is

$$y = x^2 + 5$$

The particular solution of a differential equation must be free of derivatives; consistent with the differential equation; and able to satisfy an initial condition, or conditions.

Consider now a second-order differential equation of the first degree:

$$\frac{d^2y}{dx^2} = x \tag{4}$$

written in the differential form as

$$\frac{d^2y}{dx^2} dx = x\, dx \qquad (5)$$

Integrating both sides gives

$$\int \frac{d^2y}{dx^2} dx = \int x\, dx$$

$$\frac{dy}{dx} = \frac{1}{2}x^2 + c_1 \qquad (6)$$

Integrating again gives

$$\int \frac{dy}{dx} dx = \int (\frac{1}{2}x^2 + c_1)\, dx$$

$$y = \frac{1}{6}x^3 + c_1 x + c_2 \qquad (7)$$

Equation (7) is the general solution of equation (4), and in this case the general solution contains the arbitrary constants c_1 and c_2. The number of arbitrary constants is equal to the order of the differential equation (in this case the second order).

For the particular solution of the differential equation (4), two initial conditions are required in order to determine the values c_1 and c_2. Suppose it is known that

$$y = 1 \qquad y' = 1 \qquad \text{when} \qquad x = 3 \qquad (8)$$

or in different notation

$$y(3) = 1 \qquad y'(3) = 1$$

then

$$\left.\begin{array}{l} y = 1 = \frac{1}{6}(3)^3 + c_1(3) + c_2 \\ y' = 1 = \frac{1}{2}(3)^2 + c_1 \end{array}\right\} \qquad (9)$$

Equations (9) yield the values of c_1 and c_2 as

$$\left.\begin{array}{l} c_1 = -\frac{7}{2} \\ c_2 = 7 \end{array}\right\} \qquad (10)$$

Substitution of the values in equations (10) into the general solution (7) leads to the particular solution

$$y = \frac{1}{6}x^3 - \frac{7}{2}x + 7 \qquad (11)$$

Equation (11) is the particular solution of the second-order differential equation (4).

To verify that equation (11) is the required particular solution, differentiate (11), getting

$$\frac{dy}{dx} = \frac{1}{2}x^2 - \frac{7}{2}$$

The initial condition (8) specifies that when $x = 3$

$$y' = \frac{dy}{dx} = 1$$

Thus $1 = \frac{1}{2}(3)^2 - \frac{7}{2} = \frac{9}{2} - \frac{7}{2} = 1$. Direct substitution of $x = 3$ into equation (11) gives

$$y = 1 = \frac{1}{6}(3)^3 - \frac{7}{2}(3) + 7 = \frac{27}{6} - \frac{21}{2} + 7$$

$$= \frac{27 - 63 + 42}{6} = \frac{6}{6} = 1$$

This chapter has so far established the meanings of *ordinary* and *partial* differential equations; the *order* and *degree* of differential equations; and *complete* or *general* solutions and *particular* solutions. The next section will consider the solutions of several types of differential equations.

DIFFERENTIAL EQUATIONS OF THE FIRST ORDER AND OF THE FIRST DEGREE

Differential equations of the first order and of the first degree may be represented by the general equation

$$M\,dx + N\,dy = 0 \qquad (1)$$

where M and N are functions of x and y. Functions which can be arranged into the form of (1) may be classified into four types: separation of variables; homogeneous equations; linear differential equations; and exact differential equations.

Separation of Variables

If the terms of a differential equation are arranged in such a way that it can be converted into the form

$$A(x)\,dx + B(y)\,dy = 0 \qquad (2)$$

where A is a function of x alone, and B is a function of y alone, then the *separation of variables* is achieved and solution is achieved by integration.

Example: Solve the equation

$$\frac{dy}{dx} = \frac{y}{1 + x}$$

Solution: Multiply both sides of the equation by dx/y:

$$\frac{dy}{y} = \frac{dx}{1+x}$$

Integrate both sides of the equation:

$$\ln y + a = \ln (1 + x) + b$$

Quantities a and b are arbitrary constants. Rewriting gives

$$\ln y = \ln (1 + x) + b - a$$

Let $b - a = \ln c$. This is simply to give the algebraic sum of the constants a new form. Making such a substitution gives

$$\ln y = \ln (1 + x) + \ln c$$

From this, the solution may be written as

$$y = (1 + x)c$$

Example: Solve the equation

$$\frac{dy}{dx} = -\frac{x}{y}$$

Solution: Multiply both sides of the equation by $y\, dx$:

$$y\, dy = -x\, dx$$

Integrate both sides of the equation:

$$y^2 + a = -x^2 + b$$

Again a and b are arbitrary constants whose algebraic sum is the single constant of integration. Rearranging gives

$$x^2 + y^2 = b - a$$

This is the equation of a circle with center at origin and radius

$$r^2 = b - a$$

Example: Solve the equation

$$x\frac{dy}{dx} + y = xy\frac{dy}{dx}$$

Solution: Multiply both sides of the equation by dx:

$$x\, dy + y\, dx = xy\, dy$$

Divide both sides of the equation by xy:

$$\frac{1}{y}\, dx + \frac{1}{x}\, dx = dy$$

Integrate both sides of the equation:

$$\ln y + \ln x = y + c$$
$$\ln (xy) = y + c$$
$$xy = e^{y+c}$$

Since

$$e^{y+c} = e^y(e^c)$$

let $e^c = a$, and $xy = ae^y$.

An alternate method of solution would be as follows: Integrate both sides of the equation

$$\int \frac{1}{y}\, dy + \int \frac{1}{x}\, dx = \int dy$$

To obtain the following constant of integration:

$$\ln y + \ln x + \ln k = y$$
$$\ln (kxy) = y$$
$$kxy = e^y$$

Dividing by the arbitrary constant k and letting $(1/k) = a$ gives the same results. Note that in the method above $a = e^c$ where e^c is some constant. Thus

$$xy = ae^y$$

Homogeneous Equations

Chapter 8 stated that a homogeneous function is a function such that

$$f(\lambda x, \lambda y) = \lambda^P f(x, y)$$

where λ is any quantity and p is the degree of homogeneity. Suppose that in a differential equation

$$M\, dx + N\, dy = 0 \tag{1}$$

M and N are homogeneous functions of x and y of the same degree. Then (1) is said to be a *homogeneous differential equation* of that degree. Such a differential equation may be solved by making the substitution

$$y = vx \tag{2}$$

When the substitution suggested by (2) is made, the differential equation will be transformed into terms of x and v only and the variables will become separable; then the solution developed for separation of variables may be used.

To develop the procedure for solving homogeneous differential equations, take the following steps: Find the first derivative of y with respect to x in equation (1):

$$\frac{dy}{dx} = -\frac{M}{N} \tag{3}$$

The right-hand member of (3) will become a function of v alone when the substitution of equation (2) is made. Therefore, write

$$\frac{dy}{dx} = f(v) \tag{4}$$

Find the first derivative of y with respect to x in (2).

$$\frac{dy}{dx} = x\frac{dv}{dx} + v \tag{5}$$

Substituting (5) into (4) gives

$$x\frac{dv}{dx} + v = f(v) \tag{6}$$

The variables x and v are easily separable.

Example: Solve the equation

$$(x^2 - y^2)\, dx + 2xy\, dy = 0$$

Solution (in order to show the details as completely as possible, all the steps are given): From the problem

$$\frac{dy}{dx} = \frac{y^2 - x^2}{2xy}$$

Let $y = vx$

$$\frac{dy}{dx} = x\frac{dv}{dx} + v$$

Substituting the results of step b into the expression of the derivative in step a, write

$$x\frac{dv}{dx} + v = \frac{v^2 x^2 - x^2}{2x^2 v}$$

From the right-hand member, factor out x^2 and cancel it in both the numerator and the denominator. The result is

$$x\frac{dv}{dx} + v = \frac{v^2 - 1}{2v}$$

Multiplying both sides of the equation by $(2v/v^2 - 1)$ leads to

$$\frac{2vx}{v^2 - 1}\frac{dv}{dx} + \frac{2v^2}{v^2 - 1} = 1$$

Multiplying each term by dx, write

$$\frac{2vx}{v^2 - 1}\,dv + \frac{2v^2}{v^2 - 1}\,dx = dx$$

Subtract

$$\frac{2v^2}{v^2 - 1}\,dx$$

from both sides of the equation, leaving

$$\frac{2vx}{v^2 - 1}\,dv = -\frac{v^2 + 1}{v^2 - 1}\,dx$$

Multiply both members of this equation by

$$-\frac{v^2 - 1}{v^2 + 1}$$

which gives

$$-\frac{2vx}{v^2 + 1}\,dv = dx$$

Now the variables can be separated by multiplying both sides of the equation by $1/x$, with the result that

$$-\frac{2v}{v^2 + 1}\,dv = \frac{1}{x}\,dx$$

which may be written

$$\frac{2v}{v^2 + 1}\,dv + \frac{1}{x}\,dx = 0$$

Integrate term by term:

$$\ln (v^2 + 1) + \ln x = \ln c$$

or

$$\ln (v^2 + 1)x = \ln c$$

Now write

$$x(v^2 + 1) = c$$

Substituting $v = (y/x)$ and simplifying gives the result

$$\frac{y^2}{x} + x = c$$

or

$$y^2 + x^2 = cx$$

Homogeneous differential equations may also be solved by a slightly different approach, based on the same principle discussed earlier. In making the substitution

$$y = vx$$

write the differential

$$dy = x \, dv + v \, dx$$

This procedure can be illustrated by solving the problem just discussed:

$$(x^2 - y^2) \, dx + 2xy \, dy = 0$$

Making the substitution

$$dy = x \, dv + v \, dx$$

write

$$(x^2 - y^2) \, dx + 2xy(x \, dv + v \, dx) = 0 \tag{1}$$

Substitute $y = vx$ and simplify, so that the equation becomes

$$x^2 \, dx + x^2v^2 \, dx + 2vx^3 \, dv = 0$$

Canceling out x^2 gives

$$(1 + v^2) \, dx + 2vx \, dv = 0$$

To separate the variables, divide each term of equation (1) by $(1 + v^2)x$; the result is

$$\frac{1}{x} \, dx + \frac{2v}{1 + v^2} \, dv = 0$$

Integrate:

$$\ln x + \ln (1 + v^2) = \ln c$$

The remainder of the solution proceeds as in the previous example.

Linear Differential Equations

The linear differential equation of the first order

$$\frac{dy}{dx} + Py = Q$$

where P and Q are functions of x or are constants, has the general solution

$$y = e^{-\int P \, dx} \int Q e^{\int P \, dx} \, dx + k e^{-\int P \, dx}$$

The proof of this equation is as follows:

Consider the linear differential equation of the first order

$$\frac{dy}{dx} + Py = Q \qquad (1)$$

where P and Q are functions of x or are constants. To integrate (1), let

$$y = uz \qquad (2)$$

where u and z are functions of x yet to be determined. The differentiation of (2) leads to

$$\frac{dy}{dx} = u\frac{dz}{dx} + z\frac{du}{dx} \qquad (3)$$

Substitute (2) and (3) into (1):

$$u\frac{dz}{dx} + z\frac{du}{dx} + Puz = Q$$

which may be written

$$u\frac{dz}{dx} + \left(\frac{du}{dx} + Pu\right)z = Q \qquad (4)$$

In order to determine the u which is a function of x, set the coefficient of z equal to zero:

$$\frac{du}{dx} + Pu = 0$$

which may be written

$$\frac{1}{u}\,du + P\,dx = 0 \qquad (5)$$

Integrating (5) yields

$$\ln u + \int P\,dx = \ln c$$

which results in

$$u = ce^{-\int P\,dx} \qquad (6)$$

In the transition from (4) to (5), the coefficient of z was set equal to zero. This reduces (4) to

$$u\frac{dz}{dx} = Q \qquad (7)$$

Substitution of (6) into (7) leads to

$$ce^{-\int P\,dx}\frac{dz}{dx} = Q$$

or

or

$$ce^{-\int P\,dx}\,dz = Q\,dx$$

or

$$dz = \frac{Q}{c}\,e^{\int P\,dx}\,dx \tag{8}$$

Integration of (8) results in

$$z = \int \frac{Q}{c}\,e^{\int P\,dx}\,dx + k \tag{9}$$

Substituting (6) and (9) into (2) produces the general solution

$$y = e^{-\int P\,dx}\left(\int Q e^{\int P\,dx} + k\right)$$
$$= e^{-\int P\,dx}\int Q e^{\int P\,dx} + k e^{-\int P\,dx}$$

Example: Solve

$$\frac{dy}{dx} + 2xy = 0$$

Solution: Here

$$P = 2x \qquad Q = 0$$

Then, from the general solution,

$$y = k e^{-\int P\,dx} \qquad y = k e^{-x^2}$$

To check the result, substitute the solution into the original equation:

$$\frac{dy}{dx} = -2xy = -2kxe^{-x^2}$$

$$2xy = 2kxe^{-x^2}$$

therefore

$$\frac{dy}{dx} + 2xy = -2kxe^{-x^2} + 2kxe^{-x^2} = 0$$

Example: Solve

$$\frac{dy}{dx} + 2y = 4$$

Solution: Here

$$P = 2 \qquad Q = 4$$

Substitution into the general solution leads to

$$y = e^{-\int 2\,dx} \int 4e^{\int 2\,dx}\,dx + ke^{-\int 2\,dx}$$

$$= e^{-2x} 4 \int e^{2x}\,dx + ke^{-2x}$$

$$= e^{-2x} 2e^{2x} + ke^{-2x}$$

$$= \frac{2e^{2x}}{e^{2x}} + ke^{-2x} = 2 + ke^{-2x}$$

Check by substituting

$$y = 2 + ke^{-2x}$$

into the original equation to get the following results:

$$\frac{dy}{dx} = 4 - 2y$$

$$= 4 - 2(2 + ke^{-2x})$$

$$= 4 - 4 - 2ke^{-2x}$$

$$= -2ke^{-2x}$$

$$2y = 2(2 + ke^{-2x})$$

$$= 4 + 2ke^{-2x}$$

$$\frac{dy}{dx} + 2y = -2ke^{-2x} + 4 + 2ke^{-2x} = 4$$

Example: Solve

$$\frac{dy}{dx} + \frac{y}{x} = 2x$$

Solution: Here

$$P = \frac{1}{x} \qquad Q = 2x$$

and

$$y = e^{-\ln x} 2 \int x e^{\ln x}\,dx + ke^{-\ln x}$$

Since

$$e^{\ln x} = x$$

$$e^{-\ln x} = \frac{1}{x}$$

then

$$y = \left(\frac{1}{x}\right)\left(\frac{2x^3}{3}\right) + \frac{k}{x}$$

$$= \frac{2x^2}{3} + \frac{k}{x}$$

This solution can be checked by making the usual substitution.

Exact Differential Equations

The discussion of differential equations involving separation of variables, where the equation is of the form

$$A(x)\, dx + B(y)\, dy = 0$$

showed that the solution can be achieved directly by integration. Some equations of the type

$$M(x, y)\, dx + N(x, y)\, dy = 0 \tag{1}$$

are such that the variables may not be separable. In these situations an adaptation of the technique used for solving separable-variable equations may be employed. Such a technique of solution is applicable if (1) is an *exact differential equation*.

Suppose that there exists a function $F(x, y)$ such that its total differential is

$$M\, dx + N\, dy = 0$$

where M and N are functions of x and y. Then

$$dF = M\, dx + N\, dy \tag{2}$$

Obviously,

$$F(x, y) = c \tag{3}$$

since the differential is $dF = 0$.

If there exists a function F whose total differential is exactly $M\, dx + N\, dy$, (1) is defined as an exact differential equation. Stated more formally, the necessary and sufficient condition for (1) to be an exact differential equation is that

$$\frac{\partial M}{\partial y} = \frac{\partial N}{\partial x}$$

The implications of this equality can be shown without formally proving it. By definition,

$$M\, dx + N\, dy = 0$$

is an exact differential equation, if there exists a function F such that this equation is the exact total differential of F. This requires that

$$dF = M\, dx + N\, dy$$

In Chapter 8, the total differential of a function F was shown to be

$$dF = \frac{\partial F}{\partial x}\, dx + \frac{\partial F}{\partial y}\, dy$$

This implies, then, that

$$M = \frac{\partial F}{\partial x} \qquad N = \frac{\partial F}{\partial y}$$

Differentiating M with respect to y and N with respect to x gives

$$\frac{\partial M}{\partial y} = \frac{\partial^2 F}{\partial y\, \partial x} \qquad \frac{\partial N}{\partial x} = \frac{\partial^2 F}{\partial x\, \partial y}$$

Again, from Chapter 8,

$$\frac{\partial^2 F}{\partial y\, \partial x} = \frac{\partial^2 F}{\partial x\, \partial y}$$

It follows that

$$\frac{\partial M}{\partial y} = \frac{\partial N}{\partial x} \tag{4}$$

The necessary and sufficient condition for (1) to be an exact differential equation is that the equality of equation (4) must hold.

Suppose the differential equation

$$M\, dx + N\, dy = 0$$

is to be solved. Since this is the exact differential equation,

$$dF(x, y) = 0$$

so the general solution will be

$$F(x, y) = c$$

Since

$$M = \frac{\partial F}{\partial x}$$

the integral of M with respect to x plus an arbitrary function of y will give the function F. Thus

$$F = \int M\, dx + g(y)$$

where $g(y)$ is the arbitrary function of y. The term $g(y)$ must be present since M is a partial derivative of F with respect to x. Thus the function $g(y)$ represents any terms of y which are independent of x, which will become zero when the partial derivative with respect to x is taken.

Now the fact that

$$N = \frac{\partial F}{\partial y}$$

can be used to determine the exact form of the function $g(y)$. Taking the partial derivative of F with respect to y gives

$$\frac{\partial F}{\partial y} = \frac{\partial}{\partial y}\left[\int M \, dx + g(y)\right] = \frac{\partial}{\partial y}\int M \, dx + g'(y)$$

Note that

$$g'(y) = \frac{d[g(y)]}{dy}$$

Equating this result to N gives

$$N = \frac{\partial}{\partial y}\int M \, dx + g'(y)$$

Solving for $g'(y)$ gives

$$g'(y) = N - \frac{\partial}{\partial y}\int M \, dx$$

Now integrate with respect to y to obtain $g(y)$:

$$\int g'(y) \, dy = \int\left[N - \frac{\partial}{\partial y}\int M \, dx\right] dy$$

$$g(y) = \int\left[N - \frac{\partial}{\partial y}\int M \, dx\right] dy$$

Substitute this value of $g(y)$ back into the first integration where the function F was found, to get

$$F(x, y) = \int M \, dx + \int\left[N - \frac{\partial}{\partial y}\int M \, dx\right] dy$$

$$c = \int M \, dx + \int\left[N - \frac{\partial}{\partial y}\int M \, dx\right] dy$$

The constants of integration have been omitted in this procedure since they will eventually be joined with c.

An alternate method of solving this differential equation would have been to consider

$$\frac{\partial F}{\partial y} = N$$

and then integrate with respect to y. This would yield an arbitrary function $h(x)$ in terms of x only, and by similar steps $h(x)$ could be determined. Thus $F(x, y)$ could also be found in the form

$$F(x, y) = c = \int N \, dy + \int\left[M - \frac{\partial}{\partial x}\int N \, dy\right] dx$$

Example: Solve the equation

$$(2xy + 2y - y^2) \, dx + (x^2 + 2x - 2xy) \, dy = 0 \qquad (1)$$

Solution: Here

$$M = 2xy + 2y - y^2 \qquad N = x^2 + 2x - 2xy$$

Note that since

$$\frac{\partial M}{\partial y} = 2x + 2 - 2y$$

and

$$\frac{\partial N}{\partial x} = 2x + 2 - 2y$$

then

$$\frac{\partial M}{\partial y} = \frac{\partial N}{\partial x}$$

and the equation is an exact differential equation with the solution $F = c$. In this case,

$$\frac{\partial F}{\partial x} = M = 2xy + 2y - y^2 \qquad (2)$$

$$\frac{\partial F}{\partial y} = N = x^2 + 2x - 2xy \qquad (3)$$

Determine the function F from (3) by integration with respect to y:

$$F = x^2y + 2xy - xy^2 + f(x) \qquad (4)$$

The constant of integration is $f(x)$, a function of x yet to be determined. To determine $f(x)$, note that (4) must satisfy (2) also. Differentiate (4) with respect to x and set it equal to the right-hand member of (2):

$$2xy + 2y - y^2 + f'(x) = 2xy + 2y - y^2$$
$$f'(x) = 0$$

Since $f'(x) = 0$, let

$$f(x) = 0 \qquad \text{(or any constant)} \qquad (5)$$

Substitution of (5) into (4) gives the solution of (1):

$$F = x^2y + 2xy - xy^2$$

or

$$x^2y + 2xy - xy^2 = c \qquad (6)$$

Equation (6) is the solution of equation (1). This result is easily checked by differentiation.

Example: Solve the differential equation

$$3x^2 + 2y^2 + 4xy\frac{dy}{dx} - \frac{1}{x} + 2y\frac{dy}{dx} = 0 \tag{1}$$

Solution: Multiply each term by dx and simplify:

$$3x^2\,dx + 2y^2\,dx + 4xy\,dy - \frac{1}{x}\,dx + 2y\,dy = 0$$

or

$$\left(3x^2 + 2y^2 - \frac{1}{x}\right)dx + (4xy + 2y)\,dy = 0 \tag{2}$$

Here

$$M = 3x^2 + 2y^2 - \frac{1}{x} \qquad N = 4xy + 2y$$

Find $\partial M/\partial y$ and $\partial N/\partial x$ to determine whether the equation is an exact differential equation.

$$\frac{\partial M}{\partial y} = 4y \qquad \frac{\partial N}{\partial x} = 4y$$

Since

$$\frac{\partial M}{\partial y} = \frac{\partial N}{\partial x}$$

this is an exact differential equation. From the original equation, (2),

$$\frac{\partial F}{\partial x} = M = 3x^2 + 2y^2 - \frac{1}{x} \tag{3}$$

$$\frac{\partial F}{\partial y} = N = 4xy + 2y \tag{4}$$

Determine the function F from (3) by integrating with respect to x:

$$F = x^3 + 2xy^2 - \ln x + f(y) \tag{5}$$

Substitute the $\partial F/\partial y$ of (5) into (4):

$$4xy + f'(y) = 4xy + 2y$$
$$f'(y) = 2y$$

or by integration,

$$f(y) = y^2 \tag{6}$$

Substituting (6) into (5) gives

$$F = x^3 + 2xy^2 - \ln x + y^2$$
$$x^3 + 2xy^2 - \ln x + y^2 = c \tag{7}$$

Equation (7) is clearly the solution of equation (1). It is easily checked by differentiating (7).

ECONOMIC APPLICATIONS OF DIFFERENTIAL EQUATIONS

Many problems of theoretical and practical interest in economics involve differential equations. A few examples of such applications will be considered here.

The Domar Growth Model

Domar's growth model, which was considered in Chapter 10, may be analyzed by the use of the tools of differential equations discussed in this chapter. In Chapter 10, the relationship of equilibrium was established as

$$I\sigma = \frac{1}{\alpha}\frac{dI}{dt} \tag{1}$$

where I is investment, σ is the productivity of investment, and α is marginal propensity to save. The left-hand member of this equation shows the quantity of goods supplied, and the right-hand side shows the amount of income available to buy the goods which are produced. The equation, therefore, establishes, as the condition of equilibrium growth of investment, the equality between quantity supplied and quantity demanded. Investment I is the dependent variable, whose motion through time is the desired solution of (1), a linear differential equation of the first order.

Multiplying each term of (1) by α and arranging gives

$$\frac{dI}{dt} - \sigma\alpha I = 0 \tag{2}$$

in which $-\sigma\alpha = P$, a function of time. Equation (2) is in the form of a linear differential equation of the first order. Now, since

$$P = -\sigma\alpha \qquad Q = 0$$

the solution is

$$I = ke^{-\int P\,dt} \tag{3}$$

Since

$$P = -\sigma\alpha$$

$$-\int P\,dt = -\int -\sigma\alpha\,dt$$

$$-\int P\,dt = \sigma\alpha t \qquad (4)$$

Substituting (4) into (3) leads to the general solution of (1):

$$I(t) = ke^{\sigma\alpha t} \qquad (5)$$

If

$$I(t) = I(0) \qquad \text{when} \qquad t = 0$$

then

$$I(0) = ke^{\sigma\alpha 0} = ke^0 = k$$

The particular solution becomes

$$I(t) = I(0)e^{\sigma\alpha t}$$

The Harrod Growth Model

The Harrod growth model considered in connection with difference equations requires that savings equal investment. Let savings at time t, $S_{(t)}$, be some fixed proportion α (α = marginal propensity to save) of the income at time t, i.e.,

$$S_{(t)} = \alpha Y_{(t)} \qquad (1)$$

As assumed earlier, investment is proportional to the rate of increase of income, or

$$I_{(t)} = b[Y_{(t)} - Y_{(t-1)}] \qquad (2)$$

where b is the accelerator. Equation (2) shows that the amount of investment at period t will be the fixed proportion b multiplied by the rate of increase in income over time, $Y_{(t)} - Y_{(t-1)}$. But $Y_{(t)} - Y_{(t-1)}$ may be thought of as the average rate of change over a one-period change in time, or

$$\Delta t = t - (t - 1) = 1$$

If the entrepreneurs are truly sensitive to the rate of change of income in making their investment decisions, investment must be stated as a function of $dY_{(t)}/dt$. Then (2) must be rewritten as

$$I_{(t)} = b\frac{dY_{(t)}}{dt} \qquad (3)$$

The condition for equilibrium is that savings must be equal to investment for all periods. Under conditions of equilibrium, then, $S = I$, or

$$\alpha Y_{(t)} = b \frac{dY_{(t)}}{dt} \tag{4}$$

Equation (4) is a linear differential equation of the first order and the first degree, with Y the dependent variable. To solve (4), first divide every term by α, getting

$$Y_{(t)} = \frac{b}{\alpha} \frac{dY_{(t)}}{dt}$$

Multiplying through by dt gives

$$Y_{(t)} \, dt = \frac{b}{\alpha} \, dY_{(t)}$$

The variables may be separated by dividing both sides of the equation by $Y_{(t)}(b/\alpha)$, resulting in

$$\frac{\alpha}{b} \, dt = \frac{1}{Y_{(t)}} \, dY_{(t)}$$

Integrating gives

$$\frac{\alpha t}{b} + c = \ln Y_{(t)}$$

or

$$Y_{(t)} = e^{\alpha t/b + c} = e^{\alpha t/b} \cdot e^{c} \tag{5}$$

Equation (5) is the general solution of the differential (4). To find the particular solution, let

$$Y_{(t)} = Y_{(0)} \tag{6}$$

when $t = 0$, i.e., the income of the initial period is $Y_{(0)}$. Substituting (6) into the general solution gives

$$Y_{(0)} = e^{0}(e^{c}) = e^{c}$$

The particular solution becomes

$$Y_{(t)} = Y_{(0)} e^{\alpha t/b} \tag{7}$$

Equation (7) indicates that if saving and investment plans of the economy are to be realized, national income must grow through time as specified by the exponential function (7).

Price-Level Adjustment Over Time

The model describing price-level adjustment over time which was considered in connection with difference equation systems involved finite time lags. The incorporation of a finite time lag made the model conform with the particular features of the cobweb model. Now assume that suppliers adjust quantity supplied during the current period not to price of the previous period, but instead to the prevailing price level and the rate of change of price through time. As before, assume that quantity demanded by the buyers is a function solely of the price level. These assumptions will result in a continuous dynamic model of price level adjustment over time.

$$D_{(t)} = D(P) \tag{1}$$

$$S_{(t)} = S\left(P + \frac{dP}{dt}\right) \tag{2}$$

Equation (1) is the demand function where $D_{(t)}$, the quantity demanded at time t, is a function D of price P. Equation (2) is the supply function in which $S_{(t)}$, the quantity supplied at time t, is a function S of the price level P and the time rate of change of price dP/dt. If supply and demand functions are both assumed to be linear, they may be represented by

$$D_{(t)} = A + aP \tag{3}$$

$$S_{(t)} = B + b\left(P + \frac{dP}{dt}\right) \tag{4}$$

Now set quantity supplied equal to quantity demanded.

$$A + aP = B + bP + b\frac{dP}{dt} \tag{5}$$

In (5), let $P = \bar{P}$ where $\bar{P}$ is the equilibrium price. Then (5) becomes

$$A + a\bar{P} = B + b\bar{P} \tag{6}$$

Subtract (6) from (5) and let $p = P - \bar{P}$, resulting in

$$ap = b\left(p + \frac{dP}{dt}\right)$$

Since

$$\frac{dp}{dt} = \frac{dP}{dt}$$

then

$$ap = bp + b\frac{dp}{dt}$$

or

$$\frac{a-b}{b}p = \frac{dp}{dt} \tag{7}$$

For compactness of notation, let $(a - b/b) = c$. Then

$$cp = \frac{dp}{dt} \qquad (8)$$

Equation (8) is a first-order differential equation. Multiplying each term of (8) by dt/p gives

$$c\, dt = \frac{dp}{p}$$

Integrating gives

$$ct + k = \ln p$$

or

$$p = e^{ct} \cdot e^{k}$$

Now let

$$p_0 = P_0 - \bar{P}$$

since initial conditions are $p = p_0$ for $t = 0$, and write

$$p = e^{ct}(P_0 - \bar{P})$$

Since

$$p = P - \bar{P}$$

this equation can be rewritten as

$$P - \bar{P} = (P_0 - \bar{P})e^{ct}$$

or

$$P = \bar{P} + (P_0 - \bar{P})e^{ct} \qquad (9)$$

Equation (9) is the solution of the differential equation (7). The demand curve is normally expected to have negative slope, i.e., $a < 0$, and the supply curve is expected to be positively sloped, or $b > 0$, so

$$c = \frac{a - b}{b} < 0$$

Thus (9) portrays a time motion of price adjustment such that P will tend toward $\bar{P}$.

Derivation of the Cost Function by Separation of Variables

In Chapter 6, the elasticity of the total cost function was defined as

$$E_K = \frac{Q}{C}\frac{dC}{dQ}$$

where Q is the quantity of output and C is the total cost of production. This elasticity of total cost function may be expressed as the ratio of the marginal cost to the average cost,

$$E_K = \frac{dC/dQ}{C/Q}$$

In the event that

$$\frac{dC}{dQ} = \frac{C}{Q}$$

or marginal cost is equal to average cost for all levels of output Q, the elasticity of total cost will be equal to 1, marginal cost will coincide with average cost, and both will be horizontal.

The differential equation

$$\frac{dC}{dQ} = \frac{C}{Q} \tag{1}$$

is a linear first-order differential equation whose variables are separable. Assume as an initial condition that when $Q = 5$, $C = 15$. The solution of (1) will involve the following steps: Multiply (1) by $(Q)(dQ)$, with the result that

$$Q\, dC = C\, dQ \tag{2}$$

Divide (2) by $(C)(Q)$, so that the variables are separated in the form

$$\frac{1}{C}\, dC = \frac{1}{Q}\, dQ \tag{3}$$

Integrating (3) yields

$$\ln C = \ln Q + \ln k$$

which may be written

$$C = kQ$$

From the initial condition that when $Q = 5$, $C = 15$, the value of k, the constant of integration, may be determined by substitution.

$$15 = 5k \qquad \text{or} \qquad k = 3$$

Thus the total cost function is

$$C = 3Q \tag{4}$$

Equation (4) is the particular solution of (1).

Several observations may be made about this particular total cost function. Since this is a linear cost function which crosses the origin, there is no fixed component. The average cost is

$$\frac{C}{Q} = \frac{3Q}{Q} = 3$$

The marginal cost function is the derivative of the total cost function (4) or

$$\frac{dC}{dQ} = 3$$

Thus marginal cost is equal to average cost, and they coincide at the value 3. The elasticity of this total cost function is

$$E_K = \frac{Q}{3Q}\left[\frac{d}{dQ} 3Q\right] = \frac{Q}{3Q} (3) = 1$$

The total cost function (4) thus fulfills all of the conditions specified by the original differential equation (1), and satisfies the initial condition.

Analysis of a Consumer Indifference Curve by the Homogeneous Differential Equation

A consumer indifference curve is constructed on the xy plane where x and y are two consumption goods. Along the locus of a given indifference curve, the consumer's utility (or satisfaction) does not change. Such an indifference curve may be represented by many possible mathematical functions, depending upon the nature of a given consumer's subjective preference function. In Chapter 3, for example, it was discussed how a circle, an ellipse, or a rectangular hyperbola could be used to portray the properties of isoprofit, isoquant, or indifference curves.

Consider an indifference curve of a rectangularly hyperbolic form. Suppose the only information given is the differential of the function and the initial condition. The facts available are

$$y\,dx + x\,dy = 0 \tag{1}$$

when $u = 10$; $x = 1$; $y = 5$. Here equation (1) is the differential equation to be solved subject to the initial conditions specified.

Before proceeding to solve this equation as a case of a homogeneous equation, it will be solved as a case of separable variables. The reason for solving this equation by both methods is to show their similarity.

Equation (1) may be written as

$$\frac{1}{y}\,dy = -\frac{1}{x}\,dx \tag{2}$$

Equation (2) may be directly integrated, yielding

$$\ln y + \ln x + \ln c = 0$$

or

$$c(xy) = 0$$

The initial condition is that

$$c(1)(5) = 10 \quad \text{or} \quad c = 2$$

Then the particular solution of (1) is of the form

$$2xy = 10 \tag{3}$$

Equation (3) is the indifference curve corresponding to a utility index of 10.

As discussed earlier, the solution of a homogeneous differential equation involves the substitution

$$y = vx$$
$$dy = v \, dx + x \, dv$$

Making these substitutions in (1) gives

$$vx \, dx + x(v \, dx + x \, dv) = 0$$

or

$$vx \, dx + vx \, dx + x^2 \, dv = 0$$

Dividing through by x and consolidating terms yields

$$2v \, dx + x \, dv = 0$$

Multiplying through by $1/vx$ gives

$$\frac{2}{x} dx + \frac{1}{v} dv = 0$$

Integrating yields

$$2 \int \frac{1}{x} dx + \int \frac{1}{v} dv = 0$$

or

$$\ln x^2 + \ln v + \ln c = 0$$

This may be written as $cx^2v = 0$. But since

$$v = \frac{y}{x}$$

then $cxy = 0$. From the initial condition of (1)

$$c(1)(5) = 10 \quad c = 2$$

Thus the indifference curve is again found to be of the form $2xy = 10$.

Exact Differential Equation

Suppose the equation of an isoquant is given to be

$$(K^2 + L^2)\, dK + (2KL)\, dL = 0$$

This is known to be the total differential of the production function

$$Q = f(K, L)$$

For the total differential, it is known that

$$dQ = 0$$

since output is constant when moving along an isoquant. Thus the general form of the equation of the isoquant is

$$\frac{\partial Q}{\partial K}\, dK + \frac{\partial Q}{\partial L}\, dL = 0$$

If the common notation

$$M\, dK + N\, dL = 0$$

is used, it can be concluded that

$$M = \frac{\partial Q}{\partial K} = K^2 + L^2 \qquad N = \frac{\partial Q}{\partial L} = 2KL$$

This will be an exact differential equation if and only if

$$\frac{\partial M}{\partial L} = \frac{\partial N}{\partial K} \quad \text{or} \quad \frac{\partial^2 Q}{\partial L\, \partial K} = \frac{\partial^2 Q}{\partial K\, \partial L} \qquad \text{(by Young's theorem)}$$

Since the actual derivatives for this equation are

$$\frac{\partial M}{\partial L} = 2L = \frac{\partial N}{\partial K}$$

the equation is exact. Thus

$$Q = f(K, L) = \int M\, dK + g(L)$$

By integrating M with respect to K and adding the unknown function $g(L)$, the production function, Q, can be obtained:

$$Q = \int (K^2 + L^2)\, dK + g(L)$$

$$Q = \tfrac{1}{3}K^3 + L^2 K + g(L)$$

Now the function $g(L)$ must be determined. It has been established that

$$\frac{\partial Q}{\partial L} = N$$

and Q has been found in an indefinite form. The next step is to take the partial of Q with respect L and equate this derivative to N. Note that

$$\frac{g(L)}{\partial L} = \frac{g(L)}{dL} + g'(L)$$

$$\frac{\partial Q}{\partial L} = 2LK + g'(L) = N = 2LK$$

Thus

$$g'(L) = 0 \qquad g(L) = 0 \qquad \text{or} \qquad g(L) = c$$

where c is a constant. The production function is then

$$Q = \tfrac{1}{3}K^3 + L^2K$$

DIFFERENTIAL EQUATIONS OF HIGHER ORDER

This part of the chapter will consider the methods of solving higher order differential equations, i.e., those whose order is two or greater. The explanation will be restricted to linear differential equations with constant coefficients. One reason for this restriction is that this type of differential equation appears quite frequently in economic problems. Another reason is that it is beyond the scope of this book to treat either differential equations which are nonlinear or those which have variable coefficients. Thus, the form of a linear differential equation of higher order and with constant coefficients will be as follows:

$$\frac{d^n y}{dx^n} + c_1 \frac{d^{(n-1)}y}{dx^{(n-1)}} + \cdots + c_{n-1}\frac{dy}{dx} + c_n y = f(x)$$

If $f(x) = 0$, the differential equation is homogeneous, but if $f(x) \neq 0$, the differential equation is called *complete*. For clarity, the method of solving second-order homogeneous and complete differential equations will be illustrated before returning to the nth order differential equations.

Second-Order, Linear, Homogeneous Differential Equations with Constant Coefficients

Solve the differential equation

$$a\frac{d^2 y}{dx^2} + b\frac{dy}{dx} + cy = 0$$

where a, b, and c are constants. The problem is to find a function that has the property expressed by this differential equation. Such a function would be the exponential function e^{mx} if the value of m is correctly chosen. Assume that $y = e^{mx}$; then

$$\frac{dy}{dx} = me^{mx} \qquad \frac{d^2y}{dx^2} = m^2 e^{mx}$$

Substitute these values into the differential equation to get

$$am^2 e^{mx} + bme^{mx} + ce^{mx} = 0$$

$$e^{mx}(am^2 + bm + c) = 0$$

Since $e^{mx} > 0$ for all m and x, divide through by e^{mx} to get

$$am^2 + bm + c = 0$$

This is a quadratic equation with m as the variable, which can be solved by the quadratic formula:

$$m = \frac{-b \pm \sqrt{(b)^2 - 4(a)(c)}}{2(a)}$$

Note that there are two values of m, say m_1 and m_2, such that

$$m_1 = \frac{-b + \sqrt{(b)^2 - 4(a)(c)}}{2(a)}$$

$$m_2 = \frac{-b - \sqrt{(b)^2 - 4(a)(c)}}{2(a)}$$

Thus the two functions

$$y_1 = e^{m_1 x} \qquad y_2 = e^{m_2 x}$$

will satisfy the differential equation. But this is not the complete solution, for some linear combination of the solutions above might also satisfy the differential equation. Thus the complete general solution will be written as

$$y = c_1 y_1 + c_2 y_2 = c_1 e^{m_1 x} + c_2 e^{m_2 x}$$

where c_1 and c_2 are arbitrary constants that must be determined from prescribed initial conditions such as

$$y(x_0) = y_0 \qquad y'(x_0) = y_0'$$

These will be given if the complete particular solution is required.

It is apparent by now that the solution of the differential equation is dependent upon the constant coefficients. As in algebra, the possibilities of the discriminant, $b^2 - 4ac$, must be considered, since it can be positive, negative, or zero. The types of roots will be determined by these values.

Real and Unequal Roots. If $b^2 - 4ac > 0$, then there will be two real and unequal roots m_1 and m_2, i.e., m_1 and m_2 are distinct. Thus the complete general solution will be

$$y = c_1 e^{m_1 x} + c_2 e^{m_2 x}$$

Consider the following differential equation

$$\frac{d^2 y}{dx^2} + \frac{dy}{dx} - 6y = 0$$

with the initial conditions

$$y(0) = 1 \qquad y'(0) = 2$$

Let $y = e^{mx}$. Then

$$\frac{dy}{dx} = me^{mx} \qquad \frac{d^2 y}{dx^2} = m^2 e^{mx}$$

and

$$m^2 e^{mx} + me^{mx} - 6e^{mx} = 0$$

Factoring out e^{mx} gives

$$e^{mx}(m^2 + m - 6) = 0$$

Dividing through by e^{mx} yields

$$m^2 + m - 6 = 0$$

Using the quadratic formula gives

$$m = \frac{-1 \pm \sqrt{(1)^2 - 4(1)(-6)}}{2(1)}$$

$$m = \frac{-1 \pm \sqrt{25}}{2} = \frac{-1 \pm 5}{2}$$

Separating the roots gives

$$m_1 = \frac{-1 + 5}{2} = \frac{4}{2} = 2$$

$$m_2 = \frac{-1 - 5}{2} = \frac{-6}{2} = -3$$

Thus the general solution is

$$y = c_1 e^{2x} + c_2 e^{-3x}$$

For $y(0) = 1$

$$1 = c_1 e^{2(0)} + c_2 e^{-3(0)} = c_1 + c_2$$

For $y'(0) = 2$

$$2 = 2c_1e^{2(0)} - 3c_2e^{-3(0)} = 2c_1 - 3c_2$$

Solving this system of two equations with two variables yields

$$c_1 = 1 \quad \text{and} \quad c_2 = 0$$

Thus the particular solution is

$$y = e^{2x}$$

Real and Equal Roots. If $b^2 - 4ac = 0$, the roots are real and equal, i.e., the roots are identical or

$$m_1 = m_2 = \frac{-b}{2a}$$

A solution of the differential equation will be

$$y = e^{[(-b)/2a]x}$$

but this is not the complete solution. Assume that the complete solution will be

$$y = ve^{[(-b)/2a]x}$$

where v is a function of x. Then

$$\frac{dy}{dx} = \frac{dv}{dx}e^{[(-b)/2a]x} - \frac{b}{2a}ve^{[(-b)/2a]x}$$

and

$$\frac{d^2y}{dx^2} = \frac{d^2v}{dx^2}e^{[(-b)/2a]x} - \frac{b}{a}\frac{dv}{dx}e^{[(-b)/2a]x} + \frac{b^2}{4a^2}ve^{[(-b)/2a]x}$$

or

$$\frac{d^2y}{dx^2} = \left(\frac{d^2v}{dx^2} - \frac{b}{a}\frac{dv}{dx} + \frac{b^2}{4a^2}v\right)e^{[(-b)/2a]x}$$

Substituting into the original equation and dividing through by $e^{[(-b)/2a]x}$

$$a\left(\frac{d^2v}{dx^2} - \frac{b}{a}\frac{dv}{dx} + \frac{b^2}{4a^2}v\right) + b\left(\frac{dv}{dx} - \frac{b}{2a}v\right) + cv = 0$$

$$a\frac{d^2v}{dx^2} + \left(\frac{-ab}{a} + b\right)\frac{dv}{dx} + \left(\frac{ab^2}{4a^2} - \frac{b^2}{2a} + c\right)v = 0$$

$$a\frac{d^2v}{dx^2} + \left(\frac{-ab^2 + 4a^2c}{4a^2}\right)v = 0$$

Note that

$$-ab^2 + 4a^2c = -a(b^2 - 4ac) = -a(0) = 0$$

which reduces the equation to

$$a\frac{d^2v}{dx^2} = 0$$

$$\frac{d^2v}{dx^2} = 0$$

Integrating gives

$$\int \frac{d^2v}{dx^2} = \frac{dv}{dx} = \int 0 \, dx = c_1$$

and integrating again gives

$$\int \frac{dv}{dx} = v = \int c_1 \, dx = c_1 x + c_2$$

Thus $v = c_1 x + c_2$, so that

$$y = ve^{[(-b)/2a]x} = (c_1 x + c_2)e^{[(-b)/2a]x} = c_1 x e^{[(-b)/2a]x} + c_2 e^{[(-b)/2a]x}$$

is the complete general solution. To find the particular solution, the initial conditions must be given.

Consider the following example:

$$\frac{d^2y}{dx^2} + 6\frac{dy}{dx} + 9y = 0$$

with $y(0) = 1$ and $y'(0) = 1$. Let $y = e^{mx}$ so

$$\frac{dy}{dx} = me^{mx} \qquad \frac{d^2y}{dx^2} = m^2 e^{mx}$$

Substituting and factoring out e^{mx} gives

$$e^{mx}(m^2 + 6m + 9) = 0$$

Dividing by e^{mx} gives

$$m^2 + 6m + 9 = 0$$

Note that

$$m^2 + 6m + 9 = (m + 3)^2 = 0$$

(the quadratic formula may also be used at this step). Thus

$$m = m_1 = m_2 = -3$$

and the general solution is

$$y = c_1 x e^{-3x} + c_2 e^{-3x}$$

For the given initial conditions, find $y(0) = 1$,

$$1 = c_1(0)e^{-3(0)} + c_2 e^{-3(0)} = c_2$$

and $y'(0) = 1$,

$$1 = -3c_1(0)e^{-3(0)} + c_1e^{-3(0)} - 3c_2e^{-3(0)} = c_1 - 3c_2$$

Thus $c_2 = 1$ and $c_1 = 4$ so that the particular solution is

$$y = 4xe^{-3x} + e^{-3x}$$

In order to check this result, calculate y' and y'':

$$y = 4xe^{-3x} + e^{-3x}$$
$$y' = 4e^{-3x} - 12xe^{-3x} - 3e^{-3x} = -12xe^{-3x} + e^{-3x}$$
$$y'' = -12e^{-3x} + 36xe^{-3x} - 3e^{-3x} = -15e^{-3x} + 36xe^{-3x}$$

Substituting into the original equation gives

$$(-15e^{-3x} + 36xe^{-3x}) + 6(e^{-3x} - 12xe^{-3x}) + 9(4xe^{-3x} + e^{-3x}) = 0$$
$$-15e^{-3x} + 36xe^{-3x} - 6e^{-3x} - 72xe^{-3x} + 36xe^{-3x} + 9e^{-3x} = 0$$
$$-15e^{-3x} + 15e^{-3x} - 72xe^{-3x} + 72xe^{-3x} = 0$$
$$0 = 0$$

Thus the correct solution has been obtained.

Complex Roots. If $b^2 - 4ac < 0$, the roots are complex and are conjugates. The general form of the roots will be

$$m_1 = h + ik \qquad \text{and} \qquad m_2 = h - ik$$

and the general solution will be

$$y = c_1e^{(h+ik)x} + c_2e^{(h-ik)x}$$

Recall that

$$e^{ikx} = \cos kx + i \sin kx$$

(This can easily be verified by the Taylor series for the functions.) The present general solution is in terms of complex functions. In order to express the general solution in terms of real-valued functions, rewrite as follows:

$$y = c_1e^{(h+ik)x} + c_2e^{(h-ik)x} = c_1e^{hx} \cdot e^{ikx} + c_2e^{hx} \cdot e^{-ikx}$$
$$y = e^{hx}[c_1e^{ikx} + c_2e^{-ikx}]$$
$$y = e^{hx}[c_1(\cos kx + i \sin kx) + c_2(\cos kx - i \sin kx)]$$
$$y = e^{hx}[(c_1 + c_2) \cos kx + i(c_1 - c_2) \sin kx]$$

By letting

$$c_1 + c_2 = p_1 \qquad \text{and} \qquad i(c_1 - c_2) = p_2$$

the general solution can be expressed as

$$y = e^{hx}[p_1 \cos kx + p_2 \sin kx]$$

Consider the following example:

$$\frac{d^2y}{dx^2} + 4\frac{dy}{dx} + 5y = 0$$

with $y(0) = 1$ and $y'(0) = 1$. Let $y = e^{mx}$ so that

$$\frac{dy}{dx} = me^{mx} \quad \text{and} \quad \frac{d^2y}{dx^2} = m^2e^{mx}$$

Substitute into the equation and factor out e^{mx}:

$$e^{mx}(m^2 + 4m + 5) = 0$$

Divide by e^{mx}:

$$m^2 + 4m + 5 = 0$$

Solving by the quadratic formula gives

$$m = \frac{-4 \pm \sqrt{(4)^2 - 4(1)(5)}}{2(1)} = \frac{-4 \pm \sqrt{16 - 20}}{2} = \frac{-4 \pm 2i}{2}$$

$$m_1 = \frac{-4 + 2i}{2} = -2 + i$$

$$m_2 = \frac{-4 - 2i}{2} = -2 - i$$

Thus the general solution is

$$y = e^{-2x}[p_1 \cos x + p_2 \sin x]$$

The particular solution for $y(0) = 1$ is

$$1 = e^{-2(0)}[p_1 \cos (0) + p_2 \sin (0)] = p_1$$

and for $y'(0) = 1$ is

$$1 = e^{-2(0)}[-p_1 \sin (0) + p_2 \cos (0)] - 2e^{-2(0)}[p_1 \cos (0) + p_2 \sin (0)]$$
$$= p_2 - 2p_1$$

Thus $p_1 = 1$ and $p_2 = 3$, so that the particular solution is

$$y = e^{-2x}[\cos x + 3 \sin x]$$

Complete (Nonhomogeneous) Second-Order Differential Equations with Constant Coefficients

The next problem is to solve a differential equation of the following type:

$$a \frac{d^2y}{dx^2} + b \frac{dy}{dx} + cy = f(x)$$

where a, b, and c are constants and $f(x) \neq 0$. The solution of this differential equation is the sum of the corresponding homogeneous equation and any solution of the non-homogeneous equation. The general solution of the homogeneous equation is called the *complementary* solution, denoted as

$$y_c(x) = c_1 y_1(x) + c_2 y_2(x)$$

The solution of the non-homogeneous equation is unfortunately called the *particular* solution, but this does *not* mean initial conditions are given. Let $y_p(x)$ denote a solution of the non-homogeneous equation; then the complete general solution of the non-homogeneous equation is

$$y(x) = y_p(x) + y_c(x) = y_p(x) + c_1 y_1(x) + c_2 y_2(x)$$

A set of initial conditions may be prescribed to find the complete particular solution.

Method of Undetermined Coefficients

There are a number of methods available for solving differential equations of second or higher order. The method of undetermined coefficients is very simple and is applicable to all the higher ordered differential equations to be considered here.

For the cases of $f(x)$, the general trial forms of the particular solution $y_p(x)$ will be

$$f(x) = \begin{cases} x^n \\ e^{mx} \\ \sin ax, \text{ or } \cos ax \\ e^{mx} \sin ax, \text{ or } e^{mx} \cos ax \\ e^{mx} x^n \\ e^{mx} x^n \sin ax, \text{ or } e^{mx} x^n \cos ax \end{cases}$$

$$y_p(x) = \begin{cases} A_0 x^n + A_1 x^{n-1} + \cdots + A_n \\ A e^{mx} \\ A \sin ax + B \cos ax \\ e^{mx}(A \sin ax + B \cos ax) \\ e^{mx}(A_0 x^n + A_1 x^{n-1} + \cdots + A_n) \\ e^{mx}(A_0 x^n + A_1 x^{n-1} + \cdots + A_n)(C \sin ax + B \cos ax) \end{cases}$$

A case of $f(x)$ may also be a combination of the above choices.

The method of solution is to differentiate successively the trial solution $y_p(x)$ which corresponds to $f(x)$, and then substitute the differentiated forms into the differential equation. Thus the differentiated trial solutions, which have been substituted into the differential equation, are set equal to $f(x)$. The coefficients of corresponding functions are then equated, and these equations are solved for the coefficients. Then the particular solution $y_p(x)$ of the non-homogeneous problem will be found. The general solution is obtained by summing the complementary solution $y_c(x)$ and the particular solution.

Consider the following example:

$$\frac{d^2y}{dx^2} + \frac{dy}{dx} - 6y = x^2 + e^x$$

To find the complementary solution, let $y = e^{mx}$. Then, by the usual differentiation and substitution,

$$e^{mx}(m^2 + m - 6) = 0$$

$$m^2 + m - 6 = 0 \qquad m_1 = 2; \; m_2 = -3$$

The complementary solution is

$$y_c(x) = c_1 e^{2x} + c_2 e^{-3x}$$

Let the trial solution be

$$y_p(x) = Ax^2 + Bx + C + De^x$$
$$y'_p = 2Ax + B + De^x$$
$$y''_p = 2A + De^x$$

Substitute these into the differential equation:

$$(2A + De^x) + (2Ax + B + De^x) - 6(Ax^2 + Bx + C + De^x) = x^2 + e^x$$
$$- 6Ax^2 + (2A - 6B)x + (2A + B - 6C) - 4De^x = x^2 + e^x$$

Equating coefficients of corresponding functions gives

$$-6A = 1 \qquad A = -\tfrac{1}{6}$$
$$2A - 6B = 0 \qquad 2(-\tfrac{1}{6}) - 6B = 0 \qquad B = -\tfrac{1}{18}$$
$$2A + B - 6C = 0 \qquad 2(-\tfrac{1}{6}) + (-\tfrac{1}{18}) - 6C = 0 \qquad C = -\tfrac{7}{108}$$
$$-4D = 1 \qquad D = -\tfrac{1}{4}$$

Thus the particular solution is

$$y_p(x) = -\tfrac{1}{6}x^2 - \tfrac{1}{18}x - \tfrac{7}{108} - \tfrac{1}{4}e^x$$

The complete general solution is

$$y(x) = y_p(x) + y_c(x) = c_1e^{2x} + c_2e^{-3x} - \tfrac{1}{6}x^2 - \tfrac{1}{18}x - \tfrac{7}{108} - \tfrac{1}{4}e^x$$

Several additional suggestions should be noted. Suppose e^{mx} is a solution of the homogeneous equation and e^{mx} also occurs in $f(x)$. To find the particular solution for this case, multiply the trial $y_p(x)$ by x. If xe^{mx} is a solution of the homogeneous equation and occurs in $f(x)$, then multiply the trial $y_p(x)$ by x^2. If $e^{mx} \cos ax$ and $e^{mx} \sin ax$ are solutions of the homogeneous equation and occur in $f(x)$, then multiply the trial solution $y_p(x)$ by x. This can also be generalized for nth order differential equations.
Consider the following example:

$$\frac{d^2y}{dx^2} - 2\frac{dy}{dx} + y = xe^x$$

with $y(0) = 1$, $y'(0) = 2$. For the complementary solution let

$$y = e^{mx}$$

Substituting into the equation and factoring out e^{mx} gives

$$e^{mx}(m^2 - 2m + 1) = 0$$

Dividing by e^{mx} gives

$$m^2 - 2m + 1 = 0$$

$$m = m_1 = m_2 = 1$$

Thus the general complementary solution is

$$y_c(x) = c_1e^x + c_2xe^x$$

To find the particular complementary solution, use the initial values $y(0) = 1$ and $y'(0) = 2$. For $y(0) = 1$

$$1 = c_1e^0 + c_2(0)e^0 = c_1$$

and for $y'(0) = 2$

$$2 = c_1e^0 + c_2(0)e^0 + c_2e^0 = c_1 + c_2$$

so $c_2 = 1$. Therefore

$$y_c = e^x + xe^x$$

To find the particular solution of the non-homogeneous problem, proceed as follows: Note that xe^x is in the complementary function and also in $f(x)$. Thus the trial $y_p(x)$ will be multiplied by x^2, i.e.,

$$y_p(x) = x^2(Axe^x + Be^x)$$

Thus

$$y_p = Ax^3e^x + Bx^2e^x$$
$$y_p' = 3Ax^2e^x + Ax^3e^x + 2Bxe^x + Bx^2e^x$$
$$= Ax^3e^x + (3A + B)x^2e^x + 2Bxe^x$$
$$y_p'' = 6Axe^x + 3Ax^2e^x + 3Ax^2e^x + Ax^3e^x + 2Be^x$$
$$+ 2Bxe^x + 2Bxe^x + Bx^2e^x$$
$$y_p'' = Ax^3e^x + (6A + B)x^2e^x + (6A + 4B)xe^x + (2B)e^x$$

Substituting into the differential equation gives

$$[Ax^3e^x + (6A + B)x^2e^x + (6A + 4B)xe^x + (2B)e^x] - 2[Ax^3e^x$$
$$+ (3A + B)x^2e^x + 2Bxe^x] + [Ax^3e^x + Bx^2e^x] = xe^x$$

Simplifying gives

$$6Axe^x + 2Be^x = xe^x$$

Equating corresponding coefficients gives

$$6A = 1 \qquad 2B = 0$$

so that $A = \frac{1}{6}$, $B = 0$, and

$$y_p = \frac{1}{6}x^3e^x$$

The complete solution is

$$y = y_p + y_c = \frac{1}{6}x^3e^x + e^x + xe^x$$

Two Special Types of Second-Order Differential Equations

Before considering the general differential equation of order n, two types of second-order differential equations that occur frequently should be examined.

Case I. If the dependent variable y is missing, the substitutions

$$p = \frac{dy}{dx} \qquad \text{and} \qquad \frac{dp}{dx} = \frac{d^2y}{dx^2}$$

can be made. Consider the following example:

$$x\frac{d^2y}{dx^2} + \frac{dy}{dx}\frac{d^2y}{dx^2} = 0$$

Let

$$p = \frac{dy}{dx} \qquad \frac{dp}{dx} = \frac{d^2y}{dx^2}$$

then

$$x \frac{dp}{dx} + p \frac{dp}{dx} = (x + p) \frac{dp}{dx} = 0$$

Thus the equation will be satisfied if

$$x + p = 0 \qquad \text{or} \qquad \frac{dp}{dx} = 0$$

If

$$\frac{dp}{dx} = 0$$

then $p = c$, but

$$p = \frac{dy}{dx} = c_1$$

so that

$$\int dy = y = \int c_1 \, dx = c_1 x + c_2$$

If $x + p = 0$, then

$$\frac{dy}{dx} = -x$$

so that

$$\int dy = y = - \int x \, dx = -\tfrac{1}{2}x^2 + c$$

Thus there are two possible solutions:

$$y = c_1 x + c_2 \qquad y = -\tfrac{1}{2}x^2 + c$$

Case 2. If the independent variable is missing from the equation, the substitution

$$p = \frac{dy}{dx} \qquad \frac{d^2y}{dx^2} = p \frac{dp}{dy}$$

can be made. Consider the following example:

$$\frac{d^2y}{dx^2} - 4y = 0$$

Let

$$p = \frac{dy}{dx} \qquad \frac{d^2y}{dx^2} = p \frac{dp}{dy}$$

then

$$p\frac{dp}{dy} - 4y = 0$$

$$\int p\, dp = \int 4y\, dy$$

$$\tfrac{1}{2}p^2 = 2y^2 + c_1$$

$$p^2 = 4y^2 + c_1'$$

$$\left(\frac{dy}{dx}\right)^2 = 4y^2 + c_1'$$

$$\frac{dy}{dx} = \sqrt{4y^2 + c_1'}$$

$$\int \frac{dy}{\sqrt{4y^2 + c_1'}} = \int dx$$

$$\tfrac{1}{2}\ln|2y + \sqrt{4y^2 + c_1'}| = x + \ln c_2$$

$$\ln|2y + \sqrt{4y^2 + c_1'}| = 2x + \ln c_2'$$

$$2y + \sqrt{4y^2 + c_1'} = c_2' e^{2x}$$

DIFFERENTIAL EQUATIONS OF ORDER N

The general form of a homogeneous differential equation of order n is

$$a_0\frac{d^n y}{dx^n} + a_1\frac{d^{n-1}y}{dx^{n-1}} + \cdots + a_n y = 0$$

where $a_0, a_1, \ldots, a_n$ are constants and the equation is linear. Again assume that $y = e^{mx}$ is a solution. Substitute into the equation and factor out e^{mx}. Thus

$$e^{mx}(a_0 m^n + a_1 m^{n-1} + \cdots + a_n) = 0$$

Divide by e^{mx} to get

$$a_0 m^n + a_1 m^{n-1} + \cdots + a_n = 0$$

Solve this polynomial for all values of m. If all values of m are different and distinct, then there are n unequal roots. Thus the complete general solution is written

$$y = c_1 e^{m_1 x} + c_2 e^{m_2 x} + \cdots + c_n e^{m_n x}$$

If k roots are equal and $(n - k)$ roots are distinct, the complete general solution will be

$$y = (c_1 + c_2 x + c_3 x^2 + \cdots + c_k x^{k-1})e^{m_1 x} + e^{m_j x} + e^{m_{j+1} x} + \cdots + e^{m_n x}$$

where $m_j, m_{(j+1)}, \ldots, m_n$ are the $(n - k)$ remaining roots. If the solution has complex roots, the complex roots will occur in conjugate pairs. (This is not true necessarily if the coefficients of the differential equation are complex.) Thus if a conjugate pair of complex numbers occurs in the solution, say

$$m_j = a + bi \qquad m_{j+1} = a - bi$$

and the remaining roots are something else, the complete general solution will be

$$y = c_1 e^{m_1 x} + \cdots + c_{j-1} e^{m_{j-1} x} + e^{ax}[k_1 \cos bx + k_2 \sin bx] + \cdots + c_n e^{m_n x}$$

Recall that

$$c_j e^{(a+bi)x} + c_{j+1} e^{(a-bi)x} = e^{ax}[c_j e^{bix} + c_{j+1} e^{-bix}]$$

and that

$$e^{ibx} = \cos bx + i \sin bx$$
$$e^{-ibx} = \cos bx - i \sin bx$$

Also note that

$$c_j + c_{j+1} = k_1 \qquad i(c_j - c_{j+1}) = k_2$$

When solving higher order differential equations, it is easier to use the D-operator notation by substituting

$$\frac{d}{dx} = D, \qquad \frac{d^2}{dx^2} = D^2, \ldots, \frac{d^n}{dx^n} = D^n$$

Thus the general differential equation can be written as

$$(a_0 D^n + a_1 D^{n-1} + \cdots + a_{n-1} D + a_n)y = 0$$

The solution of the non-homogeneous problem for an order n differential equation is found by the same procedure as discussed for second-order equations. First, the solution of the homogeneous problem is found, i.e., the complementary solution $y_c(x)$. Next, by using the method of undetermined coefficients, the particular solution $y_p(x)$ is found. The complete general solution is the sum of the complementary solution and the particular solution, i.e.,

$$y(x) = y_p(x) + y_c(x)$$

If initial conditions are prescribed, the complete particular solution of the complete differential equation can be found.

Consider the following fifth-order homogeneous differential equation:

$$\frac{d^5 y}{dx^5} + 3\frac{d^4 y}{dx^4} + 3\frac{d^3 y}{dx^3} - \frac{d^2 y}{dx^2} - 4\frac{dy}{dx} - 2y = 0$$

Let $y = e^{mx}$ so that

$$\frac{dy}{dx} = me^{mx}, \qquad \frac{d^2y}{dx^2} = m^2 e^{mx}, \dots$$

Substitute into the differential equation and factor out e^{mx}:

$$e^{mx}(m^5 + 3m^4 + 3m^3 - m^2 - 4m - 2) = 0$$

Divide by e^{mx}:

$$m^5 + 3m^4 + 3m^3 - m^2 - 4m - 2 = 0$$

Solve this polynomial for all roots. Observe that this polynomial can be factored in the following manner:

$$(m - 1)(m^4 + 4m^3 + 7m^2 + 6m + 2) = 0$$

And it can be factored again:

$$(m - 1)(m^2 + 2m + 2)(m^2 + 2m + 1) = 0$$

(If the polynomial is factorable, it simplifies the problem greatly). The roots are then

$$m_1 = 1 \qquad m_2 = m_3 = -1 \qquad m_4 = -1 + i \qquad m_5 = -1 - i$$

Note that roots m_2 and m_3 are equal and that roots m_4 and m_5 are complex conjugates. Thus the complete general solution is

$$y = c_1 e^x + (c_2 + c_3 x)e^{-x} + e^{-x}[k_1 \cos x + k_2 \sin x]$$

where $k_1 = (c_4 + c_5)$ and $k_2 = i(c_4 - c_5)$.

ECONOMIC APPLICATIONS OF HIGHER ORDER DIFFERENTIAL EQUATIONS

Considered here are three possible models which relate national income to national debt, and the Domar model for the burden of debt imposed on the public by governmental taxation.

National Debt Related to National Income

Model I. Suppose that income Y is increasing at a directly proportional rate a whose value is $0 < a < 1$ and that the new debt D incurred is also directly proportional to income at the rate b where $0 < b < 1$. Thus the changes in income and debt are represented by the differential equations:

$$\frac{dY}{dt} = aY \qquad \frac{dD}{dt} = bY$$

Assume that the initial values are

$$Y = Y_0 \qquad D = D_0 \qquad \text{when } t = 0$$

It is possible to solve this problem by using only first-order differential equations, but second-order differential equations will be used here for demonstration.

$$\frac{d^2D}{dt^2} = b\frac{dY}{dt} = abY = a\frac{dD}{dt}$$

Thus the second-order differential equation is

$$\frac{d^2D}{dt^2} - a\frac{dD}{dt} = 0$$

Assume the form of the solution to be $D = e^{mt}$. Then

$$e^{mt}(m^2 - am) = 0$$

Divide through by e^{mt} and solve for m, which gives the roots $m = 0, m = a$. The general solution is

$$D = c_1 + c_2 e^{at}$$

To find the particular solution, use the initial values

$$D_0 = c_1 + c_2 \qquad \text{when} \qquad t = 0$$

Note that

$$\frac{dD}{dt} = D' = bY = bY_0 = ac_2 \qquad \text{when} \qquad t = 0$$

Thus the values of the constants are

$$c_2 = \frac{b}{a}Y_0 \qquad c_1 = D_0 - \frac{b}{a}Y_0$$

The particular solution is

$$D = D_0 - \frac{b}{a}Y_0 + \frac{b}{a}Y_0 e^{at}$$

or

$$D = D_0 + \frac{b}{a}Y_0(e^{at} - 1)$$

In order to find the relationship of debt to income, the differential equation

$$\frac{dY}{dt} = aY$$

must be solved. Separate variables and integrate to obtain

$$\int \frac{dY}{Y} = \int a\, dt$$

$$\ln Y + \ln c = at$$

The general solution is

$$cY = e^{at} \qquad \text{or} \qquad Y = \frac{1}{c} e^{at}$$

Use the initial values to find the particular solution

$$cY_0 = 1 \qquad c = \frac{1}{Y_0} \qquad \text{or} \qquad \frac{1}{c} = Y_0$$

Thus the particular solution is

$$Y = Y_0 e^{at}$$

Now consider the ratio of debt to income and let the time of borrowing continue indefinitely.

$$\frac{D}{Y} = \frac{D_0 + \frac{b}{a} Y_0(e^{at} - 1)}{Y_0 e^{at}} = \frac{D_0}{Y_0 e^{at}} + \frac{b}{a} - \frac{b}{ae^{at}}$$

The limit as $t \to \infty$ of this last expression is the ratio b/a. Thus it can be concluded that the national debt will become a fixed proportion of income over an indefinite period of time.

Model 2. Suppose that the given differential equations are

$$\frac{dD}{dt} = \frac{a}{Y}$$

(an inversely proportional relationship) and

$$\frac{dY}{dt} = bY$$

Assume that the initial conditions are

$$Y = Y_0 \qquad D = D_0 \qquad \text{when} \qquad t = 0$$

Again using second-order differential equations,

$$\frac{d^2D}{dt^2} = -\frac{a}{Y^2} \frac{dY}{dt} = -(a)\left(\frac{1}{Y^2}\right)(bY) = -(ab)\left(\frac{1}{Y}\right)$$

$$= -(ab)\left(\frac{1}{a}\frac{dD}{dt}\right) = -b\frac{dD}{dt}$$

$$\frac{d^2D}{dt^2} + b\frac{dD}{dt} = 0$$

Again assume that the solution is of the form $D = e^{mt}$. By the usual substitution and factoring,

$$m^2 + bm = 0 \quad \text{or} \quad m = 0 \quad m = -b$$

The general solution is

$$D = c_1 + c_2 e^{-bt}$$

To find the particular solution,

$$D_0 = c_1 + c_2$$

$$\frac{dD}{dt} = D' = \frac{a}{Y} = \frac{a}{Y_0} = -bc_2$$

Thus the values of the constants are

$$c_2 = -\frac{a}{bY_0} \qquad c_1 = D_0 + \frac{a}{bY_0}$$

The particular solution is

$$D = D_0 + \frac{a}{bY_0} - \frac{a}{bY_0}e^{-bt} \quad \text{or} \quad D = D_0 + \frac{a}{bY_0}(1 - e^{-bt})$$

As in the previous problem,

$$Y = Y_0 e^{bt}$$

The ratio of debt to income is then

$$\frac{D}{Y} = \frac{D_0 + \dfrac{a}{bY_0}(1 - e^{-bt})}{Y_0 e^{bt}} = \frac{D_0}{Y_0 e^{bt}} + \frac{a}{bY_0^2 e^{bt}} - \frac{a}{bY_0^2 e^{2bt}}$$

The limit as $t \to \infty$ of the above expression is zero. Thus the debt will vanish over an indefinite period of time.

Model 3. For this example, assume that income is growing at a constant rate so that the differential equation is

$$\frac{dY}{dt} = b$$

Assume that the rate of change of debt is, on the other hand, directly proportional to income, i.e.,

$$\frac{dD}{dt} = aY$$

Retain the initial conditions that

$$Y = Y_0 \qquad D = D_0 \qquad \text{when} \qquad t = 0$$

Again use second-order differential equations:

$$\frac{d^2D}{dt^2} = a\frac{dY}{dt} = ab$$

Thus the problem resolves into the non-homogeneous differential equation

$$\frac{d^2D}{dt^2} = ab$$

First, find the complementary solution, D_c (solution of the homogeneous differential equation):

$$\int \frac{d^2D}{dt^2}\,dt = \int 0\,dt \qquad \text{or} \qquad \frac{dD}{dt} = c_1$$

Integrating again gives

$$\int \frac{dD}{dt}\,dt = \int c_1\,dt \qquad \text{or} \qquad D_c = c_1t + c_2$$

To find the particular complementary solution

$$D_0 = c_2 \qquad \frac{dD}{dt} = aY = aY_0 = c_1$$

and so

$$D_c = D_0 + aY_0t$$

The particular solution D_p of the non-homogeneous equation can be found by separating variables and integrating:

$$\int \frac{d^2D}{dt^2}\,dt = \int ab\,dt \qquad \text{or} \qquad \frac{dD}{dt} = abt$$

Integrating again gives

$$\int \frac{dD}{dt}\,dt = \int abt\,dt \qquad \text{or} \qquad D = \tfrac{1}{2}abt^2$$

Thus the complete particular solution is

$$D = D_p + D_c = D_0 + aY_0t + \tfrac{1}{2}abt^2$$

The next step is to solve the differential equation

$$\frac{dY}{dt} = b$$

$$\int \frac{dY}{dt}\,dt = \int b\,dt \qquad \text{or} \qquad Y = bt + c$$

To find the particular solution

$$Y_0 = b(0) + c = c$$

and so

$$Y = bt + Y_0$$

Consider the ratio of debt to income:

$$\frac{D}{Y} = \frac{D_0 + aY_0t + (\frac{1}{2})abt^2}{Y_0 + bt} = \frac{D_0}{Y_0 + bt} + \frac{aY_0}{\dfrac{Y_0}{t} + b} + \frac{(\frac{1}{2})abt}{\dfrac{Y_0}{t} + b}$$

This time, the limit as $t \to \infty$ approaches ∞ itself. It can be concluded that the debt will grow indefinitely and overcome the income.

Domar's Burden-of-Debt Model

Assume that the government continually spends with a deficit. Thus the interest on the public debt will continue to grow (unless the interest rate declines). Assume also that the interest is paid with revenue from taxes; this is the "burden" imposed on the public. The effect of the burden is not the total interest to be paid, but the effect of increments of tax imposed on the income. For example, if income is increasing, then an increase in tax may not burden the public. So the relationships are $T = iD$ where i is the interest and T is the induced tax, and the burden B,

$$B = \frac{T}{Y} = \frac{iD}{Y}$$

The previous examples have determined the ratio D/Y for three different cases; now all that is needed is to multiply the numerator of each model by i. Again assume an indefinite period of time.

Model 1: $\displaystyle \lim_{t \to \infty} B = \lim_{t \to \infty} \frac{iD}{Y} = \frac{ib}{a}$

Model 2: $\displaystyle \lim_{t \to \infty} B = \lim_{t \to \infty} \frac{iD}{Y} = i \cdot 0 = 0$

Model 3: $\displaystyle \lim_{t \to \infty} B = \lim_{t \to \infty} \frac{iD}{Y} = \infty$

The conclusions resulting here are similar to those drawn from the previous models.

PROBLEMS

1. Find the order and degree of the following differential equations:

(a) $x(y'')^2 + 3(y')^4 + 3x^2y - 1 = 0$

(b) $(y''')^2 + (xy'')^3 + 4(y')^4 + y^6 = 0$

(c) $y''' - e^{y'} = (y'')^2$

2. Solve the following differential equations:

(a) $\dfrac{dy}{dx} = \dfrac{2xy^2}{1 + y^3}$

(c) $(1 - y)\,dx + (1 - x)\,dy = 0$

(b) $2y\dfrac{dy}{dx} = 1 + x + y^2 + xy^2$

(d) $\dfrac{dy}{dx} = \dfrac{y - 4x}{x - y}$

Use $V = \dfrac{y}{x}$

3. Solve the following (homogeneous) equations:

(a) $\dfrac{dy}{dx} = \dfrac{xe^{y/x} + y}{x}$

(c) $(1 + y)\,dx - (2 - x)\,dy = 0$

(b) $\dfrac{dy}{dx} = \dfrac{y^2}{x^2}$

(d) $(x + 2y)\,dx + (2x + 3y)\,dy = 0$

4. Solve the following:

(a) $\dfrac{dy}{dx} + 2y = e^x$

(c) $\dfrac{dy}{dx} + \dfrac{2y}{x} = 5x^2$

(b) $\dfrac{dy}{dx} + y = 2$

(d) $\dfrac{dy}{dx} - x - 3 = \dfrac{y}{x}$

5. If the differential is not exact, find

$$\frac{(\partial M/\partial y) - (\partial N/\partial x)}{N} = f(x)$$

as a function of x only; then $e^{\int f(x)\,dx}$ is an integrating factor and transforms the equation. Solve the equation

$$\frac{dy}{dx} = \frac{3x - 2y}{x}$$

6. A second-order equation of the form

$$y'' + Py' + Qy = 0$$

uses the substitution $y'' = m^2$, $y' = m$, where

$$y = C_1 e^{m_1 x} + C_2 e^{m_2 x}$$

is the general form of the solution. Solve the following [check (b) and draw conclusions]:

(a) $y'' + 5y' + 4y = 0$

(b) $y'' - 4y' + 4y = 0$ (notice equal roots)

7. Show that

$$\frac{M}{Mx + Ny} + \frac{N}{Mx + Ny} = 0$$

is exact where

$$\frac{1}{Mx + Ny}$$

is an integrating factor of the homogeneous equation

$$M\,dx + N\,dy = 0$$

of degree m. [Hint: Apply Euler's theorem]

8. An equation of the form

$$y = px + f(p) \quad \text{where} \quad p = \frac{dy}{dx}$$

is known as a Clairant equation. If

$$y = xp + p^2$$

show that $y = cx + c^2$.

9. If $Q(t)$ is the quantity being consumed at the present time t, and there exists a proportionality factor K; and if Q_0 is the amount present at $t = 0$, find the amount present at $Q(t)$.

10. If $S(t)$ is the value of investment at a time t and the interest rate is 5% with the initial condition $S(0) = \$500$, find $S(t)$ and $S(20)$.

11. Solve the following Euler equations by the substitution $g(x) = x^r$ for the general solution

$$y = C_1 x^{r_1} + C_2 x^{r_2}$$

(a) $x^2 \dfrac{d^2 y}{dx^2} + 5x \dfrac{dy}{dx} + 4y = 0$ (check since roots are equal)

(b) $x^2 \dfrac{d^2 y}{dx^2} + 4x \dfrac{dy}{dx} + 2y = 0$

12. Find the orthogonal trajectories for the following, and graph the family of curves:

(a) $xy = c$ (b) $x^2 + y^2 = c^2$

INDEX

Abscissa, 69
Accelerator, 440, 443, 469
Adding-up theorem, 295, 302
Algebraic expressions, 20
Analytic geometry, 69
Angles, 142–143
Area under a curve, 395–402
Associative law, 9
Assumptions of a problem, 5–6
Average cost
  as tangent of angle, 154
  long-run, 230–234
  relation to marginal cost, 326
  short-run, 228–234
Average propensity to consume, 152–154
Average revenue, 224

Baumol, W. J., 333
Behavioral equations, 8
Bilateral monopoly, 300–301
Budget constraint, 213, 285, 292–293
Burden of debt, 496
Business cycles, 270–272
  amplitude, 150–152
  duration, 150–152

Capital growth, 404–406
Circle, 80–89
Cobb-Douglas production function, 290–295, 304–306
Cobweb model, 435–439
Collusion, 353–354
Commutative law, 9
Complex numbers, 33–36, 159–163
Conditional equation, 21
Conic section, 79–80
Conjectural variation, 359–363
Constant, 2
Constant of integration, 392–395
Constrained maximum, 343–348
Consumers' surplus, 403–404
Consumption function, 239–240, 440

Continuity, 176–179, 278
Cost functions, 224–234, 309–314
Cournot, A. A., 352–354

Decreasing returns to scale, 296–297, 301
Definite integral, 396–405
Definitional equation, 8
Demand, 8, 211
Derivative, 179–181
  higher order, 196–199
  partial, 278–280
Derivatives, rules of
  composite function, 191–194
  constant, 181–184
  exponential function, 259–261
  implicit function, 195–196, 283–284
  inverse function, 194–195
  logarithmic function, 257–259
  natural exponential function, 255–257
  natural logarithmic functions, 249–255
  power function, 184–185
  products, 187–189
  quotients, 189–191
  sums and differences, 185–187
  trigonometric functions, 261–268
Determinants, 44–51, 349–352
  equation solving, 44–45
  maxima and minima, 349–352
  properties, 46–51
Difference equations, 423
  constant coefficients, 423
  homogeneous linear, 423
  initial conditions, 423, 441
  nonhomogeneous, 429–435, 445–447
  order, 423
  second-order, 440–445
  solution theorems, 429, 443
  time paths, 426–428

Differential equations, 450
  complete, 477
  constant coefficients, 478
  degree, 451
  exact, 463–468, 476–477
  higher order, 489–491
  homogeneous, 456–459, 474–475, 477
  initial conditions, 452–453, 478
  linear, 459–463
  nonhomogeneous, 484–487
  order, 451
  ordinary, 450
  partial, 450
  second-order, 477–484
  separation of variables, 454–456, 472–474
  solutions, 451–454, 484
  special second-order, 487–489
Differentials, 199–202
  area under a curve, 395–396
  total, 282–283
Discontinuous functions, 177–179
Distance, 78–79
Distributive law, 10
Domar, E., 404–406, 468–469, 491–496
Duopoly models, 352–363
Dynamics, 422

Econometrics, 269
Elasticity
  arc, 214–215
  cross, 218–219
  demand, 214–218
  income, 219
  point, 214–216
  price discrimination and, 342–343
  total cost, 226–228
  total revenue, 219–224
Ellipse, 89–96
Envelopes of curves, 310–314
Equalities, 21
Equilibrium, 8
Euler's theorem, 297–305
Expansion path, 310

Explicit numbers, 20
Exponential functions, 128–135
Exponents, 11–13
Extremum. *See* Maxima and minima

Fixed cost, 182, 228
Fractions, 2, 57–62
Frisch, R., 356
Fundamental theorem of algebra, 53–55
Functions
  algebraic, 118–120
  composite, 191–194
  continuous, 176–177, 278
  discontinuous, 177–179
  exponential, 128–131
  homogeneous, 288
  implicit, 195
  inverse, 194–195
  linear, 22, 69
  linear homogeneous, 290
  logarithmic, 135–141
  natural exponential, 19–20, 131–135
  natural logarithmic, 19–20
  periodic, 150
  step, 177–179
  transcendental, 128
  of two variables, 278

Government expenditures, 239–243
Growth models
  Domar, 404–406, 468–469
  Harrod, 425–429, 469–470
  sales revenue, 424–425

Harrod, R., 425, 469
Homogeneous functions, 288–297
Hotelling, H., 354
Hyperbola, 105–118
Hypothesis, 6

Identity, 21
Imaginary number, 34, 156–157
Income taxation, 239–243

Increasing returns to scale, 296, 299–301
Indifference curves, 285–286, 474–476
Inflection point, 336–337
Integer, 2
Integral expressions, 20
Integral
definite, as constant of integration, 395–406
numerical methods of evaluating, 406–413
Integration, rules of
composite functions, 376–377
constant, 373
natural exponential function, 383–386
natural logarithmic function, 377–379
partial fractions, 380–383
power functions, 373–376
sums and differences, 372–373
trigonometric functions, 386–392
Intercept, 69
Interest rate, 18–19
Irrational number, 2
Isoprofit curves, 95–96
Isoquants, 291–295, 476–477

Joint maximization, 353–354

Keynesian model, 239–243

Lagrange multiplier, 343–348
Law of diminishing returns, 211
Limits, 169–176
Linear equations
horizontal lines, 71
parallel lines, 73–74
point-slope form, 76–78
solving, 22–23
systems, 38–45
two-point form, 74–75
vertical lines, 71
Liquidity preference, 117
Literal numbers, 20
Logarithmic functions, 135–141

Logarithms, 13
bases of, 18–20, 257–259
natural, 18–20
properties of, 15–17
Logistic law of growth, 134
Long-run cost, 228, 309

Marginal cost, 224–234, 326
Marginal physical product, 192, 234, 293, 305
Marginal propensity to consume, 238, 240–243, 440
Marginal propensity to save, 238, 241–243, 425
Marginal rate of technical substitution, 307
Marginal revenue, 222–224
Marginal revenue product, 192
Marginal utility, 211–214, 285–286
Mathematics in economics, 1, 7
Maxima and minima
constrained maxima, 343–348
functions of more than two variables
maxima, 349–350; minima, 350–352
functions of a single variable, 322–327
necessary conditions, 324
sufficient conditions, 324
functions of two variables
maxima, 338–339
Maximization of tax on output, 363–367
Method of undetermined coefficients, 484–487
Model structure, 8
Monopoly, 300–301
output, 330–333
price discrimination, 339–343
Multiplier, 239–243, 443
Multiplier-accelerator model, 443–445
Multiplier, Lagrange, 343–348

National debt, 491–496
National income, 237–243
Natural exponential function, 18–20, 131–135

Natural logarithmic function, 18–20
Neoclassical growth model, 304–309
Neoclassical macroeconomic model, 234–237

Ordered sequence, 169
Output, competitive versus monopoly, 330–333

Parabola, 36, 96–105, 409–410
Parabolic rule, 409–413
Partial derivative, 278–286
    higher order, 286–287
    mixed (cross), 287
Partial fractions, 57–62
Polar coordinates, 155–156
Polynomials, 20
Price discrimination, 339–343
Price-level adjustment, 470–472
Production function, 119
    Cobb-Douglas, 290–295
    neoclassical, 235
    relation to Euler's theorem, 302–304
Profit maximization, 327–330

Quadratic equations, 23–38
    Completing the square, 29–30
    factoring, 26–28
    graph solutions, 36–38
    roots, 32–33
    systems, 51–53
Quadratic formula, 30–31
    in difference equations, 441
    in differential equations, 478
    discriminant, 32

Radian, 145
Radius vector, 141–142

Rational expression, 20
Rationality in economic theory, 322
Rational number, 2
Reaction curves, 359–363
Rectangular hyperbola, 115–118
Remainder theorem of algebra, 56–57
Returns to scale
    constant, 290–295, 304–309
    decreasing, 296–297, 301, 304
    increasing, 295–296, 299–301, 304

Sales maximization, 333–336
Savings function, 425
Schultz, H., 269
Semilogarithmic graphs, 135–141
Short-run cost, 228, 309
Signed numbers, 10
Simpson's rule, 409–413
Slope, 70–74
Statics, 422
Supply, 8
Systems of equations
    linear, 38–45
    with quadratic equations, 51–53

Taxation
    income, 239–243
    maximization on output, 363–367
Theory, 6–7
Total differential, 282–283
Total revenue, 220–224
Trigonometric functions, 141–154
Trapezoidal rule, 406–409

Utility theory, 211–214, 285–286
Undetermined coefficients, 484–487

Variables, 3
Variable cost, 228